Hair Trigger 24

A STORY WORKSHOP ANTHOLOGY

COLUMBIA COLLEGE CHICAGO   CHICAGO 2002

FICTION WRITING DEPARTMENT

600 SOUTH MICHIGAN AVENUE

CHICAGO, ILLINOIS 60605-1996

Table of Contents

INTRO/FICTION WRITING I

FICTION

Preface & Acknowledgments

Hair Trigger 24 collects prose fiction and nonfiction essays written by undergraduate and graduate students in the Fiction Writing Department at Columbia College Chicago. These works come primarily from core classes—Introduction to Fiction Writing, Fiction Writing I, Fiction Writing II, Prose Forms, Advanced Fiction, Advanced Prose Forms, and Fiction Seminars—taught using the innovative Story Workshop® approach, as well as from a wide variety of Critical Reading and Writing, creative nonfiction, genre, publishing, and other Specialty Writing courses.

The success of the Story Workshop approach and those complementary approaches used in the Fiction Writing Department program is reflected in the broad range of voices, subjects, forms, and cultural/linguistic backgrounds represented in all editions of *Hair Trigger* during the more than two decades that this magazine has been published. Since its inception, *Hair Trigger* has been recognized repeatedly as one of the top college literary magazines in the country, winning first-place awards from the Associated Writing Programs, the Coordinating Council of Literary Magazines, and the Columbia University Scholastic Press Association. Numerous student writers appearing in its pages have also been honored with individual awards, and a number of them have gone on to very successful publishing careers.

Hair Trigger and the various editions of *The Best of Hair Trigger* descend from a bloodline that includes such widely acclaimed anthologies as *The Story Workshop Reader, Angels in My Oven, It Never Stopped Raining, Don't You Know There's a War On?*, and *F Magazine.* The Fiction Writing Department is also home to a newly revived version of *F Magazine* as well as the already highly regarded science fiction journal, *Spec-Lit.*

Appreciation and admiration go to the dedicated student editors, who read through hundreds of manuscript submissions and saw to it that each received equal treatment and consideration. In making selections, the editors were often forced to choose among writings of nearly equal merit. Respect for the reader, for content, for form, for point of view and language, and for vividness of telling characterize the selections printed in this volume.

Congratulations to Chris Maul Rice, who was chiefly responsible as Faculty Advisor for supervising undergraduate and graduate student editors in the overall selection and production process for *Hair Trigger 24,* and to the Coordinator of Faculty Development, Shawn Shiflett, who oversees *Hair Trigger* for the Fiction Writing Department.

Thanks to Andrew Allegretti, Jaimee Wriston Colbert, Don Gennaro De Grazia, Ann Hemenway, Gary Johnson, Eric May, Patricia Ann McNair, Polly Mills, Alexis Pride, Shawn Shiflett, Wade Roberts, Joe Meno, John Schultz, and Betty Shiflett for consulting on matters affecting the student editors' complex editorial selection process—as well as to the many other excellent teacher-writers in the Fiction Writing program.

Thanks to Creative and Printing Services Director Mary Johnson, and to Sarah Faust for cover and layout design. Particular thanks go to Deborah Roberts, Linda Naslund, and Jenny Seay for copyediting, proofreading, and supervising crucial phases of production. Thanks, too, to Nicole Chakalis, Brian Costello, Leslie Hedrick, Jamie Kallio, Stephanie Kuehnert, Tony Luce, Penny Memoli, Michael David Sims, Felicia Swanson, and Mica "The Quark Cowboy" Racine for their production assistance.

Our profound gratitude goes to Warrick Carter, President of Columbia College; to Bert Gall, Executive Vice President; to Steve Kapelke, Academic Vice President/Provost; to Leonard Lehrer, Dean of the School of Fine and Performing Arts; and to Keith Cleveland, Graduate School Dean, for their continuing encouragement of this program.

We are proud of the writers who appear in this volume, and we know that you will enjoy the prose stories and essays in this new edition of *Hair Trigger*.

Randall Albers, Chair
Fiction Writing Department

Hair Trigger 24 Student Editors
Julia Borcherts
James Hein
Steve Jackson
Bernadette Jones
Tamara Michael
Devon Polderman
Sara Sheridan
Felicia Swanson

Hair Trigger 24 Faculty Advisor
Chris Maul Rice

Hatfield's Somnabulquy

Time to dirt nap, or ain't it? That there's the question.

Wot's better'n th'other: bend over when yonder slingshot bites usns's ass
and take it,
Or shoot out the winders against th' whole passel of McCoys
And get kilt to boot? Pushin' up daisies; snoozin' in yon' hammock;
Or naw? Snoozin', we'ns aim t'feel no lovesick, no sorry,
And say we'ns'll rest in peace. Pushin' up daisies; snoozin' in yon' ham-
mock;
Or naw? Mebbe dream, but there's the fly in th' ointment,
What if when we'ns snooze, there's nightmares
'Cause usns's o'nery hateful self and murderin' grief?
It'll make ye refigure. Y'keep ploddin' on through this mis'r'ble life,
'Cause who'd keep on keepin' on with the stangs and aches of gettin'
old,
The tyrant's bullshit, the highfallutin's contemptful talk,
Love unrequited, the crooked laws,

Deb R. Lewis   1

The asinine bur'crat bastardry, and the kicks in the teeth
That thank the down an' out for tryin',
When a poor son can end it all
With a toe on the rifle trigger? Who'd carry this load,
Gruntin' and a-sweatin' under such a burdensome life,
Unless they was a-feared of what come in the afterlife,
The land over the hills, over that property line
No fool crosses twic't, and makes a body reckon
Usns'll stick to the fryin' pan,
'Cause a body cain't say there ain't no fire beneath it.
So all this thinkin' makes usns yeller bellies,
And the right sharp color of a mind made up,
Gets pale in the fog of grievin' and fear,
And all them adventures with glory and gusto
Turn into nothin' but talk
And we'ns sits on usns's porches, mumblin' 'bout nothin'.

Bodies

ERIKA MIKKALO

My name is Danielle Fayette, and I stand at the edge of roads, paths, freeways, highways, byways, state routes, numbered rural roads, broad blasting concrete carpets rolled from city to city. My thumb is my calling card, and my cunt is my welcome. I say this to Carissa while we are tripping as we watch constellations appear like blemishes on the perfect sky above the lake, all blasted up and down on Magic Mountain acid—a trip that loops us around and around like the roller coaster—and a steady stream of gin and tonics. "Hell, Carissa," I say, and swig from the plastic pitcher so that the ice cubes bury the floating chunks of lime. "I'm a bleached blonde with hard liquor: I am universally well received."

"Yeah, well," Carissa answers, reaching out with both hands to grasp the pitcher by its bottom, and drawing it back to herself with the concentration of a novice carrying the most sacred votive offering, "go get Jim to receive you well."

"If he was a man, he would." I bend forward, and the chains of the porch swing creak, a sound amplified in my mind until it sounds like a rigid sheet of ridged steel scraping the cyclone fence outside a prison. The wires whine, and I feel the individual squares on the grid go electric, then unfold themselves from my center to the ends, each fingertip a plug looking for a socket. In another hour, I might get lucky and break into discrete cubes entirely, little blocks of Danielle floating off over the lake, the hills, going into orbit around the blinking red dot on the microwave tower that now mesmerizes me. It's good to disintegrate, but I can still feel too much. I nab the pitcher back from Carissa. "Couldn't we get glasses?"

She laughs. "We should be careful. Glass breaks. Shatters. You might cut yourself." She draws her bare feet up to the edge of the seat and wraps her arms around her legs, planting her chin between her knees to squeal, "We need something childproof!"

"Hell, I need something childproof. I need to be childproofed." I belch, but quietly. The liquid's running low so I splash an ice moustache beneath my nose. "I need proof that any man that I deal with isn't a child, and if I get knocked up, I need proof that he's the one that done it."

"Come on, now, Dani, you two haven't exactly been altogether together for the last couple months, right?" I didn't mean to fuck Jim again—if you'd asked me earlier that evening, nothing would have been further from my hopes, plans, or intentions. The son-of-a-bitch even grew his hair out to a mullet—he shaved his head when we started dating, I swear, I never would have touched him otherwise. But the road to hell is paved with—I smile at myself despite the circumstance.

"Yeah, but I could tell this time. Can't you tell whenever you get pregnant?"

Carissa hiccups and takes the drinks back. "I've never gotten pregnant."

"What do you mean you've never gotten pregnant?" I can't believe it. She might as well just have said: "I've never waitressed," "I've never rolled a joint badly," or "I've never shot at empty PBR cans down at the quarry with my brother when he was on leave." Everybody has a scare sometimes.

"Just what I said: it hasn't happened."

"No accidents?" I look at Carissa's twisted eyebrows. The woman rolls her eyes up and looks like she's counting.

"Maybe, but none that stuck."

"Shit," I reply, and then say it again, drawn out like the local patois, "sheeit." I stick my legs out straight and stiffen my knees, then flex my ankles so that I can draw a straight line from my irises to my big toes. I sense the cord connecting my toenails and corneas coalescing out of bare air, so I slam my eyelids down and fold my feet beneath the seat. "Well, this one did."

"Are you going to see a doctor?" We both know that she really means the free clinic.

"Nah. I'll be fine." I blink, and the stars rearrange themselves to spell out the letters F-I-N-E over the hills.

"Have you miscarried before?" Shit. Never gotten pregnant, never mis-carried—is Carissa like a—what do they call a mule? A freemartin?

"Yeah. Two summers ago. In Philadelphia. It was bad," I tell her.

"How bad is bad?"

"I bled . . . ," I almost say "like a stuck pig," but then feel stuck, don't want to say it, don't want to see the draining pig body, slit asshole to appetite, hung from its back hooves. "A lot. I bled plenty."

"How could you tell you were pregnant?"

"Your tits hurt. And your sense of smell goes haywire, gets real sensitive."

"Why is that?"

"Damned if I know. Maybe to smell danger, to smell poison, you know, seeing that everyone agrees that the piglet's more important than you are, body goes into hormonal hyperdrive to bliss you out." I snort. "Do you ever feel like you got a raw deal, Cari?"

"What do you mean, Dani?"

"Being female."

"Well, there's not much I could do about it if I did, now, is there?"

"Sure, there is." I reach into the pitcher and fish out a cube to suck. "We could pass the hat and buy you a dick."

"You're kidding."

"Now, would I bullshit you about something like that?"

"Eeeew."

"Come on, now, it's very straightforward. You remember the surgical movies they showed at the Soggy Biscuits' show?" We did our first traveling hitching to punk shows in either of the closest decent-sized cities, one four hours away, the other five. The habit of motion stuck with me. With Carissa, it didn't. She takes the pitcher back, tries to sip, but instead takes five melted ice cubes on the nose. She shakes the water off her face like a wet dog, and then moves her head "No."

"Well," I continue, "it's completely simple. Like the film: guys, they slit it, scrape it out, and pop it up inside."

"What do they do with the balls?"

"Snip 'em and toss 'em. Biohazard bin."

"So for women?"

"They go inside and pop you inside-out, and make a long tube with a piece of thigh skin to extend it."

"Do you get balls?"

"What do you mean, 'Do you get balls?' Of course you get balls. They stretch the lips down for a ballsack, and you can get any size prosthetic balls you want, or not bother." I lean back and raise my eyebrows in consideration. "You can get your standard walnut-sized balls, or econo-sized *cojones* so that you can't put your knees together. Or you can get lentil-sized pseudo-testicles, like the ones owned by one James McDermott." I try to spit off the porch, but the globule hits the railing and hovers for a moment, the shallow dome of clear saliva then sliding towards the edge. And in this moment, I believe that gravity was invented exactly for me, and that the ball of spit contains a tiny seed of my soul that's going to be carried back to earth, and when my soul hits the ground, maybe it would get lucky and just run down some crack and fertilize a dandelion seed, or something, and then my spirit would get roots and be indestructible, beautiful, and strong. Dandelions are pretty, really. People hate them because they survive, because they don't care whether anyone likes them or not but just shoot down the toughest cord of taproot and flourish without attention, cultivation, love. Weeds are the strong ones. They call you names, insult you if you don't need them—only the fragile and dependent are praiseworthy, those that expend all their energy in pointless display, delicate, elaborate petal trumpets and simpering fronds, not plain, bold, gold buttons. But if you do need them, you're at risk, like some plants that can't even pollinate one another, or have these special bulbs that look like ginger tubers that even need to be taken out of the ground every winter.

I want to be a weed with walking roots. I look at my feet and become afraid that my toenails are going to grow tendrils, writhing down through the cracks between the boards of this sagging porch and then sinking down like magnets, like anchors, like fishhooks once they hit the ground, and I'll be trapped, unable to lose the baby, but birthing it out on the front porch in eight months, trapped in one place. I once read about some soldiers or torturers—forget when or where, as if that really matters, it seems like it's beyond time, as if history exists only to tally and relay methods of pain from one batch of whiphands to the next—Genghis Khan or our boys against the Viet Cong, like Carissa's Uncle Yar—who, whenever they came across enemy women near childbirth tied their ankles together with horse rope, tethers, barbed wire, whatever they used, to bind their legs up. Kills both ugly, obviously. There is no atrocity that humans will not perpetrate on one another. Are we taught it, or do we carry it in our bones? I saw this nature special once at Jim's where they said that whenever male rhesus monkeys take over a troupe, they just kill all the young ones. Snap, crackle, pop all the babies. "To induce estrus." I wish that I could induce my estrus, but for now all that I'm managing to do is freak myself out, and bad. I want it to stop, but I don't want to bring Carissa down by telling her about it, so I just draw my feet up—to keep them from rooting—and turn and put the bare soles on her leg.

"Hey!" she yelps. She's been talking, but I haven't been listening. "What are you doing?" she asks.

"Sorry," I mumble, "it's just that—I don't know." I open my mouth and a short bark escapes. "My feet were going to catch."

"Catch what?" Carissa looks at me like I'm a TV tuned to the wrong station, blank and agitated in the same second, buzzing with snow. My feet look huge to me, twisted, misshapen. They're about to sink into her bare leg, and we'll become bizarre acid-induced Siamese twins, an unprecedented foot/thigh pairing. We could join some cheap circus and travel on display. Our mobility will be limited, but we won't have to work again. Just put up with some rubberneckers. Now it's Carissa's turn to laugh, mechanically, at nothing. Then she begins to cry.

"My feet . . . ," I can't explain. Some uninfected outpost of my mind registers how stupid I sound and appreciates it. This is what the shit is supposed to do, any type of shit, any possible combination. Quiets the voices or slows them down to one dumb voice, a voice that you can take out for a walk in public. A voice that doesn't mind saying, "What salad dressing would you like on that?" or "Of course you can buy me a drink, sweetheart."

Now we're both crying. "Shit," I say, "my feet." I switch my gaze back to the tower. The red eye blinks. My feet won't root if they're moving. "Let's go for a walk. C'mon." I stumble down the steps and Carissa follows. We strike out towards the lake, where a small rowboat drifts on black water.

"Are you sure it's OK?" Carissa asks, as I wade towards the vessel. I snort.

"We fall in, we get back in the boat. Are you going to stand up and dance?"

"No."

"Then why would you fall in the water?"

"I don't know." Carissa watches the boat loll lazily, bouncing as I scavenge beneath the benches for paddles. "Maybe it's leaking, or something."

"Well, it's floating fine now." I walk in and stop to shudder. "Cold! Colder than the water in this lake!"

"What are you talking about?" Carissa asks.

"Jim when he looked at me and said, 'Do you know that it's mine?'"

"Well?"

"Well, what?" I found the oar and began to paddle.

"Do you?"

"Don't you even…" The bitch has never even gotten pregnant, and now she's going to pull this on me.

"Well, could it be someone else's?"

"Well, sure, but odds are it was him."

"The odds?"

"The others wore rubbers, for Chrissakes."

"So, what are you going to do?"

"I'm going to get an abortion." I say the last word extra slow, reminding myself of a "Schoolhouse Rock" animated environmentalist blurb against pollution. "PO-loo-shun," they sang, "shun-shun-shun," like "Chain of Fools." "AHHH-boar-shun," I repeat to Carissa. To ignore a wild pig? The small boat floats, rocking, a tired tin cradle on dark water. "Let's go back, I've had enough." As we paddle back to shore, the fireworks start erupting. First, a white chrysanthemum.

"Yes!" I exclaim. "Look, Carissa, now they're melting dragon tongues. They're going to lick my eyeballs. I don't want to do this too much, though: I might turn into a burnout."

"And what are you doing now?"

"What I do." That bitch. What does she do?

"And what's that?" Another burst explodes above, a long, lime green, smoky trail.

"Telling you to fuck off." Carissa sees that I'm really crying, now. Shit. I didn't mean to. Nobody's supposed to see that.

"I'm sorry, I didn't mean…"

"No, I'm sorry." I stand up, and the boat rocks side to side. I fling my arms out, and think of DaVinci's man in a wheel, each limb out straight, a female pentagram. Carissa once told me that Mona Lisa was a self-portrait. I could never have an enigmatic smile, a trace of smooth-lipped puzzle, though; I grin like a carnivore, like I'm about to bite the world.

I hear Carissa's voice, "Danielle, sit down."

"No, I'm sorry." I keep standing.

"Sit down." Carissa holds that paddle across her knees. "Sit down, sweet-ie."

"No, I haven't finished telling you how sorry I am."

"You can tell me that back on the porch." Carissa attempts another swipe through the gellid black of the water.

"No, I need to tell it now."

"Well, sit down and tell me as I row."

"Mea culpa, mea culpa, mea maxima culpa."

"You aren't Catholic." Carissa contracts her face like she's attempting to recall precisely what I am, and cannot.

"No, I'm just FUCKED UP." I turn my palms up to a series of cherry red explosions, displaying stigmata that I do not have.

"Well, isn't that how you like it?"

"You know how I like it." I clutch my fingers into fists, and then release them, fanning both. "You know how I like it."

"Sit down and tell me." Carissa looks like she's half tempted to whack me with the oar and isn't too concerned whether or not I land in the boat.

"I like it that I'm not tied to anything or any man." I throw up my chin. "I like it that I carry my home on my back, like a snail."

"You're not a snail."

"Snails have shells."

"Snails move slow."

"You're right." I lift both hands to the heavens in flat-palmed salute, just as a red-white-and-blue string of bursts punctuates the sky. "Look at the fastest snail on earth!" Then I step up on the seat, and over the edge into the water. I surface, face breaking the veil of water, gasping and shaking my head.

"What did you do that for?"

"I needed to be redeemed."

"You aren't a Baptist," Carissa snips. The idea of holding my head underneath the waves probably has a certain appeal, though.

"'You aren't a Baptist.' 'You aren't a Catholic.' What are you, my guru?" I sputter, then paddle. "Why don't you tell me what I am, instead of what I'm not?"

"I'm your friend, and I want you to get back in the boat."

"I'm fine in the water."

"You're wet." Carissa sighs and rolls her eyes. "Do you want to get back in the boat, or not?"

"My, you're repeating yourself this evening." I float on my back, limbs splayed, the black cotton dress pasted to my body as dark as the night-reflecting water. If I was filming the movie of myself, I could see the camera above so that my bare arms and legs look like doll parts, white disjointed jetsam. "I'll swim. Come on, I'll beat you."

"It's not a race. It's not a…" Carissa wants to say *competition*, probably, wants to stop and think of all the things that it's not. It's not right. It's not fair. It's not. We both know this.

"Be careful!" she calls to me. The water is wet, cold and dark. I swim through, turning my face side-to-side as I swim. Soon I feel the rocks under my feet. Some are smooth. Others are not. My toes clutch the wet rocks. They move under my feet. When I stop swimming, I hear Carissa rowing up behind me.

"Danielle." My friend's voice echoes, bouncing from the boat to the house and back. I take two steps and turn my head. The ends of my hair float out behind.

"What?" Carissa seems to strain, even rowing such a small boat. It was aluminum. Once it had been painted. Now it has a couple of aqua scales.

"Are you OK?"

"Of course I'm OK." OK? OK, I'm angry. "I'm pregnant again, maybe. I'm sick of serving omelets and burgers at the Manhattan Diner. Thanks for getting me the shifts, though." A job's a job.

"Yeah, well." Carissa stops rowing. The boat stands in the water. The water's flat and makes me think of a mirror and a rug at once. Who unrolled it? Who made the water?

Carissa keeps rowing toward me. I turn and walk to shore. My wet dress clings, hair stuck to the dress like white snakes.

The boat scrapes the bottom and Carissa steps out. "Help me with this." We carry the boat out of the water. Carissa turns it over. The bottom is not smooth. It is scraped. "Do you think that I could punch a hole through this?" She sets the oar down on top of the overturned boat. "With the oar, or maybe with my fist?"

"Don't do that, you'll only give yourself tetanus." I gather up the hem of my cotton dress, making tight folds with both hands. Then I wring it out.

Then another bout of fireworks burst overhead, every trail a discrete tendril tentacle reaching down, down to tenderly touch the interior of my ears even as the peals scream echoes and three sharp staccato rasps follow, little white flowers above, and Carissa looks like she just wants to stand at the boat and weep, cry little crystal blossoms for what we have become.

"Could I touch you?" she whispers to me.

"What?" I say. I wring out my hair now, an impossibly long rope of sun-bleached straw gone pale. It grows as I twist it, and the twist begins to coil around my feet on the gravel of the beach, then winding my shins together, a frayed freaky headless cobra circling my thighs. Carissa reaches out, and puts a hand on my shoulder. She squeezes, and the wet cloth forms a membrane that merges with her palm.

"It's going to be OK." Her words are a telegraph: I can see the yellow slip of her message, folded, a paper airplane skidding across the air and then stopping to hover outside my ear; it refolds itself to a narrow accordion and humps from the air inside toward my mind. If only it was that easy.

I laugh, sharp and bitter.

"Danielle," Carissa says, "I see soot and embers falling from your lips. They fall and build a little castle on the ground between us, black squares and glowing orange bricks. Do you see that?" she asks. I laugh and twist my hair again, then seeing it. Now the palace walls move to cage Carissa.

"Hey," I suggest, "maybe the entire lake is a moat, but one that will start rising."

"Come on, then," she says to me. "We have to get to higher ground." The fortress of laugh-charcoal has grown to my knees. It might trap us. "Let's go to the house."

My hair unweaves to become a flying carpet, and Carissa kicks away the black bricks to step upon it, and I swim through air, my hands now as impossibly long and bleached as my hair. "Squid," Carissa must have thought, because then she says it: "Squid." And the moment she says it, the steps to the front porch are flanked by two footmen, or foot squid, and I can't help but wonder if Lewis Carroll was on the same shit, or tripped from that rye fungus or opium or whatever, and the pair of six-foot squid bow from the waist in their matching brocade vests as we girls walk up the steps. The one on the left has a musketeer hat with an ostrich plume, the one on the right has an orange fez. Their eyes are the size of basketballs, big black center circles like sandwich plates. I can see the suckers on the undersides of their jelly limbs. It makes me giggle, wondering if I should explain invisible squid wearing hats to her. As I laugh, one of them teasingly taps my ankle. My hair is all mixed up with the cephalopod fins now, cold, clammy arms and wet, dank rope. Carissa must understand, because she laughs. But the laughter doesn't mean anything.

"What?" I ask her again, even though I know that there's no answer, that Carissa's just laughing not to cry, like any of us, like all of us, and I start to laugh with her, so when the first cramp tears my gut, I think that it's just part of the laughter. "Oh, fuck," I say, still clanging short yelps.

"What?" Carissa's crying now, too. Her hand is still fastened to my shoulder. My palms go to my lower abdomen, as if I could hold it in, hold in whatever it is that I need to keep, although I know that this isn't it.

"I'm losing it." Carissa cackles and weeps, nodding, and I can tell that she thinks that I'm just referring to the trip. The door gapes in alarm. The inside of the place stinks, but Jim didn't clean things out the last time that he was here. That's not like him. There must have been something wrong. Something's wrong now. I'm getting ground control to Major Tom to my brain from my woman-parts, that upside-down pear that floats beneath my stomach and on pull-down diagrams. It's squeezing. It feels like a wide stab, a scimitar or scythe or one of those blades that's a spelling-bee word, cutting a smile on my entrails. Then it feels like just a fucking knife. Just another weapon, but from the inside out. I wish that my lower torso had a cabinet, a latch that I could switch to take out my womb and tubes and wring them dry, when necessary, not unlike how I just wrung out my hair. I'm about to try to explain it to Carissa, when another one hits. I lunge into the front room, and her hand falls from my shoulder.

"Dani?" Her voice fades behind me now, impossibly small, like a child calling from the bottom of the well. I trip over dirty jeans and sweat pants. "Dani?" she calls again. Short stabs follow long ones. I make it to the bathroom. I don't want to, but I turn on the light. The wallpaper is old, neon green bamboo over silver foil. Part of it peels. My innards are peeling away now. I moan, but the sound isn't coming from me. There's some other animal in the room that carries this thing that she has to be rid of. I am attendant to this beast in pain, her impossible demands, her following crises. I turn on the shower just because the sound of the water is always nice. Rain in my room. A room full of rain. It will wash everything away, make everything good, make me clean, although I run it cold to save the hot water for later. I gather the dress up to my waist in a fat roll and peel off my shorts. There's a thin brown stain cutting across the pink and red candy stripes. Blood says hello.

"Dani?" Carissa's at the door. "Do you want me in there? Do you need anything?"

"No," I choke. Fuck. Fuck this and fuck that. Fuck it all and fuck this fucking brat. I don't want a baby that looks like that. She don't want a baby that looks like that. Bodies. I'm an animal. Am I a monster? Then I reconsider. I gasp as the meat peels. "Water." One, two, three. I wish I could scream, but my throat is plugged. "Water, and do we have any tea?"

"I'll look." Carissa's voice unwinds from the crack in the door. Her steps pad back down the hall. The lake is still on my legs. I hunker down on the toilet, damp thighs sticking to the vinyl ring. The towel rack hangs crooked, one white rag on it. Someone stole it from a Holiday Inn. Why can't it come out easy? I'm such a baby. It's just a cramp. A pre-menstrual cramp. A post-menstrual cramp. Post-menstrual syndrome: there's a phrase for a human life, a post-menstrual syndrome. Symptom. Abortion retroactive to age eighteen. "I brought you into this world, and I can take you out of it." Pain blooms again, a long pulse this time. One, two, three; one, two, three. Just like a waltz. Just like fucking *Swan Lake*. Or the *Nutcracker Suite.* Sweet. I was supposed to be a ballerina. I was supposed to be a ballerina and marry a fireman and live in a castle with a garden forever and ever and have smart and handsome children who would wear leotards and rescue kittens from burning buildings, right? Is that what I was supposed to do? Well, I'm having a kitten now, it feels like. I curl in my lips and bite down and moan. I bend over and put my cheek on my knee and pant. My hands grip beneath my knees.

"Danielle?" Carissa opens the door and leans in to put down a glass of water. "Are you OK?" Her makeup ran; she didn't wash her face from earlier today. I am assisted in my misery by the little sister of Alice Cooper. I try to smile despite everything that I even think of these things, knowing that I'm no model. If I was, what magazine would they put my picture on? *Miscarriage Monthly* with feature stories on why the hell this keeps happening, why your body persists in getting pregnant even when you don't want to and it doesn't want to let it grow? Grow like flowers. Red. I feel hot Jell-O slide with this one. I sit up and cup my right hand beneath my crotch. A doctor materializes and coaches. "Push!" he says, the lower half of his face covered in a paper mask floating above turquoise scrubs. He doesn't hold a forceps or a blanket, but one of those white paper pleated cups, smaller than a Dixie cup, that they use to dole out methadone or meds. I wonder if Carissa knows that she's the nurse? "Push!" I say.

"Danielle?" She stands in the doorway, uncertain of what to do. Stab and slide from the inside. I feel warm gelatin on my fingers. I sit up straight and lift my hand up to eye level to look at it. No bigger than a lima bean, pale fish thing in a red veil. Do you want to keep it, Jim? What should we name it?

"Danielle, can I get you anything?" Carissa's stopped crying and laughing now, charcoal sand paths in narrow ribbons on her cheeks. "Do you need tea, sweetie? Should I put the shower on hot?"

"Squid," I say, and lift my fingers towards her. "You were right, Carissa. It's my baby . . . Squid."

Vonnegut's Hat . . . or, All We Are Is Dust in the Wind, Dude. Dust. Wind. Dude.

MARK JASON HING

Caution: This story is foma* and nothing else.

My long-time love and short-time wife, Mona, is leaving me. It was bound to happen. Nowadays a divorce is always bound to happen, it's on the cusp, it's there, it's READY. Marriage is a lot like one big roulette wheel; it's a fun spin, but that ball is going to get you sooner or later. That's how life is mostly…a nice spin. But as they say, to all things an end. My marriage ended. I left my agent for a new toothier agent, while my editor is looking for newer, fresher faces with all that jazzy new writing.

So, I sit at my kitchen table with my laptop and a glass of warm soymilk, and I figure now's as good a time as any for a nice autobiography. Yes, I can hear the collective groan. "Why a biography?" you ask. "Why now?" you say. I'm at the peak of my career. I'm coming off *City Walk*; a great novel, or so I'm told by friends and family, and even the critics said it was "reasonably OK." The answer to why I'm writing this is twofold. Fold one, the reliable fold, is little Newton Hoobler. Fold two, the goodfornothing fold, is Kurt Vonnegut.

Newton sent me my very first fan letter. It went something like this:

*Cat's Cradle

Dear Hing (not Mr. Hing or Mark but Hing) . . .

Dear Hing,
I am a student at Cornell University and I am a very very very big fan of your work and I was wondering if you could tell me about yourself and I am doing an oral presentation on the process of writing, and so my question for you is, on a cold day, do you wear a hat, a scarf, or a combination of the two, or do you just go commando—with nothing?
Blah . . . blah . . . blah . . . .
Newton Hoobler.

There's obviously nothing particularly extraordinary about such a letter, except that I sent almost the exact same letter to Kurt Vonnegut fifteen years ago.

Vonnegut was someone who had a profound impact on my writing. He taught me that there's more to a joke than a punch line. He taught me that there's all these little words and phrases that most people don't even get, don't even notice, but for the ones that do notice the joke becomes a thing of beauty. And I was grateful to the man for showing me this. I looked up everything I could on him—trying to learn his history and his art. I even own a hat that once belonged to him. But Kurt Vonnegut never wrote me back, not that he needed to.

So here's to Newton, this one's for you, kid. You wanted to know me, well, you can have me. Whatever. I got up from the kitchen table and made some phone calls. I called my mom up and got stories about me sticking M&M's up my nose. I called my friends and got a story about me doing a Sean Connery imitation for two months straight. I called everyone I knew and got every story I could, and the following is my story . . . .

Little Kurt hid under the porch steps of his house; there was a small hole in the crisscrossed pattern of wood that boarded up the sides of the hollowed-out cavity. His older sister, Alice, hobbled about looking for him, calling out, "Come out, come out, wherever you are." She was seeking and he was hiding.

The dirt under the porch was thick and lovely, tickling the creases between his bare little four-year-old toes. It was cool and refreshing and slow and easygoing under the stairs on an otherwise hot Indiana summer day. Alice would find him soon enough—Kurt would probably giggle or forget he was even hiding and pop his little head out of the hole.

And where was I? Where was I in all this? Who was I?

I hid under the backyard deck in my Sunday best. The cat lived under there for the most part...the cat and me. That cat once attacked me when I was a baby and left a small white scar down the left side of my cheek. Or maybe not—maybe it was always there and it took a cat for it to be noticed. Anyway, I didn't cry when that cat drowned in our pool so many summers from now. But that was later, now was my time in the dirt.

My mother hollered for me, "Mark! Mark! You better not be under the deck!"

It was time for church. I hated church, although I didn't know at the time that I hated church. I wasn't old enough to know the intricacies of hatred. All I knew was that there was no cat and no cradle. A matrix of strings between my fingers amused me greatly. Give it a name, give it a name, and give it a life: cat's cradle. No cat, no cradle, no god. Words are just grunts that are supposed to have some sort of meaning...but sometimes, sometimes they're just grunts.

Kurt sat in a big easy chair with an empty crystal glass slinked in his left hand. Thick rivets of salt and pepper hair sprouted from beneath an old hat, and Kurt's equally graying push-broom mustache wiggled under red blood-shot eyes. Without the scotch as a buffer the big rocks of ice clinked and clattered around the glass like a baby's annoying rattle. Half a bottle of sleeping pills slowly dissolved in the pit of his stomach—plop, plop, fizz, fizz, oh what a relief it is. Relief . . . .

He tilted his old hat over his tired eyes and drifted off into space. Kurt murmured to himself, "If I ever get really pissed off, screw it all! SCREW IT ALL!" And then to someone in the distance he called out, "Oh, Momma . . ."

. . . *isn't it wonderful, I can see you on Mother's Day,* Kurt wrote in the last letter he would ever write to his mother. He was a strapping lad of twenty-two, and Kurt was currently on a train rushing toward Indianapolis, Indiana, toward the house he grew up in. Lightning crashed outside and the train moved wobbly onward. Onward to glory...onward to Momma. The chagga chagga chagga chagga of the immense, black, coal-driven engine trickled to his big ears, not to mention the giggle giggle giggle of the blonde across from him. The ladies do love a man in uniform. He smiled and flicked an invisible fleck of dust from his army greens. He nodded toward the blonde with her hair like some boogie-woogie drummer girl, and he absentmindedly massaged his mustache...which consisted of nothing more than two Errol Flynn wisps at the time.

And somewhere between Knoxville, Tennessee, and Indianapolis…somewhere between that lovely blonde and a plump brunette and a freckle-faced redhead, somewhere between May 13 and May 15, and somewhere between Saturday and Monday—somewhere, Kurt's mother, Edith, killed herself with an overdose of sleeping pills.

Of course, I came into all this much later. I was a grad student struggling to write the great American novel. So far, I only had one word: mayonnaise. Mayonnaise smack dab right in the middle of my computer screen. Mayonnaise is a tough hill to climb, but I'm there, I've been at the top of the summit for six months. The view is killing me. Mona kissed me on the temple and rubbed my shoulders.

"Having a hard time?" she asked.

"Yeah," I blinked a few times, "I'm just having trouble getting inspired." I spun around and pulled her to my lap. "Can you think of any inspiration?"

I ran my hand through her thick black hair, and she smiled that golden smile of hers—that 1.21 gigawatt smile. "I think I have something that could help," Mona said as she leaped off my lap. She dashed off into the other room and came back carrying a small oval box.

She handed it to me and said, "Let's just call this an early Christmas/birthday present."

I beamed. "Oh, Christmas and my birthday, this must be a doozy."

With nervous Chinese-noodle fingers and much anticipation, I opened the box and found a hat. A hat. It was the kind of hat from a Mike Hammer novel or maybe the kind of hat a cub reporter wore in the 1950s. This wasn't my usual style; said style consisted of simple words like *Knicks* or *Giants*. I released my very best valiant smile and said, "Um…thanks, honey."

Mona didn't miss a beat. She simply rested her hands on her hips and said, "Look inside the hat, Mr. Smarty Pants…at the lining."

So I looked. There were some words scribbled with a felt-tip marker. A signature. I made out the big K and the big V and the rest fell into place. "Kurt Vonnegut," I said. I said it like "Rosebud" in the movie *Citizen Kane*, the last breath of a dying man.

"Do you like it?" she smiled.

"Is this for real?"

"He wore that hat when he was a police reporter . . . I'm sure he wrote a couple of novels in it, too," Mona said with a wink.

She took her spot on my lap and wrapped her arms around my neck. "So you never answered my question. Do you like it?"

"I love it…Kurt Vonnegut," I repeated in a whistle. "How did you ever get this?"

She laughed and said in a Russian accent, "I av my waas."

"I'm sure you do. I'm sure you do," I mumbled as I covered her neck and shoulders with kisses, but my eyes were on the hat.

Even after we made love, I sat up and stared at the hat. I caressed the two dimples of the peak with my fingertips and gently sniffed the insides: it smelled vaguely like cigars. It smelled like 250,000 cigars, 3,000 quarts of scotch, and two wives, Jane and Jill. I slipped the hat on my head; it fit perfectly, like a surgical glove or Mona's fuck-me dress. And that's when the universe shattered.

Kurt was a skinny, tall kid who seemed to hover through the halls of Shortridge High School. Scurrying from the gym to the cafeteria, writing news stories for the Shortridge Daily Echo about jock itch or potato salad or whatnot. Mostly whatnot. In the classroom it was always, "Why can't you be a little more like your brother Bernard?" Bernard, Bernard, Bernard. Of course, there was the occasional, "Alice was quite a gem," but it was mostly all about Bernard. Except in the newsroom—with a pencil and paper, with a typewriter and a carbon strip, with scissors and glue, he could be a god. Kurt was no longer writing for that snivelly Mr. Rosewater and his English class, but he was writing for the masses of Shortridge High. The power, the ecstasy, in meatloaf sandwiches, tuna melts, sock hops, and freshly sharpened number 2 pencils.

Although that's not why he spent so much time in the newsroom. The real reason he spent so much time holed up in that little room was Archie Kilgore. Archie was a big lump of lard and muscle with a continual dirt smudge that clung to his neck, or necks as the case may be. Archie hated Kurt for reasons unknown even to the bully. Hate is a lot like the lottery; sometimes your number just comes up.

Archie would jam a big finger into Kurt's chest and say, "Hey Vomitgut, where do you think you're going?"

"I'm looking at you, Vomitgut."

"I'm watching you, Vomitgut."

"When you least expect it, Vomitgut. BAM!" he said, smacking his meaty fist into an equally meaty palm.

Sometimes there was a crowd, sometimes there wasn't, sometimes Jane was watching. Jane Marie Cox, who Kurt knew and loved from kindergarten, had pigtails then. Now her hair was long and flowing and her breasts had swelled nicely. She had a dimple in her cheek . . . a dimple that would spread and deepen when she smiled. A dimple that would vanish whenever Archie would push Kurt around. Archie was the type that pushed ahead in life; no one ever got in his way, and he pushed and plowed his way to the front of the line. He was among the first to die in the Battle of the Bulge. Kurt was there too, a young battalion scout with the 106th Infantry Division, and although he didn't see it, he could dream it—he could see that bullet split through Archie's forehead, drilling through fat and blood, and splintering bits of skull here and there. Unlike others, Kurt didn't die during that battle. His fate was worse. His fate was Dresden.

I had never been in a fight before…this was to be my first. This was my fourteenth year of life and a year of many firsts for me. I asked out my first girl, and I also received my first rejection. It was not the typical rejection of "I'm washing my hair" or "I don't want to ruin our friendship." It was more of a hysterical blind laughter. Zinka, Zinka Wesollow, she wasn't even pretty; hair that was dull and lifeless, a nose that was bony and slightly upturned, and a somewhat lazy left eye. I carefully calculated that she was well within my league; that's the only reason I asked her out—I guess I forgot to carry the one. I also finished my first short story that year, a masterpiece about a man without destiny and the Grim Reaper that loved him. I sent it out and received a letter saying, "Obviously, you're not half as talented as you think you are…try harder next time. And please proofread."

The last thing I needed was a fight, but it was the only thing I was receiving. The cafeteria students parted like the Red Sea, and they quickly swarmed and towered around Trout and myself. Trout, whose real name was Ivan Trotsky, was a big Hungarian kid like a living giant meatball or whatever the hell they eat over there. He wore those long khaki shorts that let slivers of his ankles tiptoe out. I don't know what his problem with me was. Maybe it was because I was smaller, maybe it was because I was younger, or maybe it was because I was me. Whatever it was, it couldn't be stopped or changed or avoided because Trout's fist plunged into my stomach. Which isn't entirely bad…there's a peace and calm with no air in your stomach or lungs—all that old, stale mojo and hoodoo is knocked right out of you. The pain doesn't start until you try to breathe, until your lungs reach back and find nothing.

I slumped to the greasy cafeteria floor and clutched at my gut. I came to two conclusions that day. One: I would eat my lunch in the library from now on. And two: I would become a writer, I would show them all. I would show everyone what I was capable of, once I got my breath back.

Kurt sat at his typewriter trying to remember how to breathe. Six years ago he sold his first novel, *Player Piano*. It had been almost eight years since he quit his job at General Electric to become a full-time writer. But a full-time writer was about the last thing he was. What he was was a teacher to little idiots. What he was was an advertiser. What he was was a Saab dealer. What he was was broke. He was broke with a wife. He was broke with two kids. He was broke with a dead sister.

Alice died of cancer. Her husband died in a train crash. Twenty-four hours apart. What were the odds? The odds were 2,712,003,892 to one. Kurt mumbled to himself, "Life's just a series of accidents." I heard myself murmur from the fathoms of another space and another time, "We're all victims." "Victims," Kurt huffed, "victims of a series of accidents." Could he hear me? He twitched his nose at that statement and started typing. The ticker-tack of his old folding Corona filled the room like a great organ. He hunched over the machine and typed until the wee hours of the morning…it was as if he was following the sirens' call, *The Sirens of Titan*.

Kurt could hear the sirens from deep within the bowels of Dresden…air raid sirens. Kurt and the other prisoners were forced to make vitamins for pregnant women in an old slaughterhouse. They were growing thin and pale, skeletons in beat-up army uniforms, and the only thing that kept them living was the occasional nip from the vitamin syrup. Kurt chuckled every ten minutes. His friend, Billy, looked at him and asked, "What are you laughing at?"

"We're in a slaughterhouse," Kurt answered.

"Yeah, so?"

"So," Kurt giggled, "so, don't you get it? We're protected in a slaughterhouse. In a slaughterhouse. A slaughterhouse."

Billy shook his head and murmured, "You're one weird fuck, you know that, Vonnegut?"

And then the whoosh of a firebomb filled their ears. Dresden had zero in war machinery and was supposedly off-limits to allied bombing. However, no one told the bombs that. In a matter of minutes, 135,000 innocent civilians were burned to a crispy crisp. The only safe spot was in the heart of death, in the slaughterhouse. The Soviets quickly occupied the smoldering ash that was once called Dresden. The newly freed POWs ate and looted; Billy was carrying around a lamp in the shape of a boat. Someone else had a sword. Someone even pried the gold teeth out of a corpse. The trinkets and belongings of the dead and departed were their just reward. Kurt just wanted to go home and put this whole mess behind him.

This would be the year of Mark. I know I said that last year would be the year of Mark and the year before that one, too. But I had a good feeling about this year. I didn't write today. I didn't write yesterday. Today, I looked up

Albanian kittens for six hours on the Internet. I spent six hours researching what would take up half a line in a short story. But I needed that half a line, because there's nothing like a good Albanian kitten. There's no substitution for perfection.

Instead of writing, I attacked the pile of dirty dishes. It seems like all I do is clean and eat nowadays. Eat. Shit. Clean. Eat. Shit. Clean. Eat. Shit. Clean. But I do enjoy scrubbing the dishes. Nothing beats warm water and soap…and after you scrub and scrum off the gunk, that red spaghetti gunk, after you've scrubbed off the gunk and the plate is gleaming before your eyes, you look at the plate and say, "I beat you." There's few things left in this world that a single solitary man can beat, and a dirty plate is one of them.

And I can beat writer's block. So I sit at my computer and gaze at that blank screen. I will fill the screen up and I will say, "I beat you." So, I start typing in my sporadic singsong of pecks and clicks. It was nothing but random jabberwocky at first, but it narrows down as I think of Mona. She's the girl in my English class with the short dark hair and the elfin face…there's just something about her, something about the way her shoulders hunch or her back arches. Every time I try to ask her out, I end up flipping around like a foosball player and taking off with my head between my legs. I can't talk to her, but I can write to her.

Alice and Kurt and Kurt's imaginary friend played tag in the backyard. Bernard no longer sat over an anthill with a magnifying glass in his hand and a devilish smile on his face…at eighteen he was beyond such childish things. However, as he read his chemistry book under the warm sunlight, the devilish smile stayed all the same. The flowers were in bloom, and the grass was a sharp shade of green; giggles and frolicking floated through the air and eventually through the window of their large house. It floated through the kitchen and down the hallway and around the corner and to the living room. The faint laughter fell on Edith Vonnegut's ears, but she cried anyway.

Great gobs of sprinkler tears flowed from her eyes. This was at the dawn of the Great Depression, and she was greatly depressed. No longer was she a rich jet-setter with her mink stole, doing the Charleston on top of the Eiffel Tower. No longer was there money in the bank. No longer was there a reason for living.

Kurt galloped into the room shooting a toy gun at his imaginary friend, who was now a make-believe Indian. Suddenly a pretend arrow pierced his little heart, and he clutched at his bloody chest. Kurt slithered back and forth on the floor mumbling, "Ouch" and "Eee," and "I'm dying, I'm DIE-ing." He looked up with one winking eye to his audience and to see his applause but saw his mother crying instead. Did she have a booboo?

The young boy wanted to ask her what was wrong, but she got up quickly and left. He turned to his imaginary friend and said, "Momma doesn't want to be disturbed."

I shrugged my shoulders and said, "There's nothing wrong with a little disturbance."

"Yeah, but what if she's been drinking or has been possessed by demons and she kills me with strange mental powers or a knife?"

I laughed and said, "Oh, Kurt, someday you're going to find out there's fates far worse than death."

I coughed and hacked and gave the old evil eye to all who passed me. Seventy-one years, thirty-three novels, six hundred and twelve short stories, and what did I have to show for it—an old-age home. And my kids can take more credit for that than myself. Incompetent, they said. I'll show them incompetent . . . if they ever come to visit me.

I rocked back and forth in my chair as a nurse tried to feed me soggy Wheaties. I looked at her and said, "Where are my Discover Card ads?"

"What, Mr. Hing?" she asked.

"Where are my fans? All my life I got one fan letter. One letter. One!"

"All right."

"I never lectured at Harvard, either. I would have done well at Harvard . . . I would have played big there."

The nurse shook her head and said, "I never lectured there, either."

"You ever read *City Walk*?"

"No."

"Really? It's about the country hunchback that, that, that goes to school in the city. It was big; it was on the bestseller list . . . *New York Times*. I wrote that."

The nurse frowned and said, "Well, I never read that."

"How about *Alphabet Soup*?"

"No."

I scratched my head, right under the old hat I've worn for fifty years, and said, "Um . . . *Slaughterhouse-Five*?"

The nurse nodded her little brown-haired head and said, "Oh, that's a wonderful novel. Um…Vonnegut, right?"

"Go fuck yourself."

"What?"

I took a deep breath and said, "Can you believe that Kurt didn't want to call it *Slaughterhouse-Five*? He wanted to call it *The Children's Crusade: A*

Duty-Dance with Death. I talked him out of that one."

"Um . . .OK, Mr. Hing. How's your medication doing?"

I gave her my famous evil eye and said, "Do you want me to snap? Is that what you want? Because I will snap all over your ass!"

She flopped the spoon down in my mushy bowl and left. I watched her thick hips sashay out, and I called to her, "I did! I helped Vonnegut! I did! Me! I'm not lying!"

Then the doctors arrived with their sweet, sweet sedatives.

Kurt was hard at work on his fifth novel and was having a hard time of it. When he wrote he always had his Kurt character and his Bernard character and his Alice character, but this novel was missing something. And he sat at his new IBM Selectric with nothing to fill it with.

The cigarettes were dropping faster than the pages, and then eventually it was just cigarettes dropping. So I whispered my stories in his ears to help get the creative juices flowing…tales of machines that run the world, tales of Jesus coming from a planet far, far away, tales of maniacs in the fourth dimension, and tales of dancing fools and planet gobblers. And Kurt typed as I talked.

He wrote of a man that couldn't write to save his life. A man with wonderful ideas but horrible prose. A man who was only published as filler for tits and ass. He wrote of a man who received only one fan letter all his life. He wrote of a man named Kilgore Trout.

From two beach chairs on the little moon that was Titan, all that could be seen was Jupiter. It loomed beautiful and orange and huge before us. Two men sat on those two beach chairs with identical hats on their heads and identical neon green margaritas in their hands. Kurt Vonnegut sipped from his glass, and icy green margarita mix clung to his mustache. He waved his hand at the universe and said, "This is just lovely. It's not about descendants and books and a legacy that will live on and on. Someday this is all going to go up like a celluloid collar by-and-by. And it's all about you and me and this lovely moment because this and every moment is going to last forever and ever."

I smiled and said, "You think so, huh?"

"I know so," he answered.

I sipped my margarita; it tasted sweet and salty and alien and earthy. I said, "I figured it out, you know."

"Oh, you have, have you?"

"Yep, well, my lot in life at least."

"Well, let's have it then," Kurt said with a smile.

I leaned in close and tried to get as personal as I could, and said, "I'm Kilgore Trout." It felt like I was saying, "I'm Batman."

And Kurt laughed like I had said I was Batman. He said, "For such a smart kid you really are an idiot. Look, it's not that you are such and such and I am who and who. Kilgore Trout, Kurt Vonnegut, Billy Pilgrim, Mark Hing— we're all the same in this cosmic soup. 'Man is something that shall be overcome'—Nietzsche."

I shook my head and said, "'All we are is dust in the wind, dude. Dust. Wind. Dude'—Bill and Ted."

"Wise men," Kurt nodded. "Wise men, indeed."

"Mayonnaise" stared at me from my computer screen. Mona was making dinner, and I was trying to get some writing done. She gave me my Christmas/birthday present two days ago, and I've been wearing it nonstop ever since—I was hoping it would bring me a little help. Maybe a little magic. I was about to give up, not just the story but my life as well. "Life" not meaning death, but "life" meaning work. I was seriously contemplating getting a job working for my dad when I heard a voice. I thought it was Mona at first, but it was a voice of a man. And he whispered in my ear and I typed.

Mayonnaise was the creamy spread of choice for the Nazi party. It was white and velvety and filled with wonderful fat much like the hookers that Hitler often frequented. And I typed and typed and typed well into the morning hours. I hadn't even noticed the plate of food sitting next to me and didn't even notice that the plate was now empty and scraped clean.

My fingers were cramped, and my eyes were bagged. I took off my new hat and plopped it on top of the computer screen. I gently touched the brim of that old hat and said, "God bless you, Mr. Vonnegut."

What It's Like to Be Dead in Kalamazoo

DEVON POLDERMAN

Not back in the Zoo a week and already I can't think straight. And it's *not* the five days of booze. I was raised on that shit, man, me and Bobby Bug every day, every day from age ten on. Drink you right into the sweatshirts.

It took New York to dry me out. Mostly. And it wasn't for any sophisticated television reason. I never had a moment of fucking "clarity." (I was only twenty when I moved.) I quit because I'm a personal trainer, and I got sick of having to train asswipes at seven in the morning while I was all shook out. Emotionally, I was still a motherfucking prince.

But no matter how many days, months, years, or parts of years you're dry, your body never forgets. It's wormed into your muscles, your bone, the whites of your eyes, tissue and organs and cells forever sodden. Falls somewhere between air and your mom's voice—not essential, but every once in a while the only comfort that'll wring you out of the day. Even now, almost twenty years mostly clean, I still feel like I'm in the Zoo.

I don't drink, but I like to drink.

After five drunken days of carefully avoiding any place he imagined she might be, Phil finally stumbled across Sandy at Uncle Bug's funeral that morning. It was only dumb luck the two hadn't crossed paths yet, anyway; if you don't talk to someone for almost twenty years, even if you did accidentally run into her once ten years ago and screwed her, you really have no idea where she might or might not turn up in Kalamazoo. The next table over? Hidden in Bobby's trunk? Where was she? And think what he wanted, she wasn't any more eager to revisit her Phil Lockwood past. Even love will give you a hangover. The bitch of it was that half the time he hoped he would see her, though he wouldn't admit that for all the beer in Bell's Brewery.

But at the funeral there was no avoiding it—she'd grown up alongside him and Bobby Bug, three weeds in the woods. She'd just had the sense to take that one giant step back from Bobby that Phil hadn't. Claimed Bobby's perpetual leer made her feel like she was under a spotlight, even that summer Bobby'd moved in with the two of them. Maybe especially that summer. "Why don'cha smack 'im one?" Phil suggested, but she'd just laughed, knowing Bobby'd take it as an invitation. "You don't know your friends very well, do you?" she chided. "Much time as you two spend together, that's like not knowing yourself, dummy."

Phil rubbed the tender tomato Bobby had laid on his cheek last night and winced. Well, fuck her. She'd never been able to completely let his dead weight sink, either. And since she had never left town (regrettably, Phil would decide later), and Bobby'd never left town (which amounted to Kalamazoo taking a bullet for the rest of the country), the three of them finally gravitated to the common ground of the funeral. Phil dropped his hand from the bruise and slammed the car door behind him.

The service was held in a small chapel on a hill in the center of the cemetery, and by the time Phil arrived the chapel's lot was spilling cars onto the paved carpaths threading through the graves. After the long night at the Elephant Bell with Bobby, he'd awoken too late to ride with his folks. He would have rejected it anyway. It was one thing to be thirty-eight years old and hungover in their house again as they creaked about like the dead all day, and another to ride to Uncle Bug's funeral trapped in grim silence. Might as well hitch with the hearse. So he drove alone, purposely late and even bringing a change of clothes so he wouldn't have to go back afterward, and parked on the cemetery's far south end where he could enter and escape unnoticed. This week had shown him enough ghosts to last a lifetime.

It was a cold morning, proper December gray with light snow dropping soundlessly through the still air. Crunching across the grass for the chapel, Phil craved a drink and decided he needed a reunion with Sandy and Bobby like he needed a noose. He bunched his bare hands in his pockets as he sulked uphill, gaze ranging over the headstones. "And now you, Uncle Bug," Phil thought. "You're next. Sleep with the rest of Kalamazoo's dead."

As if in answer, the maroon tent shielding Bug's freshly cut pit gaped before him.

The earth piled beside the tent was a cold, cold brown, looked as hard as granite. Like rubble. A roll of green Astroturf lay beside the dirt. Up the hill he could feel the people hurrying into the chapel, but he couldn't pull his eyes from the hole. Magnetized, Phil floated across several plots, beneath the awning to the hole's sheer edge. It dropped to a flat hard bottom. Graves shouldn't have bottoms. They should just keep spiraling from sight to whatever world comes next, forever and ever, amen, so that you never have to know how far there is to fall. Phil traced the four corners of the bottom, automatically measuring how much space his big carcass would demand. So goddamn small. And as he wondered how they'd ever fit Uncle Bug down there, he suddenly felt honor bound to hop into that too-near bottom, hide in a corner shadow and wait for Bobby's dad to plop in beside him. He finally craned his heavy neck away to glare at the surrounding graves, angry at all the fucking dead people. Just waiting around for something to happen. He spat, then tore himself from the hole to trudge towards the chapel.

He let himself in the chapel's back door, and the hum of the organ did nothing to help him feel any less sullen. The bright lights stung his eyes, the air felt a little close. Phil hid himself in a back corner to scan the dark pews. It was a full house, though no one ever said Uncle Bug wasn't popular. Many drunks have many friends. But the faces he could see didn't make any sense, just a grinning blur. Finally a head turned, his mother's matronly radar picking him out. His folks sat on the aisle to the far left, perfectly positioned for a quick getaway, Phil noted. He raised his hand meekly, and his mother gave him a curt nod and faced forward, and that freed him to begin identifying more faces. A collection of the Daddy family had commandeered the row ahead of them, and Spence was up a few more. There were others, along with faces Phil recognized but couldn't place. But anyone who dies here draws roughly the same crowd. Their configuration just depends upon who's in the box.

Bobby sat on a folding chair at the front, back to Phil, brother Mattie beside him. They were nearest the casket, with their mother, the ex-Mrs. Bug, seated with her husband right behind and surrounded with folks close to the family—his secretary and boss, respectively sniffling and muttering; a couple guys Phil recognized as Bug drinking cronies (even gussied up for a funeral, they looked rumpled and anxious). Several of Bug's brothers, each indistinguishable from the others, finished the row. Bobby twisted in his seat to whisper at his mother, snagging Phil's attention again.

The welt tattooed over Bobby's right eye shone dully, but underneath that angry mark the thing that struck Phil was Bobby's expression. Utterly placid. His dead father ten feet away, and Bobby looked bored as a fisherman. Probably asking when it'll be over, Phil guessed. The most Bobby was ever going to care about his dad's death had come last night, slobbering around a mouthful of whiskey to voice to Phil what a fucking crumb his old man had been. Fighting for it. Like it was a secret. Uncle Bug could be the Kalamazoo mascot.

Except Bobby's worse, Phil thought. And I'd be walkin' dead right beside him. Random images of Bobby and Uncle Bug collided through his head, and to make it stop Phil forced himself into one of the remaining seats in the rear of the chapel. On the seat was a memorial pamphlet.

The cover photo showed old Uncle Bug cavorting on his patio bricks, wrapped in an apron and brandishing a hot-dog fork at the smoking grill beside him. A tall glass of scotch glistened in his other hand. Grinning, drunk, lake blue as a bird behind him. Could have been snapped practically any day of his adult life. Phil thumbed the cover open, and on the inside flap was a quote:

> The proverbs of Solomon son of David, king of Israel:
> for attaining wisdom and discipline;
> for understanding words of insight;
> for acquiring a disciplined and prudent life, doing what is
> right and just and fair;
> for giving prudence to the simple, knowledge and
> discretion to the young....
> The fear of the Lord is the beginning of knowledge, but
> fools despise wisdom and discipline.
> Proverbs 1:1-7

Phil snorted, then saw that the NRC would be administering the service. Predictably, Bobby and Mattie had left the selection of the eulogist to the ex-Mrs. Bug, and as a final comment on her dissolved marriage she'd chosen not Pastor Robbins, the family sympathizer for decades, but some dinosaur from the goddamn Netherlands Reformed Church. She wanted everyone to know Uncle Bug was going to Hell. Kalamazoo is still a Dutch town, which means the Netherlands Reformed Church still holds court, and it is the perfect religion for this grumbling place. The NRC commands you praise the Lord hotly, condemn everyone you meet, die, and burn in Hell forever because that's where everyone goes. Take comfort in remembering that God loves you even though you don't deserve it. These people make the Catholics look like goatish orgiasts. Phil collapsed further into his seat, and on cue the organ stopped humming.

The preacher entered the chapel behind Phil, cutting an ornery path up the aisle to the pulpit beside the casket. Dropping a Bible the size of a rucksack onto his lectern, the old man forked a hand through a wild crown of silver hair and scowled at the assembly, poised to bring the doom. The rows of well-dressed mourners separating Phil and the preacher stiffened in their seats.

"The Lord our God!" he thundered, thick Dutch accent edged in gravel and tempest, "delivered his Proverbs through Solomon, son of David King of Israel, so that we may attain wisdom, discipline, and understanding, and wise Solomon heralds His instruction with a rebuke. 'The fear of the Lord is the beginning of knowledge, but fools despise wisdom and discipline.'"

The minister paused, glared, and slammed his fist upon the pulpit. His black figure swelled, dwarfing Bug's casket as he filled the high arch he ministered beneath. The mourners shrunk from him.

"The fool despises and *ignores* the wisdom of the Lord!" he roared. "While those who would seek the knowledge and His answer and promise *fear* our one true Savior!"

Suddenly his fiery face calmed, though it wasn't the calm of a man at peace with his wisdom. It was the calm of a man using his wisdom to condemn. Phil wanted a drink almost as badly as he wanted to see Bobby's face.

"As the Bible tells us to hate the sin and love the sinner, we must love Robert Theodore Burg. But like each of us here, Robert was a sinner. And as the Lord our God and His Son Jesus Christ who gave His life for our sins promised us, the wages of sin are death, and the Hell to follow."

He flattened his hands atop his black book, and his iron brow began to arch into a stiff glare, rising until the congregation tried to hide collectively in their own pockets.

"You may recall Robert fondly. This past week I have heard countless tales of his generosity and goodwill. Assisted his neighbors each spring with their docks or broke bread at backyard barbecues. Always a kind word. And as I counseled those who came to me, Robert was not *overtly* malicious. I myself can still recall him at worship with his family, a thin, quiet boy who dutifully studied his scripture." He stabbed his finger like a bayonet at the congregation, and his voice dropped to a whisper. "But even then the sin festered within his heart. As it does within the heart of each and every one of you!

"The Lord was not the master of his work! The Glory of God not Robert's aim! Worldly temptations enslaved this man. His devotion to the scripture fell to the pursuit of worldly goods: gas grills and power tools and pontoon boats.

And his pleasure derived no longer from the Lord, but from…the grape."

More thunder.

"Drink! Alcohol! Robert's lust for alcohol is no secret. As the Lord promises, it led to nights in the jailhouse, and ultimately the end of Robert's earthly days. But not before estranging him from the House of the Lord, destroying his family, destroying himself. In Proverbs 23, verses 29-35, through Solomon the Lord asks, 'Who has woe? Who has sorrow? Who has strife? Who has complaints? Who has needless bruises? Who has bloodshot eyes?'"

Phil pawed blearily at his own eyes, bumped his bruise and winced.

"'Those who linger over wine, who go to sample bowls of mixed wine. Do not gaze at wine when it is red, when it sparkles in the cup, when it goes down smoothly! In the end it bites like a snake and poisons like a viper. Your eyes will see strange sights, and your mind imagine confusing things . . .'

"'They hit me,' you will say, 'but I'm not hurt! They beat me, but I don't feel it! When will I wake up so I can find another drink?'"

All the black robes in the whole wide world couldn't hide the preacher's contempt for Uncle Bug and for Kalamazoo and everything else in the world. A week ago, Phil couldn't have given a shit about the old lush, and now this God-gurgling cocksucker had him thinking the dead guy was some kind of hero. Phil tuned the preacher out and silently recited his own little eulogy:

Ghosts and strangers, we gather here today to hoist one last shot in the name of Uncle Bug. Lover of life. The King of Kalamazoo. Among us today are people I've never had a drink with, and that's OK. We are still alive, we can still do that. And there are also those here who, before right now, I thought I should never drink with again. You know who you are. Bobby, Sandy, stand up and speak in tongues, because I say the three of us owe our lives to that man. *Everything* between us, we learned from oiled Uncle Bug. How to mix stiffly. How to get more after the stores quit selling. How to know any idea you have drunk is the right idea. That's the scripture that bound us, Hallelujah! We studied in this dead man's basement and went into the world to witness, spreading the good word until we'd made Kalamazoo a notch on a belt. And I, for one, love him for it, because he taught me that it's OK to be dead. As long as you have a little whiskey. He was fearless.

Last night, Bobby, that's the shit you and I should have laughed over. *Before* last night. But *especially* last night. Except you're still walking around here happily dead and drunk while I'm killing myself to live dry somewhere else. Boy, did we learn well. Shit, Sandy, for all of this, I don't even know where you fit anymore. I guess you just got pushed out. We all did. That's funny enough to laugh to, though it'd be a bad laugh for us, edgy and too familiar to really feel good. But it would have still been better. Now I don't want to laugh with you.

That's all I wanted to say. Amen.

The snow had begun to fall more steadily during the service, but there was still no wind, so the flakes fell like damp ashes over the mourners as they filed through the graves for the maroon canopy at the bottom of the hill. The headstones jutted like scabs from the bare lawn. The pallbearers led, Bobby and Mattie and some older men Phil only vaguely recognized, and the casket looked to weigh a thousand pounds as it pulled them along. There was no forced laughter, chagrined laughter, relieved laughter you usually hear on the way to the final graveside address. The unforgiving minister had satisfactorily kicked the celebration of passing from everyone, and like Phil everyone now just itched to escape.

Phil was in the middle of the line, and even with his head hung he was taller than the rest, rising above them like the crest of a wave. He marched consciously, measuring each step to avoid eye contact. The tug at his elbow caught him completely off guard, as insignificant and insidious as that little snippet of glacier runoff that cut the Grand Canyon. Before he turned, he heard her even voice.

"Phil Lockwood."

He revolved slowly, taking a year for every inch he spun, heels corkscrewing into the ground. Forever turning, dragging against the sight of her. Phil felt the mourners stream past, rushing faces, their eyes completely foreign. As though they were there to grieve him. To grieve them, Phil and Sandy.

"Hi, Phil."

She stood primly, heels of her boots together, hands folded around a purse she held at the belt of her long blue coat and staring up his chest at him. She'd dyed her hair. No…let it go natural. To blonde. Not red. Not orange. She wore it swept off her forehead, a pair of unfunereal turquoise earrings as blue as her eyes twinkling above the space where her hair spilled over the collar of her coat. Talk about your ghosts. He suddenly felt small and obsolete, caught. He wanted to crouch behind a grave and hide, but remained stoic. He pulled his hands from his pockets, then plunged them back in to anchor himself.

"Sandy." The name felt like ice on his tongue. "Hi."

"What happened to your cheek?"

"Talking with Bobby last night," he mumbled, and when she nodded and looked up earnestly he changed the subject with a meek, "How are you?"

"OK, I suppose, considering." She clicked the corner of her mouth and glanced forward in the mourning line. "Poor Bobby."

If you'd heard him last night, Phil thought, you wouldn't worry. But then, she probably knew better. Sandy wasn't dumb. The mourners continued past them. Phil towered over Sandy, unsure of his next words. Finally he just replied, "Yeah."

Sandy let the silence hang a moment, then said, "C'mon, Phil. Let's walk."

"OK."

They took their place in the line, side by side, not touching. The pace killed Phil. Small step. Small step. Small step. Like an inchworm. He wanted to bound over the people ahead of them and through the graves, and if he wasn't lucky enough to land in Uncle Bug's pit, just skip all the way back to Brooklyn and hide in his closet. Instead, he kept his head bowed, marking the heels of the person in front of him. The procession forced him to match the length of her short strides.

"So when'd you get back, Phil?" she asked.

"Couple days ago."

"How're your folks?"

"Good."

"Have you seen Spence?"

"Yeah."

"How's he?"

"Fine."

Sandy rolled her eyes, grabbed his arm, and stopped. "Phil?"

Phil jerked to a halt beside her and looked all the way down at her, slightly surprised. "Yes?"

"Is New York full of savages?"

"What?"

"Are there savages around your house?" She stared up at him earnestly, smirking. She'd folded her arms around herself. "You know. Painted savages, like *National Geographic*." She arched her eyes. "Because I was wondering if someone had cut out your tongue."

The anchor pinning Phil down reeled off his back into the heavens, and he straightened to full height. He gazed down at her warmly. She'd gained a very few wrinkles at the corner of her eyes, and her chin and neck looked a little softer. The coat hid her body from him, so he couldn't tell if she'd been working out in the past ten years. But otherwise, she was the same person. She sounded like the same person. Bobby had become a walking wreck. Everyone else had wound down like old clocks. But Sandy, she glowed. He hadn't wanted to see her, then he did, and now that he had he couldn't fathom how he would have felt if she'd withered like the rest of his memories had. If anything, she was brighter, and that brought him an unexpected relief. His gaze drew involuntarily to her left hand (the gym had trained him to spot wedding bands like a crow), but it was folded under her armpit. She followed his stare and pretended to shiver and stamp her feet so she could step back. But her smirk held.

"So how're things, Phil?" she asked. "How's the city?"

"Can't complain."

She clucked at him.

"Things are real well, Sandy," he said gently. It had crept over him stealthily, but now he felt compelled to convince her how well he was in a way he hadn't needed to convince anyone else. He began walking, head up and staring at the gray sky more easily. It didn't seem quite so high as it had before. The canopy bloomed at the bottom of his sight. They weren't far from the grave now. She fell back in step, too, keeping his side.

"I run a bigger gym now. Up on the East Side. Train a lot of people you probably see on the TV. Soap operas. Magazine models. Few music people, but I couldn't tell ya what they sing. All that shit." Phil shrugged his jaw back and forth, acclimating to the talk. "I don't know, I guess it's cool. Celebrities and shit. Lets me…feel a little bit bigger, of all things. I suppose."

He waited for her to react, and after a moment Sandy laughed politely to appease him. Phil didn't notice her pause.

"Kinda miss working out with real lifters, though," he continued, coolly lost and content. "I mean, it's not like with Spence or the guys back here, or even the body builders I trained with when I first moved out. Those guys fucking worked, man…cranking that shit for hours…practically hear their muscles. I miss it. I miss that sweat and the dirty weight rooms and blasting stadium rock. Now I wear a gay uniform, the gym's painted all pastels like a damn Ladies' Room, the PA runs this endless loop of junior-high-prom dance shit. I spend ninety percent of my time making sure people got no reason to sue us." He clapped his hands, turning a few surprised faces. Sandy glanced up, too.

"The only thing that's supposed to matter," Phil finally added, looking off again to the big sky, "is how much you sweat…last time you saw a good collar-to-waistband sweat stain?"

"Oh, it's definitely been awhile," Sandy sighed, still looking up at him. His eyes were clearly elsewhere. "Can't say I miss it though."

"Exactly," he replied. "I got a lot of pull now, but if I completely had my way, I'd change that fucking place around, all right. Rip out the goddamn juice bar and tar over the plumbing. Paint the motherfucker black. Make the faggots quit playing grab-ass when they lift. Classic rock, naturally. And gambling. You could gamble on how much dickheads could lift, throw money down on the mat and make 'em go at it like a pitbull for his cut. Mirrors all the way to the shitter so everyone in the place can see it.

"Remember when Spence and me built that little weight shed near the woods? Weights? Shit, we made 'em out of railroad ties and concrete blocks. Well, we had this bet with Bobby . . . ," and on and on, blithely rattling on about groins and weight belts and injuries. His mind reeled a million times faster than his mouth could have with twenty tongues. That's what Sandy did to him, and sometimes he didn't notice till it was too late.

"That sounds really great, Phil," Sandy interrupted. They were only about ten yards from the open grave, and through the mourners that had begun to collect under the canopy they could see the pallbearers wrestling the casket onto a short scaffolding beside the hole. The casket was clearly winning. Sandy and Phil stopped walking and turned to face one another. Phil gazed down at the small space between them. The minister pushed down the path from the chapel to speak his final angry words over Uncle Bug.

"Really, Phil," Sandy continued, looking up at him earnestly. "I'm glad to hear it. Sounds like you got exactly what you wanted." Someone behind him waved, distracting her, and she returned the wave before returning to him. "Guess you did it, huh?"

"Guess so."

I got it, he said to himself, *I did it.* His mantra. He didn't even realize he still said it, but they were there, those two short sentences sharp as the horns on a small black whispering imp. Lurking in the webbing of his muscles as he lifted, skating across his wet cock after he screwed. In the subway shadows, behind him at the show, dancing from top to tippy-top of the Twin Towers when Phil admired them from his Brooklyn roof. Phil had grown callous to it, the constant reminder.

Right now, however, the only thing on his mind was Sandy and how she'd managed to avoid slowing to a lurch like everyone else he'd seen again. He took a confident step toward her. He wanted to hear her talk, to keep testing if it was possible to stay here and live here. He grinned, conveniently forgetting that they'd been able to talk since they were kids. Listening was the problem, mostly because they quit doing it. Sandy remembered, though, and mistrusted an eager Phil Lockwood.

"Well, Phil," she began, deliberate with her words, "I keep real busy."

"What do you do?"

"You mean job?"

"Yeah." He winked. "Now who's got the cannibals?"

She gave him a weak grin back. "I work out of my home. About nine years ago I started keeping the books for Uncle Henry's quarry, and then I got some tax work, too, so now I've got about thirty regular clients. Plus what I pick up every April." She wondered why he didn't know this, considering she did his brother's taxes. "I had Uncle Bug's books until, you know . . . ,"

"That's great," he blithely interrupted. "Sandy DiStaunt, my little entre-preneur."

The tops of her ears flashed red. "Don't condescend to me, Phil."

"Huh?" Then he chuckled. He'd just wanted to see her response to having her last name thrown at her. And since she hadn't argued that, he was game for her. "I'm sorry, honey."

Oh no.

Phil felt the word curdle on his tongue before he even finished saying it. *Honey.* No term of endearment was harmless between Phil and Sandy; the small slip-ups are the ones that set ex-lovers on edge because between them nothing is incidental. They both stiffened, and Sandy's face began to redden. Groping for what came next, Phil searched again for her left hand, now exposed, for a clue. No ring. His face brightened, and when Sandy nabbed him looking this time, she set her jaw, eyes violent as sparks. She raised her bare hand and waved it in his face, startling not only Phil but an older couple pass-ing the grave.

"This what you're looking for, Phil?" she asked indignantly.

"Yeah," he admitted.

"No ring, Phil. Never had one, either, in case you were wondering. How 'bout that?" He felt a pang, but not enough to dull the enthusiasm for that naked finger.

"Sandy, don't be mad. I—don't take this the wrong way, but I'm thrilled."

"How could I take that the wrong way, Phil?"

"You know what I mean." He raised his head and took a deep breath. The space under the canopy was nearly full, and with each new mourner that crowded under, he felt his time winding shut. Thank God, he thought. If there was one thing he could count on Kalamazoo for, it was pressure.

"Look, I'm not back very long, so I'll be straight. Anyone take up your time nowadays?"

A little incredulously, she replied, "Yes." She stepped forward and took his hand, not tenderly, not bitterly, but firmly, to make sure he listened to what she was about to say. "Phil. I know what you're trying to do, but the answer is no. Even if I ignored . . . everything—and that would be dumb—I wouldn't . . . ."

"Look, Sandy, all I'm asking is, I don't know, let's just sit and talk or something."

"Phil," she challenged, marking the unusual candor in his voice, but still disbelieving him. "You've been welcome to sit and talk practically your entire life. You know where I live."

"You're still in the house?"

She smirked at him sardonically. "Time flies when you don't keep in touch, huh? Yes, I'm still there. Where else am I going to find a place that size? I need that house."

"I'm only in town till the New Year. Bargain ticket."

"Come over tomorrow, if you like."

"I will." Her chin twisted, and he knew she didn't believe him. "Get ready, Sandy, 'cause I will."

The minister finally brushed past them behind the last of the mourners, and Phil motioned Sandy with his head to follow him under the canopy. He left his hand in hers, not giving her a chance to let go. As they moved through the crowd for a place to view the casket, because he felt like he owed it to her, he added, "And don't worry, I won't be a dick. Talk shit about you or this guy, you know."

"I really don't think you could change my opinion of . . . ."

"You selling me short?" he grinned, trying to lighten the mood before Reverend Hellfire got boiling again.

"Phil, the guy taking up all my time is Rigg, and right now that's exactly how I want it." She smiled broadly—*touché*—and Phil faltered in pulling her behind him toward the front of the mourners.

"What's a rig?"

"Rigg is a person," she said sharply. She glared at him, still holding his hand, but amazed at how callous he could be.

Rigg. The name sounded vaguely familiar to Phil, but he couldn't quite place it. "Who's Rigg?" he asked innocently. "Do I know him?"

Sandy stopped. He outweighed her by more than a hundred and fifty pounds and towered a foot and a half over her head, but her little hand stopped him like a gunshot.

"What are you saying? He told me he met you in the woods, Phil."

"Who?"

She searched his face, but it was wide and dumb. "Rigg. Phil, I thought you knew. Rigg is my son."

The anchor sank back onto Phil, his neck throbbing. The kid. The fucking kid. Every morning, sitting on the overturned wheelbarrow beside the wood-pile while Phil worked the stumps from his folks' backyard. Asking Phil how much wood he thought he could split. Yanking his orange hat over his eyes when Phil raised the maul. And he'd come traipsing out of the woods, from *her* direction, probably down the same path he and Sandy used to take to each other's houses. The fucking kid. Phil suddenly felt almost betrayed that the kid had told his mom he'd met Phil, accidental meetings for the squirt to hang out with a big guy.

"I . . . I . . . ," he slouched under his words.

She looked at him, standing like clay in front of her, and her tongue melted. She'd never meant to ambush him. She thought he knew. That's why she'd been so precise, waiting for it to come up. The murmurs of the crowd quieted for the sermon, and Sandy locked her fingers tighter around his hand, like handcuffs, so he couldn't get away, and used the grip to hold her tongue, too. Phil Lockwood had always been the sort to need his bad news in small doses.

"Whose...?" But before Phil could finish the minister exploded into a fresh tirade.

"We, who gather here today to mourn the death of this sinner before his soul passes on to Hell for the rest of eternity, are complicit in the downfall of Robert Burg. Because we all, like him, are sinners."

Sandy pulled Phil with her to the front of the crowd to force him to stay, for the good of them both. The minister stood in his robes at the head of the casket, arms raised like rickety old Death himself on a house call. Phil stared hollowly at the apparition. Bobby stood just beyond the preacher, looking at the ceiling of the tent.

"Robert was a fool in the eyes of the Lord, and the Lord through Solomon tells us, 'A whip for the horse, a halter for the donkey, and a rod for the backs of fools! Do not answer a fool accordingly to his folly, or you will be like him yourself. Answer a fool according to his folly, or he will be wise in his own eyes.'"

The crowd sagged beneath every word. Phil swayed in the front as though he were drunk, drawing the attention of the ex-Mrs. Bug, Bug's relatives, even his own parents. Only Bobby did not notice.

"Who here among us took such a step with Robert? With any of our neighbors?" The minister's voice dropped into a cruel whisper. "With *ourselves*?" And back to Bible voice. "A fool repeats his folly.'"

Phil wanted to jump in the hole, but Sandy's grasp held him back. She squeezed his hand white, nearly breaking her own hand before her grip registered on him. It consumed Phil wondering, *What did I miss?*

"The Proverbs were given us to learn by, so the question before all we hell-bound sinners today is, What may we learn from this fool, Robert Burg? What can we as followers of God take from this death in order to ascend to His heavenly host and avoid our rightful place beside Robert, damned to the burning Hell of fools where we shall be roasted until time's end by Satan's devils with their pointy, pointy pitchforks? Bah!" Without ceremony the minister buried his hands into the sleeves of his robe to stomp furiously from the grave.

A moment of confusion ensued before a gnarled old groundskeeper and his hale young assistant materialized to lower Uncle Bug into the dirt. Phil watched the casket sink from sight, as slowly and deliberately as the bottles he and Bobby Bug used to submerge over the edge of the boat, and instead of air bubbles slipping out as it descended, Phil felt his hope and good will burble into the hard steel sky. No more, Phil thought. A funeral director began to shepherd people to the chapel basement for the reception (though most left to raise a glass in a nearby bar just to avoid Pastor Deadbones in his house of death). As the crowd began to mill, Bobby appeared to them from out of the swirl.

"Thanks for coming," he said mechanically, placing his arms around them just enough to take the free elbow of each. Sandy's nose flared, and Phil guessed the bourbon was Maker's Mark—it was an occasion, after all. Bobby'd drunk enough to coax a spider's web of sweat around the bruise over his eye. Phil glanced back to Sandy and wanted a drink so badly he'd about kiss Bobby just to suck a shot out of his old friend's tongue. With a flat voice and a clumsy nod, Bobby concluded, "It means a lot to me."

Then he released them and turned away, vanishing into the crowd before reappearing on the far side to shamble around the graves for the cars on the northern carpath. Phil and Sandy stood rooted in place. A number of the bereaved stopped to offer the clearly shaken large man their sympathies, but Phil didn't notice, not even his brother, not even his folks when they each gave Sandy a warm arm. She stood by Phil's side holding his hand the entire time, keeping him on his feet with that simple grip, and when most of the group had dispersed and Phil found enough strength to begin walking away from her without a look, she pulled him round one more time before letting him go.

"Phil."

He stared at her vacantly. Before long he would be angry, very, very angry, and he would drink, too, the way Uncle Bug had taught him. But right now he was still empty.

"Phil, come over tomorrow. We'll talk." He nodded vacantly, half-registering what he was agreeing to. "But Phil, you must stay calm. If you come to my house, where my son lives, you must be calm."

He nodded again, and she felt satisfied that she'd made her point. She couldn't offer him anything more than telling how things must be. He turned to leave. She watched his broad back sulk through the headstones, slanting off from the other mourners to the south.

"Oh, and Phil," she called from behind him. He didn't turn, but he heard. "By the way. Rigg likes you."

Sandy turned to leave before he'd disappeared into the welt of graves.

In New York, in my life away from Kalamazoo and the ghosts, I fuck someone or lift weights every day. Every goddamn day. Why? Because it's good to be alive. Old-fashioned visceral living: Muscles. Work. Sweat. Cum. Every time I lower that bar to my chest, I have to *live* to press that mother-fucker into the air again. Rack it, add weight, pick it up, and do it again. And again. And again. What more proof could you want of your own vitality than plying that hard cold metal off your body with raw, warm flesh?

Sex. Toes dug into the dirt, back bare to the air, aspirating woman wide and warm, four legs kicked out like that diagram by Da Vinci. Cock high and hard, animal and alive and so goddamn electric. And then I become muscle and bone, sweat thorns out my back and horns out my head, just fucking cap-tured alive. Just like the weights, always an inch from rupturing that part inside that feels the most like me. Goddammit, man. Not having sex is a crime.

Growing up in Kalamazoo, we used to fish a lot, Bobby and me. Good hangover sport, because everything is slow. And when we were too hung over even to fish, we would just troll, just kick back in the boat and drift about the lake letting our lines drag and hope that slow drift would hook a fish. Happy just to be in the boat. Those fish we caught trolling never tasted as good as the ones we caught actually fishing by wrist, you know, maybe because they had so little life in them as to be caught by an indifferent line.

The gym reminds me of trolling.

I fall in love a million times a day at the gym, because that's where I work, and because women are in front of me, flexing and stretching and flattening and swelling and bouncing, bouncing, bouncing, striped in lycra and sweat and waiting for me to hook them. And I wonder, and fall into a quick some-thing I call love, and even when I fuck them and the fucking's good, it's never more than exercise. We are essentially dead to one another. I redefined what falling in love means, and it's made my life a lot easier. That's what I learned living in New York.

Here's the thing: These thoughts—I don't have them. If I thought more and trolled less, these are the thoughts I'd have. Maybe. I thought when I quit drink-ing I might have them. But I don't. That's how I know I'm different from Bobby Bug and his dad. For me, it was never the booze. My gift is in hard, cer-tain, physical acts. Weights. Sex. Fighting. Never has that hit me more square-ly than feeling hopeless with Sandy at Uncle Bug's funeral. Wanting so badly to slide back under her skin. I am dead to her. She killed me with her son.

The Art of Losing: Death

LILA S. NAGARAJAN

Joseph's first job was as the boy who massaged my grandfather to sleep every night. He was eleven years old then. He died some thirty years later as head coffee-lorry driver for my grandfather's estates. When he crashed the truck painted bright red for good fortune and loaded with newly picked coffee beans, our entire house had been asleep. There was no phone call or long, sad siren that signaled a death in the village, but at two o'clock in the morning, every single one of us woke up with our hearts pounding. And then the dogs howled and howled until the sun finally broke into the sky. We're a largely superstitious family and did not return to our beds. Instead we wondered who had died or who was going to die or who might die.

At six o'clock that morning a blue Jeep with four policemen in it drove through our gates and stopped just inside our compound. My father walked out to meet the inspector, who wanted to be called "Mr. Mani, not Inspector, if you please, sir," and asked him what the trouble was.

"We found your lorry, license number TN4543, turned on its side on the road to Madurai, sir. There is a large amount of coffee scattered all around the truck. Pity also because it looked very ripe indeed. According to papers found in the lorry, the driver's name is Joseph, yes?" My father nodded, pulling his glasses off and pressing his thumb and index finger against the bridge of his nose.

"According to skid marks, Joseph was driving much too fast for the roads and the time of night. Too dark to see, isn't it? The lorry is like a big animal, sir, and Joseph was very stupid to be driving so fast. It squished him right under it. We employed an elephant to lift the lorry from his body. I must inform you, sir, even without conducting a test; I know this man was sipping too much from the bottle. I could smell him five kilometers away. He died fast, I think." There was a short, uncomfortable silence, and when my father didn't say anything, the inspector asked if Joseph had any family. Still pressing the bridge of his nose tightly, my father gave the policeman the names of Joseph's wife, son, and two-month-old daughter.

I was sixteen when Joseph died, and when he died, my whole body let out a long sigh of relief. When Joseph died a part of a secret died. I must have been only two or three when he kissed me. But the memory sticks to my brain like a picture tacked to a wall. I'd had this playroom, with high ceilings and two fans spinning, always spinning, and floor-to-floor mattressing. This was so I could run all over the room, and it wouldn't matter if I fell. There were toys everywhere, too, colorful plastic ones that broke the first time I put them into my mouth, and brown wooden ones with wheels and shapes and painted doors. It was a safe room, so I could be left there alone. When it was time for me to eat, my mom or grandma or one of the servants came and got me. One day, Joseph came.

He picked me up and threw me into the air and caught me, and of course I laughed. And then he pulled me against his chest and kissed me on the lips. When that memory comes to me, so does the thickness of his tongue and how wet it was, slipping between my lips and filling my mouth. Then he wiped my lips with the palm of his hand and carried me to my mom.

At four on a Friday morning, Jaya tiptoed through the only door of their hut and out into the small vegetable garden her husband grew tomatoes and lima beans in. She walked ten steps to the far end of the garden and pulled out an iron spoke that helped hold a shaky wire fence up. She untangled it and carried the spoke back towards the hut. Jaya felt oddly relaxed as she did this, first focusing on the weight of the iron in her hands and then on the coolness of the mud under her bare feet.

Once back inside the hut, Jaya walked over to where her husband slept on his back with his mouth wide open. His arm hung loosely over the edge of the cot, the tips of his fingers scraping the terracotta floor. She raised the iron spoke, pointy edge down, at chest level. She'd planned and designed this for a month now, ever since he'd thrown a bucket of boiling water straight into her face. Her face was all she'd had left of her identity, of the "Jaya before marriage," as she referred to that part of herself. He'd even stolen that from her. She knew she'd have to use all her body weight, so she held it tight at chest level. That way she could throw her whole self into the action of lunging down on his sleeping body. And she did, right into the middle of his chest. She saw his eyes tear open and his arm swing up from the side of the bed to try and pull her off him, but all that didn't last long. He soon went limp. That's when she pulled the iron spoke out of him and returned it to its original spot in the garden, holding up the flimsy fence.

Jaya took the sickle her husband used to chop firewood and tender coconut with to separate his hands from his arms and his legs from his hips. She chopped her husband up and stuffed the pieces of him into a suitcase they'd received as a wedding present, a dark blue one with a canvas cover and gold-colored zippers on it. Then she dragged the pieces of her husband through the street to the bus stop and left him next to a bus with passengers' luggage, headed for Bangalore. "Going somewhere, Jaya?" A neighbor, sweeping the night's dust off her doorstep, called out. "No, no. I must stay at home. It's my husband going away for some time," she'd answered.

When other neighbors saw Jaya pull a cot to the garbage dump and burn it along with a stained sheet they sat in circles and speculated on what had happened.

Days later the newspapers said that a bus conductor found the suitcase first; he went to pick it up and saw it all covered in blood that had leaked through the canvas. He called the bus driver who called the bus company who called police. And then he fainted. The police went to the town the bus originated in and interviewed its people.

No one blamed her, and no one really answered the questions asked over and over again by police. "I could hear her screaming at all hours of night when he was there," one neighbor told them. "Good riddance to bad rubbish. He was no good and now I can sleep peacefully every night."

"He never wore a belt in his life," a man who worked with Jaya's husband informed the police. "But he kept one under the cot just to beat her with. He got his just desserts."

"She came to work with blisters the size of table-tennis balls all over her face one day. She didn't tell me," Jaya's missionary employer said to the police, "but I'm quite sure he threw hot water or something right at her. He was a disgusting man. I would've liked to kill him myself."

It was a small town, so it did not take long for the police to find Jaya. When they did, she did not even lie to them. She said that if she could, she'd do it again. The police had to take her to jail, but then they couldn't keep her there because no one in the town would cooperate and help them build a case against her.

Seven roads meet at a faded sky blue police bunker at the heart of Kurinji. This area is called Seven Roads, and is a little like Michigan Avenue without the name brands and limousines. There are stores here and snack shops and restaurants and gift shops and ice-cream parlors and the Milk Union. If you are at Seven Roads on any afternoon at around four, you'll see a tall, dark, beautiful woman. She wears loud bells on her feet and bright, shiny saris and dangly earrings and red lipstick and heavy bunches of flowers strung through her hair. She's the Queen of Seven Roads and Kurinji's number-one-requested whore. She's also mute, just like her brother, who's a taxi driver and part-time muscle for the Queen and the Mayor.

The Queen's pimp is a man named Nath, and the word around town is that he got whacked by her brother last night. And I don't mean "whacked" as the Mafia uses the word. I mean whacked with the flat side of a cricket bat, whacked right at the back of his head so hard that a couple of his teeth fell right out of his mouth and a big hole gaped from where the bat made contact.

That's just the word; I didn't see it with my own eyes. But Mani, the lady who sells us mushrooms, was there, and this is how she said it all went down.

"The Queen of Seven Roads has a special customer, and everyone knows that. He'd buy her things all the time, that's why she can dress the way she does. Men always buying her this and that. Well, last week he bought her this sari fit for a bride, a beautiful red sari with real gold sewn into it. And with the sari he gave her a pair of gold anklets, so that every time she took a step, the bells on her ankles would ring and music would follow her. He also bought her flowers for her hair and color for her lips. And then after all that, he asked her to marry him. He would leave his wife, he said. She kissed him on the lips the way his wife never would and nodded her head yes.

"Well, Nath came to hear of this, and it made him crazy, they say. He rushed into the Queen's room and slapped her across the face and said no, she could not marry the bastard. The Queen was his prize whore, you see. She brought in the most money; when politicians were in town, they only wanted the Queen; the Mayor only wanted the Queen, and the rich, rich boys at Kurinji School asked only for the Queen. He could not afford for her to become some man's wife. Then he locked her up in the room and wouldn't let her out until she promised that she would not get married to that man. Well, everyone knows. The Queen is mute and could not say anything at all from behind a closed door, so Nath kept her there for a week.

"Now, just to let you know, the Queen had a room fit for a queen. They say there was a cooling box in that room filled with pomegranates and mangoes and bunches of grapes and bottles of coconut water. The floors were covered with soft rugs of sheep wool dyed dark red brought all the way from Kashmir, and her bed was covered with satin sheets also dyed red. She had her own telephone and radio and even a television. But the room did not have windows or even a sun light. Nath did not want his customers to worry about curious, peeking eyes.

"We both know Kurinji is a small town, and the mute taxi driver soon heard of his sister's problem. He took his cricket bat and went to the whorehouse. He banged on the door, and when no one answered, he let himself in. He found the pimp asleep, face down, on his bed. So the brother raised his cricket bat high up over his head and brought it down hard on Nath's head. Whack. And then there was blood everywhere. He let his sister out of the room she was in, and they left that house.

"And you know, the Police Inspector probably fucks the Queen, too, because she still walks around Seven Roads like nothing ever happened."

Brother George is a convert. He is the worst kind of convert, an Indian one who used to be Hindu but then found God. The Real God, that is. He came to high school assembly one day—it was a Friday, because Friday's assembly was always a religious one. Anyhow, he came to tell us students about God and how he found Him and how wonderful He was. Brother George found God by murdering his own family.

"We were poor," he started, clutching the microphone stand with both hands. He stood on stage, and three hundred of the school's five hundred students sat silently below him. Some scribbled in notebooks, and others openly rolled their eyeballs. How many times had they heard this very same opening on a Friday afternoon? "I was a poor man and could not send my own children to school. I had three children." Brother George took a breath and continued speaking. "We depended on the good people of Saint Joseph's Church for food and clothing. And God forgive me, I prostituted my own beautiful wife for money." A few students stopped drawing circles in their books and looked up at him for the first time. "I was an alcoholic, young ones. And most of the money she brought home I squandered on Shiva's Rum and Kingfisher Beer. My life was a dark one, I tell you." Rolling eyes again. Someone in the audience sighed.

"It got to be too much for us to cope with. The children were diagnosed with malnutrition, and my wife had contracted gonorrhea. So my wife and I, we decided to commit suicide. Both of us, with the children. Who would take care of three starving strays, after all? So we went up to Green Valley View, better known as Suicide Point. I am sure you all know the place next to the golf course." Now everyone was listening, and a girl in the second row had her mouth open so wide he was sure she would pass out from lack of oxygen. Brother George pulled a white handkerchief out of his pants pocket and dabbed it at his eyes. He wiped the edges of his mouth and coughed into it. Holding it close to his neck and still clutching the microphone stand with his left hand, he continued, "I am the man in the family, so I did the job of pushing each one off the point one at a time. My wife begged to go first, so she would not have to suffer the sight of her children falling to their deaths. Then I pushed the children, starting with the oldest and ending with the youngest." Brother George paused once more, bringing the hanky back to his mouth. Someone slipped onto the stage and handed the man a tumbler of water. The students waited, unmoving. They could not believe what they were hearing.

"When it was my turn to jump I was unable, as you can plainly see." His voice had lost its shaking, and he pushed the hanky back into his pants pocket. "I peered over the edge of the cliff, and all I saw was miles and miles of endlessness that could only result in sure death. I tried to jump two or three times. Just hold my breath inside of me and jump, like taking medicine or getting a vaccination. But I couldn't. So I went home instead, and I got drunk. I found the sharpest knife my wife kept in the kitchen and prepared to slit my wrists. I sat on the floor and first numbed the area I would cut with ice. Then I pushed the tip of the knife into this part of my wrist. See? I still have the mark." Brother George rolled up the sleeve on his left arm and shook it at the students.

"That is when I heard the holy voice of God speak to me. Son, it said, why do you not see me? Why do you not take me into your heart and love me? I have sinned, I told the voice. I have committed a great sin. How can anyone love me? And the voice said, For God so loved the world, he gave his only Son . . ." Then Brother George paused again, the kind of pause their English teacher called a pregnant pause. The students were whispering amongst themselves, looking at the man on stage like he was a maniac, a serial killer, a psycho of some sort. "God bless you," he said. "I was saved, and you can be too."

Gulshan had a problem with his sinuses. His father was a well-known surgeon in Zambia and decided that Gulshan's discomfort could be removed by a simple surgical procedure, a simple surgical procedure that his very good friend Dr. Patel could perform right there in his hospital. That way Gulshan's father could be right there when his son woke up, and say, "See, now you are able to breathe easily."

Gulshan did not want the procedure. He was thirteen years old, and the thought of shots and knives and cutting things open put a dark, gurgly feeling in his stomach. We were on vacation then, and while I sat talking with my grandma in her bedroom, the office boy brought in a letter to me. The envelope had three Zambian stamps stuck to the right-hand corner. I excused myself and moved into the living room to read it. I sat sideways in my favorite armchair and swung my legs over the armrest. Then, leaning my head against the back of the chair I slid my finger under the flap and opened the letter carefully because I collect stamps. The letter was from Gulshan, and this is what it said.

> Dear Lila,
> The whole thing will be done by the time you get this letter. I go in for surgery this afternoon, and I'm embarrassed to say this, but I'm scared. I've always been scared of needles and scalpels and shit like that, the shit my dad used to give me to play with when I was younger. He'd look at me playing with the things out of his hard black bag and laugh and say, "My son will be a doctor like me." Imagine what he'll say when he finds out I want to go into theater. Shit, I think that'll be worse than this fucking surgery. So, I'll be seeing you in about three weeks. Don't remind me of this letter. I think I'll go and vomit now, I hear him calling me. Fuck.
> Always, Gulshan

Three weeks later, wearing new clothes and new perfume—and some people with new hairstyles and book bags and stories to tell—we all waited for the year's first all-school assembly to begin. I didn't even look for Gulshan because we'd all heard that the Zambian group's flight had been delayed in Bombay, and they'd only get to school that night.

"Eh hum, eh hum." And the five hundred students crowded into the gymnasium quieted down. "First I'd like to welcome you all back, parents, students, faculty, and staff." As always, our principal looked tall and serious and very, very white in his white suit with his white hair and beard and shoes. "Before we continue with assembly I have some sad news. Gulshan Patel passed away following surgery in Zambia three weeks ago." There were a few gasps, and some of Gulshan's friends started to cry. The school chaplain came to the microphone and said a prayer, and then there was a moment of silence. I wanted to vomit. Had he died after writing that letter to me? How did he die?

Was he alone? Who made him die, why did he die, why weren't they telling us anything?

I left the assembly and went home. I asked my mom to find out what happened, and this is what she came up with: Gulshan had trouble breathing from time to time because of his sinuses. A new doctor, also by the name of Patel, came to Zambia to work in his father's hospital, and they became friends. This new Dr. Patel was well known for taking care of breathing/respiratory problems and promised that Gulshan would breathe much better if he had a very minor surgery. The surgery went fine—it only lasted about ten minutes—and Gulshan's father was there the whole time. Gulshan was still knocked out after the procedure was finished, and his father had other patients to tend to and his doctor did, too. It was the nurse's fault, I guess. She forgot to turn Gulshan over from one side to the other every half hour. So the blood clotted in his nasal passage, and he suffocated and died. "It was all just a big, big mistake."

Daddy's Babygirl

MARYA PATRICE SMITH

The afternoon I was to meet my grandmother, my maternal grandmother, for the very first time was only one of two Sundays in my entire
childhood that Daddy didn't swing me up into the air and twirl me around and
then place the wettest kiss his full brown lips could on my forehead and lead
me by the hand to Nacho-Mama's Ice Cream and Snack Shack on the corner
of Thirty-first Street. We walked over together hand in hand and talked about
this and that. For the most part, he did all of the talking until I got older, an
opinion, and an attitude.

One question I was sure to get every week was, "So what is my babygirl
gonna be when she grows up?" Daddy asked each time with mysterious eyes
and an excitement that would make you believe we had never discussed my
future before that very day. "You gonna be like your father? You gonna be a
doctor?" And his eyes would twinkle and shine and fill up with more pride
than it seemed his body could take. Then he'd stop in his tracks, gaze into the
far-off distance, past Nacho-Mama's Shack, and then those chestnut eyes of
his would plop down on me. "Or maybe . . . ," his face twisted in consideration,
"maybe you'll be the president of some big university. Yeah, that's it. My baby,
my Red's gonna be the first black woman to be president of a huge university."

Daddy would squeeze my hand, sometimes so hard the bones in my fingers would rub together, and then he'd kiss me on the forehead and ask me what kind of ice cream I wanted this week.

I got the same thing every week: a banana-split sundae with strawberry topping only and goo-gobs of whipped cream, no peanuts. Mama Della knew just how I liked it, and sometimes she had it made up for me before we even got to the order window. Mama Della was sort of family, or at least I looked at her like family. She dated my grandfather for a while, and from then on she treated me like I was one of her own grandchildren.

Mama Della was kind of like the community mother. When she wasn't at Nacho-Mama's, she was out and about helping people with this or that, or breaking up all the after-school fights, or keeping the older kids and their bad influences away from the young and still innocent, or making sure that no young boy with fierce hormones did any more than walk his pick of the week home and that some young girl with a seasoned and ripe body didn't invite him in.

Some folk didn't like Mama Della because they thought she was always in everyone's business and needed to get a life of her own. But we were her life. If you lived anywhere from Twenty-ninth to Thirty-fifth Street and Martin Luther King Drive, Mama Della was watching you, sometimes with compassionate eyes and sometimes with judging eyes. Daddy had been upset with Mama Della a few times before, but only one that I can remember clearly. It was the summer Daddy left Mama, my mama, and shacked up with Flo (FreeFlo most everyone called her—behind her back, of course) for three months, and Mama Della told him that he was a triflin' pig. Now, Flo, you could say, had a shack of her own though she wasn't in the business of food preparation. No matter what day, month, or year it was, somebody was shacking up with her. The day Daddy moved in Vincent Green moved out, and the day Daddy moved out, Leland Green (Vincent's little brother) moved in.

Now, I loved Mama Della more than I think I ever told her before she died, but I don't doubt she knew. Mama Della was to me what I didn't have and longed for: a grandmother. I probably wouldn't have longed so deeply if Mama had not told me that my only living grandmother wouldn't have anything to do with me. From then on there was this huge void, this emptiness, a deep growing pit in my stomach that blossomed into something toxic in my mind. So when I heard the news of meeting my grandmother I was overwhelmed. I was only ten years old and had enough on my plate with fourth grade starting in just a week.

On the morning of her arrival, Mama had a cleaning list prepared for me and a sort of checklist of things I needed to make sure someone had done and, if they had not, to do them. My major project was my bedroom because she would be sleeping there. My room was almost always tidy, so I was instructed to change the sheets and dust. "Mother hates dust, Red. Be sure to do a good job," Mama warned.

So I dusted well, and then ripped the sheets off my bed, tossed them in the corner, and began to spread the clean ones over the mattress. I stopped, almost like Daddy did every week when he went back and forth about my future, and leaped off the bed and over to my small brass vanity. I looked over my ten-year-old face and fingered my thick, bushy, amber hair. With erect arms, I flung the sheet around my body and over my head and softly tucked the edges behind my ears.

Backing away, I flipped the sheet like I had seen all the glamorous models do and tossed my newfound hair from left to right. Energy filled my blood, and I danced around my room, alone, to a song of my own. I jumped on my bed and held my hair carefully so as not to step on my precious ends. And then Mama's voice crept under the crack between the floor and door and filled my room. I buried my head under my pillow to drown her out. But Mama's voice wouldn't leave—it wouldn't go away. I remembered it like it was yesterday. The day I got up the nerve to ask about my grandmother. The day I learned that sometimes not knowing is better.

Almost four years had passed since I sat in the misty bathroom on the floor hugging my knees to my chest.

"Red, why are you asking about your grandmother? Has anyone said something about her?"

"No, Mama. I was just wondering because Latisha always talks about her grandmother, and she comes to visit at least once a month, and her grandmother lives all the way down south. How come Grandma doesn't ever come and visit us?" I watched Mama with her honey blonde hair piled on top of her head and too much black eyeliner smothering her eyes as she scooted way down in the bathtub so that the bubbles covered almost all of her. I sat on the floor beside her, like I always did while Mama took her baths.

"Red, your grandmother probably won't ever come and visit us here."

"Why not? Doesn't she want to meet me ever?" I leaned in closer and Mama scooted further down, so far down there was nowhere else for her to scoot without her legs popping completely out of the water.

"Probably not, Red," Mama sighed, "probably not. I mean, it's not that she doesn't want to meet you; it's that she doesn't really like things that are different from her." Mama blew a wad of feathery bubbles away from her mouth that landed on the foggy faucet and slowly slithered back into the tub like a large fluffy snowflake.

"What do you mean, 'different'?"

"Look, Red, you're seven years old. Maybe when you get older your grandmother will want to come and visit. OK?"

"Well, what if I'm still different? And how am I different? How can I be the same?" My words tangled and whipped together, all searching for a comfortable place to rest.

"You're just different from her, Red. Different—different like your hair." Mama sat up and turned on the hot-water faucet until it leaked at a slow steady pace; then she quickly disappeared beneath the bubbles again.

"What about my hair, Mama? How's it different?"

"Just different, Red," Mama's voice snapped, "different like your hair is nappy, and to her nappy is ugly."

Mama's voice crept out of my room just as it had entered from underneath the door crack. I was glad it had left. I wanted to stomp on it, so I opened my door and chased it to the edge of the hallway and into the bathroom and quickly shut the door behind me to trap it there. But when I turned the light on, I was completely alone, standing with my bedsheet flowing down my sweaty back.

The sheet. The sheet didn't even lie flat on my head but looked more like a crown and poofed up over my hair. I yanked open blue oak drawer after blue oak drawer, rummaging through each, one after the other, taking seemingly rehearsed glances at myself in the mirror. I grabbed Daddy's small brush with the thick bristles and stuck it under the bathroom-sink faucet. After it was completely wet, I ripped the soiled white sheet off my head and brushed my hair, each stroke harder than the one before. I kept hoping the weight of the water would make my hair lie down, but after each stroke, it sprung back up with more life than ever. "I look like a wild animal," I whispered. Masses of my curled and frizzy hair, now damp and shimmering, gathered together as if in communion, hands locked.

To the left of the sink rested Daddy's electric razor. Before I had time to think it through, I plugged it in and pushed the little button that read POWER. But thoughts of severely cutting my head took over, so I set the razor back down. Its black-and-silver shell vibrated and hummed against the countertop.

"Matches," I whispered, holding the glossy gold-and-black matchbook with *The Liar's Joint* scribbled across it. That was it, I thought, I could burn it off…that would be fast. My small fingers fumbled with the glossy book until, shaking, I struck the match and lifted it to my head and the tip of my hair caught fire. I watched in amazement as the fire ate away at strands of hair and moved quickly up, spread, and warmed my ear. The room was overwhelmed with an awful odor that I was sure Daddy would soon smell from downstairs.

So, frantically, I slapped the left side of my head until the fire was completely out. Anxiously, I stepped off the stool and flicked the fan switch on. The bathroom was hot, and my forehead glistened, the ceiling light reflected off small beads of sweat.

"Red, come downstairs," Daddy called. I stood in front of the mirror, controlled by panic and fear. Blindly, I returned my hands to the bottom of the open drawer and continued my search. The tips of my fingers touched something cool and solid. And slowly, I lifted Mama's black-handled metal scissors.

Someone was coming up the stairs so I ran over to the door.

"Red?" I heard Kahrim coming up to the door. I knew he would try to open it, so I threw my left shoulder up against the door to stop him and slammed it shut just in time to push in the small raised silver button that promised he couldn't enter.

"Red, what's wrong with you…slamming the door in my face?" Kahrim, on the other side of the door, stretched out his long neck and placed his ear against the wooden surface.

"Nothing, just go away." My eyes were frazzled, and I was fidgety and felt nervous and compulsive.

"Daddy said come downstairs 'cause Grandma is on her way and gonna be here any minute."

"OK, Kahrim," I walked back over to the counter and stroked the scissors. "OK." I stood there and didn't move until the sound of Kahrim's bare feet scampering down our rickety steps ended. With a final look at my fluffy source of shame I placed the cold scissors against my scalp and squeezed the two small black circles together until they met. I did this, again and again, over and over, until all my reddish brown hair fell, drifted, and soared in fluffy balls, filled the sink, covered the carpet, and disguised the countertops.

"Red," Daddy's rich voice was abrupt and intrusive. "Red." Now he was on the other side of the door, twisting at the knob. "Open the door and come downstairs."

I hurriedly chopped the last bunch of hair and hid the scissors back in the drawer. "Just a minute, Daddy."

"Have you lost your simple-ass mind?" His voice was loud and bold as he stood holding the doorknob, thinking only that there would never be a day that his child would ever have the audacity to lock him out of any part of the house. "Open it *now*, Red."

I knew by his tone that not another moment could pass with the door remaining shut, and furthermore, locked. I slowly scooted back over to the door and twisted the silver knob, releasing the lock, and inched the door open.

I guess he couldn't contain his anger and wanted to make sure that I never locked another door. Daddy started shouting before the door was fully opened and, caught up in his frustration like a fly in a spiderweb, didn't even look at me but grabbed me by the forearms and pulled me close to him, my face to his, until his eyelashes tickled mine. "I don't know what's gotten into you, but Red, as God is my witness, don't make me whup you. Don't you ever not come when I call you. You do what I say with goddamned urgency." He pulled his hovering face away from mine and loosened his grip on my arms. "No doors are ever to be locked in *my*—" Daddy stopped midway through his sentence and stood up, nice and tall and straight, and his eyes filled with astonishment and confusion as he looked at me completely and saw the few small patches of remaining hair that scarcely covered my pale scalp. "Red, what...what happened to your hair?"

I couldn't do anything but lower my eyes. "I cut it, Daddy." My words mumbled together and sounded spineless. And Daddy looked down at me, full of disgust and pity, because Daddy did not believe that women should cut their hair.

"Why, Red? Why?" he asked, but his eyes said that he already knew. His words were now soft and careful. Daddy hadn't looked at me, really looked at me for a long time. And the more he looked the less he recognized me. He saw my ten-year-old eyes, and saw for the first time that they were older, had seen things, and had been hurt, though I would never admit it. Daddy saw that there was something missing, the look that he thought should be on the face of all children, that look of carefree innocence and desire for discovery. Instead, he saw shameful, insecure, aged eyes, and the thought of this crept into him like a disease, spreading rapidly and taking over his entire body. How had he not known, not seen this change in *his* babygirl before now?

"Grandma's coming, Daddy. She'll be here any minute and . . . *and I want her to like me*. She'll like me now, right? She'll like me now, Daddy." My head flopped down and hung, like a puppet with a string tied to my chin that someone kept pulling down. Daddy couldn't look at me anymore, and so he walked past me and over to the counter. His hand dove and swam around in the sink full of my hair and then he turned to me and pulled me to him. "Oh, Babygirl..." He cupped the back of my cool head into his palm and pressed my face into his chest. I shamefully hid my wet eyes in his white button-down shirt with blue stripes and protruding stomach. Shameful because I was glad it was gone. I wanted it gone, but I knew Daddy thought women weren't supposed to cut their hair. But I had Daddy's love; it was my grandmother's I was after.

"I just wanted her to like me, Daddy."

"I know, Red. Damn, I know." He bowed his head and rested his lips on the top of my fuzzy scalp and then gently kissed me, just once.

Mama Della was the only person who didn't ask me about my hair. And she was the only person I told the truth to. And probably the only person I didn't have to tell.

May the Force
Be with You

JULIA BORCHERTS

The minute I saw Darth Vader walking through the door of the gay bar, I knew I was going to end up lying to my wife. It was Halloween night, and we were driving home from my parents' house, the twins asleep in their chocolate-smeared Winnie-the-Pooh costumes, their chubby fists still clutching the plastic pumpkins that held the rewards of their evening expedition. Cindy's dark ponytail swung around as she daubed their faces with baby wipes, and she patted my arm as I drove. For her, the entire world seemed to exist inside this car, and she liked it that way.

I loved my wife, and most nights that was enough. But the sight of that mysterious, black-clad figure made the heat shoot up through my legs and into my crotch, and the next thing I knew, my dick was straining against my khakis, and I felt like I was about five seconds from pole vaulting out of that Volvo and into the club to find him.

Now, as I've said, I love my wife and, strictly speaking, I've never given her any reason not to trust me. Oh, there's been the occasional quickie blow job, complete with condom, on the way home from work (which really doesn't count since it's about the same as taking a shower in a raincoat), and when she's back in Michigan visiting her mother, I've been prone to head over to the gay bar after her ten-o'clock check-in phone call. But I don't consider myself a restless man, and it makes Cindy proud to have a husband who likes to volunteer as a coach for the Little League but doesn't flirt with the mothers. She hasn't said anything to me about it, but I know it secretly makes her feel secure that she has never once seen me ogling another woman.

But sometimes after she's scrubbed her face and put on a Laura Ashley nightgown and tied her hair up in a ribbon and gone to bed, I'll sneak downstairs to the den, pull a box out of the back of the closet labeled "Old IRS Forms" and select a movie from the *Star Wars* trilogy. I pop it in the VCR, take off my pants and boxer shorts, and lie down on the leather couch. I fast-forward to the scenes where my Prince of Darkness arrives, stroking my penis with a silky black scarf till it grows hot and red and wet at the tip. When Darth steps into the Death Star and breathes heavily with those scuba-mask sounds, I stick my fingers into a jar of Vaseline and thrust them, one at a time, up my butt while I masturbate. And then, when he grips the joystick of the Death Star as he chases Luke Skywalker across the galaxy, I grab the Darth Vader Action Figure from the bottom of the box, and slide it, head first, in and out of my rectum while I finish jerking off into the scarf. The whole procedure takes about fifteen minutes, and I've been doing it since I was twelve. I have asked Cindy to buy black sheets for our bed, but she prefers pastel florals. All the same, I often wonder if she'd wear a gas mask to bed if I asked her to.

I looked over at Cindy, who was humming to herself, completely oblivious to the tent pole sticking up in my pants. I briefly considered whipping around into the parking lot and leaving her and the kids in the car with the motor running, but I knew that the shock of seeing me commit an illegal U-turn would immediately alert her that something was wrong even before I muttered whatever lame excuse I could concoct for having to dash into a gay bar for fifteen minutes. I pulled my windbreaker tighter over my hips and tried to think of old nuns, but the voluminous black habits led to thoughts of Darth Vader's cape, so I forced myself to concentrate instead on sheep, which have never been one of my kinks.

"What are you thinking about, honey?" Cindy asked, damn near causing me to lurch off the road.

"The petting zoo," I replied, patting her knee. "Maybe we can take the kids there tomorrow. And how about you, all lost in thought?"

She smiled at me with wide green eyes and tucked a strand of fine, dark hair behind her ear. "I was thinking it might be time to plan for another baby."

"Well, we're out of condoms anyway," I joked.

"No, I'm serious," she said.

"We've already got two, we never sleep as it is, and we're running out of bedrooms." I put on my best Ricky Ricardo face. "Please 'splain, Lucy."

"The twins are almost three, and I miss having a baby around the house." She snuggled up to me over the gearshift. "And you're so good with them."

In a way, I liked the idea. Despite the fact that my wife didn't exactly knock my shorts off, I loved creating a family with her. There was something worthwhile and satisfying about welcoming tiny versions of myself into the world and nurturing them through their various stages. It didn't hurt, either, that so far, all of my kids looked like me. And it was a comforting sort of proof that everything was OK, to have an adoring family that looked up to me to provide for them.

But another part of me heard a trap snapping shut in her words. And in the meantime, I had to figure out how I was going to ditch them and get back to that bar before it closed, or worse, before Darth Vader left and went somewhere else. My mind jerked like the gears of the Volvo that I kept distractedly gnashing. What could I tell her? That I was running out for cigarettes? Nobody smoked, unless the twins had taken it up while I wasn't paying attention. A forgotten wallet back at Mom's? No, Cindy would sensibly insist on calling my mother herself to make sure the wallet was there before she let me drive all that way back over. A sudden craving for tacos? She knew I wouldn't eat anything that might give me gas. Jesus!

I marched into the house with a twin on each hip. We got them ready for bed together, with me getting more frustrated as each minute ticked by without getting any closer to a plausible excuse. This was going nowhere. When the kids asked for their bedtime story, I just about slapped them. I asked Cindy to read to them for a change, and told her I was going into the den, where it would be quiet, so I could concentrate on some work I'd brought home. I strolled down the hall, shut the door tight behind me, and plopped into my desk chair.

I tried to think. A sudden medical emergency? She'd insist on going with me, or worse, sending my parents. A forgotten office party? No, she knew everyone there on a first-name basis and would insist on calling whatever house I said I was going to and asking if she should send a bottle of wine or some homemade chip dip along with me. A sudden errand at Kinko's? What could possibly be so important that it couldn't wait until at least Sunday?

In frustration, I spun the chair around and snapped on the computer. Maybe I could have virtual sex with someone. That might take the edge off, since I wasn't any closer to getting out of the house tonight.

I cruised through the chat rooms, distracted for a few minutes at a fisting site, pausing for a few minutes more at a debate over bare-backing, the proponents of this backlash trend insisting that sex had become too sterile in the last couple decades, and that you'd never know a mind-blowing orgasm until you let go of all your inhibitions and surrendered to the danger inherent in breaking that last taboo. It didn't take long to find what I was looking for. Another guy who had the video hookup so we could watch each other jerk off. I had heard of the old-fashioned way, where people typed smut back and forth, but it didn't seem too erotic to try to type with your left hand and masturbate with your right. Besides, I'm a man, so I like to have visuals.

So, I found this guy. No Darth Vader costume, but not bad looking. Typical tall, dark, handsome, muscle shirt and blue jeans. Great big cock. We unzipped, pulled them out and started to get down to business. I leaned back in my chair and watched him pull up his shirt and tweak his pierced nipples while we stroked ourselves. I could tell he was staring at my penis, and it turned him on. My breathing was coming out in harsh gasps when I heard the door behind me open. I let go of my cock and whipped my head around as Cindy came in with a plate of sandwiches. I dove for the monitor and slammed it off, noticing as I did that my video Romeo had stopped playing with himself and was laughing uncontrollably.

I grabbed my zipper and yanked it through half the pubic hair on my testicles, which caused me to scream, although fortunately, my cock went into an immediate wilt, so I didn't have to explain any unsightly bulges. I flipped my shirttails over my half-zipped fly and turned my rage on Cindy and her sandwiches. "What the HELL are you doing, bringing me goddamn TUNA MELTS at midnight?"

She looked at me like I'd hit her. "I just thought you might be hungry, sweetheart." She continued to hold the plate out toward me, and her chin trembled a little, which made me feel guilty and furious at the same time. Then I noticed her looking at the bottle of Lubriderm on the desk, and then over at the video monitor. I needed to head this off before it went five seconds further, and, as everyone knows, the best defense is a good offense, which I've found to be especially true when dealing with my wife. As I mentioned before, she likes her world to stay small and is therefore pretty passive about allowing arguments to be deflected to keep the status quo.

"I told you I wanted to CONCENTRATE, and you can't even leave me alone long enough to do that! Well, I've had it!" I yelled, an idea coming to me. "I need to get out of this house right now! I'm going out for a drive in the car so I can have some peace and quiet and some time to THINK!" And I zipped up my jacket and stomped self-righteously out of the den, with Cindy and the sandwiches trailing behind me.

"Honey, what's wrong with you?" she asked as my greasy hand slipped off the doorknob into the garage. "You're not acting like yourself at all, and you never use profanity with me. What's the matter?"

"Just let me cool off for a bit and I'll be fine," I said, wiping my hand off in my jacket pocket and looking her squarely in the face but avoiding her eyes. "You know I'm under a lot of pressure at work right now, and it's not any easier when you stand here and hound me. I'm going out to drive around for a while, and then I'll be fine." I walked into the garage and opened the car door.

"But are you sure you should be out?" she asked. I knew she still smelled a rat, and it worried her. "They're predicting a storm later tonight, and the winds are supposed to get up to sixty miles an hour. The National Weather Service said to bring any patio furniture in from the deck, and they've issued a small-dog alert."

"Can't you just FOR ONCE leave me alone?" I shouted, as I pictured my car getting totaled in the parking lot of the gay bar by flying poodles. I started the Volvo, and all that backed-up semen made me rev the engine while I waited for the garage door to go up.

"Well, at least take an umbrella," she offered, but I roared out of the garage and pulled out of the driveway before my conscience could get the better of me.

Once out of the driveway, I switched the radio from NPR to a pulsating Top Forty dance-mix station and dove into the glove box for a breath mint. I forced myself to drive the speed limit to the bar and combed down my hair with my fingers at every red light. I checked and rechecked my teeth in the side-view mirror, certain I'd find a black speck or a hanging sliver of lettuce. After ten of the longest minutes of my life, I pulled into the parking lot of Fort Dicks.

For those of you who have never been there, Fort Dicks is not an army base, but an alternative-lifestyle nightclub housed in what used to be a National Guard Armory building on the edge of town. The exterior hasn't changed, other than the discreet sign that flashes above the door. But where the inside used to be filled with guns and ammo, it's now home to a whole different sort of weapon. I couldn't wait to get my hands on one.

I raced the Volvo around to the back of the building and lurched into a parking slot next to a truck, forcing myself to slow down as I strode to the entrance at the back of the building. The first time I'd come here, three years ago, I was so terrified that I'd circled the block for half an hour with a wad of condoms stuffed in my pocket and a Brigham Young baseball cap shoved down to my nose, unable to drive up to the building but unable to go home, either. When I'd finally worked up the nerve to go in, I kept whipping my neck around like a periscope every time a man appeared in my peripheral vision, panicked that I'd be caught red-handed, so to speak, by a church usher or a VP from the brokerage house who had seen me sneaking in. Fortunately, I had never once run into anyone even remotely familiar, so the terror that used to squeeze my gut subsided into the jumpy sort of warm flood you get when you feel like you're about to start really living your life.

I walked up to the door and checked my reflection before pulling it open. Khakis pressed, mustache trim and neat, windbreaker zipped up only halfway so as not to appear too uptight. I turned sideways a little. Stomach still pretty flat thanks to three days a week in the company workout room, receding hairline not too visible thanks to the frantic hair fluffing in the car. I opened the door and walked in the entrance. The light was dim, and the hall was narrow, with a coat check off to one side and a Joan Crawford look-alike checking coats. At the end of the hall was a good-looking man, tall and crewcut, dressed in a pink vinyl halter top, black patent-leather lace-up Daisy Dukes, fishnets, and heels. To top it off, he was wearing bunny ears, a bow tie, and a cotton-tail. He was collecting a cover charge from a couple who had come as a nun and a Nazi.

I walked up to this Playboy Bunny gone bad and pulled out my wallet while she welcomed me to Fort Dicks. I peered over her shoulder while she introduced herself—her name was Eureka Fish—and tapped my foot while she pulled a roll of bills from her halter top to give me the change back from the twenty I'd given her. I put the bills in my wallet, declined the hand stamp, and walked into an acid trip of Transylvania. Liquid spiders and furry bats dropped from the ceiling and retracted back up. The walls were covered with black and orange reflective paper, and dry ice steamed out of cauldrons in the corner around tombstones and wooden crosses. A lifelike cypress tree draped itself next to the entrance, its curved branches clammy and drooping like a witch's claw. Voodoo candles lined the bar, interrupted with plastic jack-o'-lanterns. Some of the pumpkins were filled with candy, others with condoms. The condom pumpkins were labeled TRICK, while those with candy said TREAT. The only other illumination was provided by the staccato strobe lightning bolts, which kept time for the Janet Jackson remix that was booming across the dance floor.

The strategically posed platforms that normally showed off go-go boys in construction boots and tighty-whitey Fruit of the Looms had been replaced by elevated coffins. And the undead who rose up from the pinewood boxes in their Halloween drag ranged from a Jeffrey Dahmer impersonator who danced around his coffin clutching a giant barbecued turkey leg (who on earth did he think he was going to get lucky with in that getup?) to a Girl Scout complete with a beret and a sash full of badges. The worst was a guy who had dragged out in a white tank top and a red-and-white checked cooter skirt with daisies on it. He was wearing enough makeup to make Tammy Faye Bakker look cornfed, and he had glued matching curly brown wigs to both his head and his crotch, so that he had both a giant perm and a huge bush sticking out of the skirt. His Virginia Slim Menthol 100 kept sliding off his crimson lips as he teetered back and forth across the coffin on six-inch white patent-leather platform heels. Fascinated and repelled at the same time, I crept closer through the flashing haze. As he thrust that giant cloud of pubic hair out into the crowd in some bump-and-grind stripper imitation, I noticed an unwrapped condom stuck in the fur. She was truly more frightening than that Jeffrey Dahmer.

I suddenly felt like the most conspicuous person in the room. I normally wear Docker khakis and oxford shirts so that I'll feel like I blend in. Short hair, no jewelry, not even a watch, Doc Martens low tops. But in the middle of this surreal S&M scene, my outfit screamed "novice." I became instantly terrified that someone would notice and drag me off to some corner as a sacrificial virgin.

And then I saw the object of my affection, Darth Vader, walk through a door at the other end of the bar. I dove across the sweaty cesspool of the dance floor and immediately had a spike heel ground into my instep by Mae West.

"Ouch!" I yelled, glaring at her. She kept right on dancing, and looked down her long nose at me, daring me to be so gauche as to mention her dance-floor faux pas. I decided to anyway.

"Would you please get rid of those killer heels?" I demanded. "Don't you have a purse or something that you could stuff them in?"

"Sorry, darling," she cooed airily, "but all I have room for in my evening bag is a tube of lipstick and a revolver."

Darth Vader had disappeared again, and I was getting crabby. "Well, watch where you're stomping," I yelled at her. "Even in heels, you dance like an elephant." I tried to push through the crowd, but Madonna had started singing "Ray of Light," and a wave of dancers surged out of nowhere, flinging me back into Mae West.

"You think you're so butch in your little Eddie Bauer getup," she snarled, "but you aren't half the man your mother was." And she spun on her spike heel and flipped the back of her wig into my face.

I plunged across the dance floor, elbowing my way past the entire cast of The Village People attempting the lambada, and a schoolgirl who accidentally hit me in the nose with her Donny Osmond lunchbox. I saw a black cape swirl over to a corner and ran over to my intended as he paused at the entrance to the men's room. I tapped him on the shoulder. He spun around, and I discovered, to my horror, that it wasn't Darth Vader at all, but a very predatory-looking Dracula. He grabbed my wrist, dragged me into the men's room, pinned me against the wall next to the condom machines, and bit me on the neck.

"What the fuck did you do that for?" I yelled, as I slapped at him and dodged past his cape.

"I know that look, you boy-next-door, you," said Dracula. "Here, take my card and call me when you calm down."

"You'll be hearing from my lawyer," I screamed as I ran back into the club.

The music had switched to a Toni Braxton ballad, and the movements on the dance floor had slowed to a rainbow sludge, except for Mae West, who had discovered another Mae West in identical drag and was preparing to scratch her eyes out if she didn't leave. I circled the perimeter, my eyes adjusting to the slower bursts of hazy light. A couple walked off the dance floor, dressed like Bert and Ernie, but with the added touch of bondage gear: Bert and Ernie in black leather chaps, studded leather armbands, leather vests and masks. A gingham-checked Dorothy, straight from Oz with her ruby slippers and perfect brown braids, was checking me out as I made my way around the far side of the dance floor. As I got closer, I noticed that Dorothy was at least fifty years old and had a gray goatee. I smiled at her and kept walking. She didn't smile back.

And then I saw him. He was sitting on the floor by a tombstone, clutching something in his black-gloved right hand. I stopped short, gasped, and felt my dick get hard. I didn't even notice an out-of-control nurse run up the back of my heel until she yelled at me to get my brake lights fixed. My vision narrowed until I felt like I was watching a movie. Smoky light, chalky tombstone, startling black figure. I crept closer, almost holding my breath. I could make out narrow shoulders and long arms under the cape. Black engineer boots, probably a size twelve. Long legs in leather pants, bent at the knee and spread apart. Other than that, he was long and lean, the only thing I could tell about Darth Vader was that to sit like that, he had to be young. I got closer and saw that what he was holding was money. A rent boy? No problem. I had money.

I walked up and stood in front of him. His mask tilted in my direction, but he didn't get up. I held out my hand, a twenty-dollar bill in it. He took my hand, stood up, and led me through the crowd, slicing through the boas, veils, and chiffon, all striking poses and vogueing to Cher. We walked back to the same bathroom Dracula had dragged me into, not saying a word, which was how I wanted it. Darth Vader held open the door to the large handicapped stall at the end, and I entered. He closed the door, locked it, turned to me, and motioned to the furry restraints mounted to the wall above my shoulders. I wanted to leave one hand free, but I snapped the other wrist and leaned up against the wall as he dropped to his knees and unzipped my pants.

My erection sprang out and smacked him on the side of the black plastic mask. I was delirious. I closed my eyes, and visions of Darth Vader unleashing that glowing, phallic sword as he faced Obi Wan Kenobi ran through my head as he lifted the mask enough to suck me in. No condom. Pretty bold. Even for a hustler. It made me go rock hard. I felt a ridge of narrow, slightly crooked teeth, full lips, and a tongue that knew what it was doing. I thought about Darth Vader swirling gracefully around the metal floor with that huge pink phallus as he gracefully beheaded Obi Wan Kenobi and caressed the side of the mask. I wanted to explode, but something wasn't quite right. Two things, actually. First, with that mask pushed up, I kept getting distracted away from my fantasy and confronted with the unwelcome idea that this was not really Darth Vader, just some trick. And second, the fantasy always involved me jerking off with him up my ass. I put my hand on his shoulder. "Put your mask back on and fuck me," I told him.

He pulled my pants down below my knees. I swiveled my locked left wrist around and bent over, grabbing my penis with the other hand and looking over my shoulder at him. He grabbed my hips and ripped me open as he plunged up inside me. No condom, no lube, and it hurt like hell, but I didn't care. It was happening, it was really happening! My jaw dropped, and I exploded all over the wall as that black mask loomed over me and receded, and those black-gloved hands pinned my hips. And then I heard him start to groan, and he shoved all the way up and damn near tore my wrist out of the wall, jerking my ass back toward him. He pulled out, and I leaned against the cinder-block wall, panting, as I watched the trickle of semen and blood run down the inside of my leg. I heard the leather pants zip up. I kept staring at the wall. And then he reached around to unlock my wrist. The black sleeve slid down from the end of the glove, and I noticed tanned skin, a scattering of fine, dark hair and . . . a lesion.

No, it couldn't be. It had to be a birthmark. Had to be. Darth Vader unlocked my wrist, handed me a wad of toilet paper, and walked back into the club. I locked the door, sat down on the toilet and convinced myself that I hadn't seen that. Purple spots from the orgasm. My conscience playing tricks on me. Someone slipped a drug into my drink. Oh wait, I hadn't had a drink. What the hell had I done? I wanted to go home.

I stuffed a wad of toilet paper up my ass, pulled my pants up and staggered out into the bar. It was a bruise. Someone had handcuffed him earlier. Just a bruise.

The music had moved on to Ministry. "Every Day is Halloween." I hoped not. I replayed the scene over and over in my head while the strobe lights flashed violet through the eerie, mechanical vocals, desperate each time to notice a detail that could drain the malignancy from that mark of the devil on his forearm. A black cape swooped past me, and I almost fainted, but as he landed at the bar, I noticed it was only Batman. My legs got stronger, and I hurried out of there, flat-out running past the crew-cut Playboy Bunny at the door and into the parking lot. I leapt into the Volvo, locked all the doors, and floored it out of the parking lot.

I sneaked into the house, praying that Cindy wouldn't be waiting up for me, and thanked God that it was dark. I crept down to the hall closet, groped around in the dark till I found one of her Summer's Eve douches, hoping like hell it was the vinegar one, and locked myself into the guest bathroom. I cranked the water up as hot as I could stand it, grabbed the douche, discovered that it was Springtime Flowers, but took it into the shower with me anyway. I scrubbed every inch of my skin, over and over, inside and out. I stayed in that shower till it ran cold. I stepped out and took two fluffy towels and buffed myself till I shone bright pink. I tiptoed into the bedroom, opened the door to the "his" walk-in closet, and pulled out some pajamas. I grabbed my slippers from the shelf and my robe from the hook. I walked outside and threw the empty douche into the neighbor's trash, then came back into my house and into the kitchen. I turned on the light and walked to the granite counter.

Cindy had left me a plate of oatmeal cookies with a note that there was a glass of milk in the fridge. I took them over to the breakfast nook and leafed through a gardening catalogue, mentally noting what I'd like to plant for a perennial border. The pineapple basil might make a nice winter herb garden addition for the sunporch, I noticed, as I glanced around the kitchen. This was my home. This was my life. This was where I belonged. I loved my wife and kids. This was what I wanted. It was permanent. What happened earlier wasn't real. This was real. The other was a fantasy. It hadn't happened. I had to put it out of my mind.

I heard Cindy stirring back in the bedroom. I put the catalogue away, rinsed my dishes, put them in the dishwasher, and wiped the table. I rinsed the dishcloth. I walked back down the hall to the bedroom, hung up my robe, and set my slippers on the shelf. I walked over to the bed, slipped under the covers, put my arm around my wife, and kissed her cheek. She stretched out, and I rubbed the beginning of a hard-on against her nightgown, flannel to flannel. She turned around and smiled at me, rubbing her tongue across my lips and sliding it into my mouth. Her left hand slid down my abdomen and closed over my erection, her need for reassurance apparent under the veneer of lust.

"Are you all right?" she asked me, putting her other hand up to my face, my signal that there weren't going to be any repercussions from the Tuna Melt incident.

"Everything's fine, honey," I reassured her, pulling her towards me. "Now let's get serious about that baby."

The Whole Ball of Wax: The Meshing of Point of View, Time, Event, Language, Image, Scene, and Tone in Vladimir Nabokov's *Lolita* and *King, Queen, Knave*

MICHAEL CURTIN

Vladimir Nabokov tells us in "Good Readers and Good Writers" that of the three points of view from which a writer may be considered (storyteller, prophet, or enchanter) it is "the enchanter in him that predominates and makes him a major writer."[1] Nabokov is never bashful about standards he proposes. *Lolita*[2] and *King, Queen, Knave* (KQN),[3] arguably Nabokov's two best fictional works, offer the good reader the opportunity to see the techniques a writer may leverage to evoke this "enchantment," as he calls it.

Lolita, which still generates controversy some forty years after its original publication, is a first-person narrative told by the infamous Humbert Humbert, a pedophile in every sense of the word, a lover of "girleens," or "nymphets" as he so often refers to them. Written by Humbert from the confines of a prison cell, complete with a fictional introduction by one Dr. John Ray, and "published" after Humbert's death by heart attack, the novel finds its immediate sense of address in a jury which is to decide Humbert's fate. The arc of the narrative follows Humbert's despicable, desperate, and yes, loving obsession with Dolores Haze, the pubescent daughter of Charlotte Haze, the woman from whom Humbert first rents a room, and later marries as a way to cover his designs on Charlotte's daughter. No less dark in its subject matter but with many archetypal precursors, *King, Queen, Knave* is a twisted riff on the classic love triangle, following the young and impressionable Franz to Berlin, where he finds employment with his uncle, Dreyer, a clothier married to the beautiful and manipulative Martha. An affair between the inexperienced Franz and (his aunt, by marriage) the experienced Martha, ensues. They soon realize, as do we, that there is no other way: Dreyer must be killed, simple as that. But, of course, their tale is anything but simple.

An uninitiated reader may find the premise of either novel unsavory enough to convince him or her to stay far away from the frontier of that first page. And truth be told, there are certainly some repellant slices of human nature on display in both novels. But the other more singular truth is that Nabokov elevates these books beyond their subject matter to the level of art. And what elevates them is precisely the brand of enchantment or magic he speaks of.

To say a book succeeds strictly because of its dialogue or use of image or flexibility of point of view is much like trying to define the singular spice in a recipe which brings off a grand repast—all the ingredients are at once necessary and irreducible. Still, one might argue that certain ingredients in certain dishes are more crucial than others because they influence by their sheer gusto the character of all other ingredients. If one extends this meal metaphor to the story elements in *Lolita* and *King, Queen, Knave,* one could argue that it is Nabokov's generous infusion of ironic distance which renders these books so savory. Ironic distance keeps them from sinking under the weight of their dark material and makes these novels most keenly resemble each other. We see a good example of this when Humbert Humbert is fantasizing about killing Charlotte, Lolita's mother, to more easily have his way with the daughter:

> …all I had to do was to drop back, take a breath, then grab her by the ankle and rapidly dive with my captive corpse. I say corpse because surprise, panic, and inexperience would cause her to inhale at once a lethal gallon of lake while I would be able to hold on for at least a full minute, open-eyed under water….But what d'ye know, folks—I just could not make myself do it!!

Similarly, in *KQK*, when the young Franz becomes sick during one of Dreyer's parties, we follow him to the toilet, where he "…emitted horrible sounds, recognizing in the intermittent torrent a medley of food and drink the way a sinner in hell retastes the hash of his life."

Both scenes—one an imagined murder, the other the visceral description of a character vomiting—are successful because of a distanced wit which enlivens what in the hands of a lesser or *less aware* storyteller could only be rendered as oppressively disturbing or disgusting. So how does Nabokov manage to cast light in such dark quarters? Part of it lies in the power of creative language. The alliterative quality of "captive corpse" and "lethal gallon of lake" or the playful quality of "intermittent torrent" and retasting "the hash of his life" disarms the reader. The precise positioning of language curbs what would be a reader's common emotional response to such descriptions. The prose is winning and funny. Attached to the voice of the overall storyteller is a very controlled tone of bemusement. Any misstep in language would otherwise impart an unintended emotion (what Poe called the "single effect"), and thus veer the story or the reader's participation in the story off course (if, for example, Humbert included a realistic, horrific, physical description of Charlotte drowning; or if, say, the overall storyteller in *KQK* did not view Franz with the mixture of empathy, fondness, and disdain which he does). These examples of ironic distance are peppered throughout each book, and like a pungent, tasteful ingredient, are what most shade the stories' other elements.

For an insight into the way Nabokov handles *event*[4] one can begin by looking at how it influences the chapter structure in each book. In *KQK* each chapter very much has a beginning, middle, and end with a nearly self-contained arc of movement to it, as Nabokov provides a central event or series of events which give these chapters their ballast and balance and form. Chapter One rather naturally begins with Franz's departure on the train and ends with the train's arrival in Berlin—an ideal, if obvious, merging of event and structure. Chapter Two, while less simplistic, finds Franz (nearly blind, having stepped on his glasses) venturing out into Berlin, with the centerpiece being his initial visit (of many) to the Dreyers' villa. Chapter Six methodically, through a series of brief scenes and the subtle movement through time, sketches the architecture of Franz's and Martha's affair, and how it affects their thoughts about and relations with Dreyer. The central event in Chapter Twelve is the race, or bet, which Martha and Franz have devised as a means of murdering Dreyer. You get the idea: event is propelling the action at regular, finite, orchestrated intervals, building tension and momentum in minicrescendos (such as in Martha's first visit to Franz's apartment, which sets the story's second "act" into motion; or later, when Franz and Dreyer are attempting to push open the door to Franz's apartment while Martha, on the inside, pushes back). Concurrently throughout the novel, a series of internal events takes place within each of the major players: for Franz, his lust for and preoccupation with

Martha is offset only by his occasional thoughts of his home as well as his curiosity about his strange landlord; for Dreyer, his desire for Martha is eclipsed by his penchant for playing the jokester, as well as his business interests; for Martha it is her obsession with Dreyer's flaws and her simultaneous desire for and blindness toward Franz, the "warm, healthy young wax that one can manipulate and mold till its shape suits your pleasure."

Lolita has its own lion's share of plotted events which propel the action of the story—Humbert's memory of the first girl he loved (who died of typhus), Humbert's (good? bad?) luck in stumbling onto the Hazes, Charlotte's accidental demise upon reading Humbert's journal and running out into the street where she is killed by the Beale Packard, Humbert's and Lolita's cross-country odyssey, Quilty's murder in the final act, and so on. But in contrast to *KQK* which adheres to its pattern of a central event or events in each chapter, there is no real pattern of event in *Lolita*. Humbert will often break the flow of action to make direct entreaties to his audience (the jury) or linger long in memory upon a past event, or stop such a telling in midevent, begin a new chapter, and then pick it up again as if there was no break, as in the close of Chapter 22: "'There's this man saying you've been killed, Charlotte.' But there was no Charlotte in the living room."

Then, Chapter 23: "I rushed out." Many of *Lolita's* short (and by strict comparison anemic) early chapters read like perplexing asides that only make sense later, time for obsessive Humbert to discuss the many merits of nymphets or his own good looks, as in chapter seven, where he asserts, ". . . well did I know, alas, that I could obtain at the snap of my fingers any adult female I chose; in fact, it had become quite a habit with me of not being too attentive to women lest they come toppling, blood ripe, into my cold lap." Part of this is a built-in construct and inherent advantage of first person, wherein the pull of voice can carry the narrative for stretches without much happening (Holden Caulfield of *Catcher in the Rye* fame is a perfect example), and part of this structure is necessary—the form of the novel allows Humbert the freedom of a classical argument whereby he can concede some points and refute others. Hence, by seeing Humbert's manipulation of event-telling in *Lolita*, we as readers are let in early with respect to his unreliability as a narrator. Humbert's version of things cannot be trusted. Conversely, the third person narration in *KQK* we accept as accurate and reliable—which is closely linked to how *time* is handled.

We learn as Franz exits his apartment for the last time that "…all that had been brought into this room or had accumulated there in the course of ten months, disappeared in those two suitcases…" Ten months—where have they gone? And yet this time—the time arc of the novel, two hundred plus pages of the most ultrasmooth, pothole-free ride through time you are likely to find—seems and sounds right. Fictionally, it reads like ten lived months, which is not to say it is particularly detailed or labored. Rather, the combination of event and gentle time jumps present the subtle illusion of ten months having flitted by. Nabokov does some of his best work with respect to shaping time in the middle section of the novel, specifically Chapters 4 and 5, where we see the passage of time move through the half-models and brief models and effortless time jumps of hours or days, and in the process renders a simulacrum of reality to the ways in which two people (Martha and Franz), through revealing gestures, adjust and change in the prelude to and consummation of their affair.

> ...During the first few days Franz, dazed and self-conscious, and trying not to shiver...simply stood in a corner trying not to attract attention, avidly following the actions of his colleagues...and then abruptly, with unbearable clarity, imagining Martha...In a month or so he had grown completely accustomed to his work...he now washed his feet at least twice a week and changed his starched collar and cuffs practically every day...almost night (and what monstrous melancholy lurked in that "almost") he would visit the Dreyers...she was generally alone; Dreyer, a fantastic but punctual person, would arrive exactly in time for what Franz called supper...he would compute within half an inch the exact degree to which she showed her legs while walking about the room and while sitting with her legs crossed...at every new visit he added something to the collection of enhancements which he would gloat over later in his solitary bed...there was an evening when he saw a minute brown birthmark on her arm...that night he realized as one becomes abruptly aware of suffering from a fatal illness, that he had already known Martha for more than two months...tomorrow came... "how can one love a man whose mere touch makes one feel sick," she confessed to Franz at one of their next meetings...the room had grown more attractive...on the table three pink dahlias were on their last legs in a dark-blue vase...lacy doilies had appeared here and there...Love helped to mature Franz...warm, warmly flowing happiness filled physical Franz to the brim...his hands had now grown more nimble...for other motions and contact, also rapid and nimble, causing Martha to purr with pleasure...

Even a phrase as simple as "love helped to mature Franz" connotes some brand of change or implied stepping through time. Nabokov's use of brief models, simple jumps ("It all began one Wednesday in mid-November…"), and evocative phrases such as the one above to give the *impression* of constant motion through time, without calling the reader's attention to it—a hallmark of the best novels, a pushing through time, as seamlessly and soundlessly as a jet's nose through the elevated air.

The frame alone in *Lolita* (the entire novel is Humbert's reflection; Humbert has an agenda to keep as well as a story to tell; we, the readers are reading it as Humbert and Dolores Haze are dead in a present fictional tense) produces some interesting considerations with respect to the handling of time. Part One of the novel creates little sense of real time (Humbert repeatedly interrupts the flow of the narrative to plead his case or clarify his affliction). The narrative will build a brief nest of real time, then Humbert will quickly dash it with one of his diatribes or historical comparisons or self-psycho-analyses—interesting to consider, if Humbert is trying to deconstruct and diffuse his previous actions to the jurors. That is not to say that within those pockets, Nabokov does not stretch a mere instant out to epic proportions. In fact, if one contrast can be noted about the handling of time between *King, Queen, Knave* and *Lolita*, it is that the former generally does not stretch, accelerate, or slow down time to the elastic extent that Humbert does in *Lolita*. Nowhere in *KQK* does time wind down to quite the same palpitating beat as in a passage such as:

> …I was still walking behind Mrs. Haze through the dining room when, beyond it, there came a sudden burst of greenery—"the piazza," sang out my leader, and then, without the least warning, a blue sea-wave swelled under my heart and from a mat in a pool of sun, half naked, kneeling, turning about on her knees, there was my Riviera love peering at me over dark glasses. It was the same child—the same frail, honey-hued shoulders, the same silky supple bare back, the same chestnut head of hair. A polka-dotted black kerchief tied around her chest hid from my aging ape eyes, but not from the gaze of young memory, the juvenile breasts I had fondled one immortal day…all I know is that while the Haze woman and I went down the steps into the breathless garden, my knees were like reflections of knees in rippling water, and my lips were like sand…

This comes just pages after a swift compression of time—the years Humbert summarizes regarding his failed marriage to Valechka. Humbert, like the best first-person narrators (Jack Burden, the narrator from *All the King's Men*, makes time crawl when he's remembering the Anne Stanton of his youth), uses and abuses time to fit his need at that moment, which, in Humbert's case, goes hand in hand with scene and image, what he tells and what he leaves out. The most brisk sections of Part Two are the celebrated travelogue, when Humbert takes Lolita on a cross-country odyssey; the most measured section (maintaining a sense of real time) comes much later, during Humbert's farewell scene with the new Dolly "Schiller" (Lolita). Time slows again, just as their first meeting, but it is a different kind of slowing. The time being paid attention to is the realistic time between characters—the silences and pauses and revealing gestures. Keep in mind that in this scene Humbert knows he has lost Lolita, knows that she is eighteen and married and pregnant, that she is no longer a nymphet, that she is asking solely for money which belongs to her and which Humbert has been keeping for her:

> "We—e—el!" She exhaled after a pause with all the emphasis of wonder and welcome. "Husband at home?" I croaked, fist in pocket. I could not kill her, of course, as some have thought. You see, I loved her. It was love at first sight, at last sight, at ever and ever sight. "Come in," she said with a vehement cheerful note. Against the splintery deadwood of the door, Dolly Schiller flattened herself as best she could (even rising on tiptoe a little) to let me pass, and was crucified for a moment, looking down, smiling down at the threshold, hollow-cheeked, with round pommetes, her watered-mild-white arms outspread on the wood. I passed without touching her bulging babe. Dolly-smell, with a faint fried addition. My teeth chattered like an idiot's. "No, you stay out" (to the dog). She closed the door and followed me and her belly into the dollhouse parlor.

This indelible image of Lolita, as well as the very first time Humbert sees her, are prime examples of how Nabakov creates lasting images. We find that the intensity of image (colors, smells, gesture, metaphor) is directly proportional to the speed of the narrative telling (slowwwww). When time slows, an impressionist image begins to take shape. When the sentences start to lengthen, this is the barometer of Humbert's internal state. Image is the weather vane by which we measure the storm inside Humbert. He is loquacious always, but when he locks onto the object of his obsession, there is a heat and vibrancy and exacting compulsion about the language of image:

> There my beauty lay down on her stomach, showing me, showing the Thousand eyes wide open in my eyed blood, her slightly raised shoulder blades, and the bloom along the incurvation of her spine, and the swellings of her tense narrow nates clothed in black, and the seaside of her school-girl thighs…As I looked on through prismatic layers of light, dry-lipped, focusing my lust and rocking slightly under my newspaper, I felt that my perception of her, if properly concentrated upon might be sufficient to have me attain a beggar's bliss immediately…

By comparison, the language and use of image in *KQK* is decidedly cooler, restrained, though just as visually present—that is, clearly and precisely seen in the writer's imagination and by extension to the page, and thence in the reader's mind. In short, we see more or less intact what Nabokov saw. If Humbert's eye is obsessed with one object (nymphets), then the overall storyteller-narrator in *KQK* is just as interested in fleshing out the odd detail, the fringe-sights which render a probing intelligence and peculiar subversive quality to many of its images, as though the "seer" is examining the character for clues into their internal lives, as when:

> Martha wandered back to the dining room and stood lost in thought behind the chair Franz had vacated. Then with irritation she lifted the tablecloth where the water had been spilled, and slipped a plate bottom up under it. The looking glass, which was working hard that night, reflected her green dress, her white neck under the dark weight of her chignon, and the gleam of her emerald earrings. She remained unconscious of the mirror's attention, and as she slowly went about putting the fruit knives away, her reflection would reappear every now and then. Freida [the maid] joined her for a minute or two. Then the light in the dining room clicked off, and nibbling at her necklace, Martha went upstairs to her bedroom.

Here, Nabokov does two things with respect to image that occur frequently throughout the novel. First, he casts a cold, unsentimental, and almost clinical eye at Martha, as he is just as apt to do with Franz or Dreyer, and he brings to life the mirror which regards Martha with a sort of indifference she would never otherwise tolerate. This is only one image of many in which Nabokov personifies simple household objects in fleshing out the periphery of a scene or image, or in making other latent comments, perhaps about his characters, perhaps about the fickle and fierce nature of human relations, as when Dreyer "slowly sipped up the last sweet drop, threw his napkin on the table and hurried out; the napkin slowly crept off the edge of the table and fell limply onto the floor." Why does that seem to be saying something about Dreyer and what he doesn't know? Or, later, when "a blue tinted cork…hesitated for an instant, then rolled in a semi-circle to the edge of the oil-cloth table, hesitated again, and jumped off. With the help of the lashing rain the wind tried to open the window but failed. In the rickety wardrobe a blue black-spotted tie slithered off its twig like a snake."

Over the course of the novel (and this speaks to tone as well as image) these images provoke an odd undercurrent, a distant echo as from the call of a canyon, a strange sense of things coming undone—as though another unnamed and as yet unseen character is there with Martha and Franz and Dreyer (bringing to mind the phrase "if only walls could speak") and, dare I say, judging them. The strongest and most accusatory image of this kind occurs in the latter stages of the novel, on page 184: "(Martha) tried the accursed desk again. It cringed and stood holding its breath at her menacing approach. The drawers began clacking like slaps on the face. Not here! Not here! Not here!" Starting with this image of the clacking desk, the personification assumes a more conscious level, as in Martha's and Franz's last meeting in his apartment: "The little room was aware it was being talked about and was assuming a more and more strained expression," or during the ride in the rowboat when all of nature seems to be peering out at Martha's and Franz's intended murder: "The oarlocks creaked, an inquisitive gull circled over them, a wave lifted the boat to inspect it."

This story element is one more angle Nabokov uses to leverage *point of view*, which in the case of *KQK*, similar to Joyce's "The Dead" or Woolf's *To the Lighthouse*, continually shifts from one character to the next, sometimes from line to line within sentences, or gesture to gesture. One pattern is that of Nabokov's inclination to begin chapters from a way pulled-back angle of view and then slide gradually into one character's vantage point or point of view. Chapter twelve, for instance, begins "the main thing of course was the sea: grayish blue, with a blurred horizon, immediately above which a series of cloudlets glided single-file as if along a straight groove…" Way pulled-back. Then, we gradually shift into Dreyer's internal point of view, his musing about why anyone would go rowing on that "desolate expanse of water." Then we slide from a final image—"leaning near them against the wall some kind of net: a bag of pale-bluish gauze on a ring fixed to a rod of light metal" to a brief dialogue beginning with Martha *explaining for us* the image just described— "Shrimp catchers," said Martha (*thus the character assists the overall story-teller* in what is taking his attention). At this point begins the conversation that remains pulled back, refrains from any internal point of view until "Dreyer strolled off alone," at which point we follow Dreyer and leave Franz and Martha behind. This is a common occurrence in *KQK*—switching points of view in order to go where the strongest tug of story is taking place, pushing the movement forward, as characters enter the scenes or depart, while the narrative may go any number of directions. Nabokov establishes this early in the first chapter, as point-of-view switches work overtime to characterize Martha's and Dreyer's marriage, their individual opinions of Franz's initial impression of Martha. Because Nabokov will readily switch internal point of view at any moment, by the time we switch immediately from Franz's dream into Martha's point-of-view, the shock is blunted:

> Now he seemed to be in a mirrored hall, which wonderously opened on a watery abyss, water glistened in the most unexpected places: he went toward a door past the perfectly credible motorcycle which his landlord was starting with his red heel, and anticipating indescribable bliss, Franz opened the door and saw Martha standing near the bed. Eagerly he approached but Tom kept getting in the way; Martha was laughing and shooing away the dog. Now he saw quite closely her glossy lips, her neck swelling with glee…he was about to clasp her hips but suddenly could no longer contain his boiling ecstasy. (Internal point-of-view switch) Martha sighed and opened her eyes. She thought she had been awakened by a noise in the street: one of their neighbors had a remarkably loud motorcycle.

(Keep in mind here that Martha is on the other side of Berlin while Franz is dreaming of her.)

Nabokov is not above using devices (e.g., dreams) to alter point of view, as when Dreyer makes the much-anticipated call to Franz (whose POV we have been close to), and then switches, following the course of Dreyer's day after the phone call is taken care of. Another keen double-switch point of view hinges upon the device of a photograph:

...she (Martha) wordlessly showed him a snapshot...it showed a smiling Dreyer, in a Scandinavian ski suit, clutching his poles...(SWITCH) ...When the photographer had clicked the shutter and straightened up, Dreyer, still beaming, moved his left ski forward...and with a great flourish of ski poles he tumbled heavily on his back...in the snapshot, though, he looked like a real skier, and he admired it before slipping it into the envelope...it would be fun to catch Martha's soul unawares, and see whether she should let escape a radiant smile of surprise...(SWITCH BACK)...Franz ripped the photo into little bits which the wind carried across the wet lawn. "Silly," said Martha, "why did you do that?" "He's sure to ask if I pasted it in the album." "Some day I'll tear up the album too," said Franz. An eager Tom had come running toward: (SWITCH) he hoped Franz might have thrown a ball or a pebble but a rapid search revealed nothing.

As both Martha and Franz, racked by guilt and fear, lose their hold on reality near the novel's end, Nabokov chooses to revisit their points of view and not explicate the confusion they are experiencing, as when we slide into Martha's internal POV without any warning or indication: "...presently from the balcony they (Dreyer and Franz) saw the ambulance enter the drive. (SWITCH) Over the waves, small angular waves, that rose and fell in time to her breathing, Martha floated in a white boat, and at the oars sat Dreyer and Franz..."

The constantly shifting, uniquely flexible point-of-view structure allows Nabokov to move freely throughout the story, to investigate scenes as varied as Dreyer, now Kurt (his first name), running into an old lover, all the way to Franz discovering that his landlord's wife is really a wig and a stick (and knowing as readers, too, that this guy is having Franz "erased," since he "invented" him, after all). The end result? We get to see these characters in many different, contrasting angles, get to know their motivations and their guile and their weakness.

Conversely, the point of view in *Lolita* is all Humbert. What keeps it from getting myopic is Nabokov's awareness, his ability to pull back through Humbert, and, when necessary, find the proper vantage point, tell it with sufficient ironic distance, as when Humbert does his best active-narrator impression in this passage:

So let us get started. I have a difficult job before me. Main character: Humbert the hummer. Time: Sunday morning. Place: sunlit living room. Props: old, candy-striped davenport, magazines…she wore that day a pretty print dress that I had seen on her once before, ample in the skirt tight in the bodice…she had painted her lips and was holding in her hollowed hands a beautiful, banal, Eden red apple.

Clearly, Humbert's point of view. But it is not the point of view of the movement. Rather, it is the pulled-back point of view of hindsight which informs many of Nabokov's scenes and images. The telling is that of a stage distance—it is as if Humbert is replicating, from memory, the sight of Lolita and himself, rather than the close-in perspective of himself in scene, of seeing from his own eyes, or over his shoulder. This is crucial to the seeing and to the movement. This stage distance becomes most prominent when Lolita is about to be compromised, as in chapter 29:

The door of the lighted bathroom stood ajar; in addition to that, a skeleton glow came through the Venetian blind from the outside arclights; these intercrossed raps penetrated the darkness of the bedroom and revealed the following situation. Clothed in one of her old nightgowns my Lolita lay on her side with her back to me, in the middle of the bed. Her lightly veiled body and bare limbs formed a Z. She had put both pillows under her dark tousled head; a band of pale light crossed her top vertebrae.

How, then, do all these elements come together to inform the development of character in *Lolita*? A slippery question, for many have argued that Humbert's character does not evolve, that he is the same lecherous, morally bankrupt man at the novel's end. His character is static, some might say. We get some evidence to the contrary, though, when we take into account the gradual, nearly 180 degree shift in tone from the novel's opening pages to the last. What begins as a lighthearted, hilarious, and exaggerated romp ends as tragedy, straight-faced and earnest, as we see in Humbert's final observations, just moments before the police catch up with him:

Reader! what I heard was but the melody of children at play, nothing but that, and so limpid was the air within this vapor of blended voices, majestic and minute, remote and magically near, frank and divinely enigmatic—one could hear now and then, as if released, an almost articulate spurt of vivid laughter, or the crack of a bat, or the clatter of a toy wagon...I stood listening to that musical vibration from my lofty slope...and then I knew that the hopelessly poignant thing was not Lolita's absence from my side, but the absence of her voice from that concord.

It seems hard to believe it is still Humbert narrating, but it is. We can only imagine that it is a decidedly different Humbert from the one we thought we knew. It is the artful execution of Nabokov's craft, a sleight of hand writers employ in the best first-person narrators, wherein the narrator is revealed in the process of concealing.

Another clue lies in the final scene between Humbert and Dolly "Schiller," who herself undergoes an amazing transformation by the novel's end—she is not the same girl characterized earlier in the novel. Life has dealt her some hard knocks, and the weight of that is (quite literally, with her pregnancy) upon her. How Humbert reacts to her, though, speaks volumes about him. If Humbert had not undergone some level of transformation by this juncture, we would surely see him disavow her, now that she is well beyond that age of nymphets, and very much an ordinary young women in the middle of her ordinary domestic life. Yet, his final descriptions of her are all drenched with empathy and longing. Aside from Humbert and Lolita, no other characters hang around long enough, or are given the opportunity to change or develop. Humbert could really care less. Humbert sees other people as specimens whose appearances, habits, shortcomings are scrupulously itemized. All, of course, except for Lolita.

Character development in *KQK* is slow but fully realized. Nabokov spends the first third of the novel "winding up" his characters, so to speak. We see the patterns of behavior which make Franz, Martha, and Dreyer utterly real, if somewhat static. Then, gradually—first with the affair, then with the murder plot—we see these three people begin to change. The middle section of the book is not surprisingly where the tone (similar to *Lolita*) darkens substantially and the novel finds its gravity. Innocent, horny, and ignorant Franz becomes impatient, greedy, and vindictive. We see this especially in his thoughts towards his uncle, whom he comes to loathe to the point that he sees not the living, real Dreyer, but an ineffectual one already murdered in his mind. At the same time, we see, ironically, the softer side of Martha bloom in Franz's presence even as she manipulates and prods him. Even Dreyer begins to experience a welling up of his own mortality, foreign thought to him, as he feels "suddenly very sad" while walking along the local storefronts. In the closing chapters of the novel, we see the development of Martha and Franz manifest itself in their different brands of madness. Franz is too benumbed to choose between "plain brown or the heather tweed," while Martha, living in her cloud of delusions, dreams the boat murder scene over and over in her mind, where something is always amiss, until she dies of pneumonia. Only Dreyer, and a shaken one at that, is the last one standing while Franz is left to mutter, "Is it?…it?" In fact, Nabokov's overall storyteller provides us with a rare glimpse of an older Franz looking back on the events that constitute the novel.

> In those days—which as a very old and very sick man, guilty of worse sins than avunclicide, he [Franz] remembered with a grin of contempt—young Franz was oblivious to the corrosive probity of his pleasant daydreams about Dreyer's dropping dead.

This glimpse affords us the luxury of knowing more than what Franz knows in the present time, and by extension we know just how far-reaching and complete his bitterness will be.

Endnotes

[1] "Good Readers and Good Writers," *Vladimir Nabokov: Lectures on Literature* (New York: Harcourt, Brace, Jovanovich, 1980), p. 5.

[2] *Lolita* (New York: Vintage International, 1997). Citations will be given in text as *L*, followed by page number.

[3] *King, Queen, Knave* (New York: Vintage International, 1989). Subsequent citations will be given parenthetically in text as *KQK*, followed by page number.

[4] An operative definition of *event* in story terms, would be a noteworthy occurrence. A series of occurrences could also denote one story event.

Flippin'

PHYLLIS PORCHÉ

I admit it, I'm one of those people who cringes when there's a news story on television, and the only person the reporter interviews is the brotha in the shower cap who just happened to be standing on the corner and witnessed the whole thing. And the minute brotha opens his mouth and pieces together the accident or the crime or the fire in his Ebonical words, I just want to rip up the carpeting, crawl up under it, and hide from the world because I know that there was some articulate black person on the scene who also could have given an account of the events. Some suited, brief-cased brotha or sista who would have been able to tell Mr. and Mrs. America, John and Jane city and suburban the same story as clearly as the reporter had. I know that the reporter sought out Mr. Shower Cap to interview because his comments would be spicy, gritty, and urban, or whatever term reporters use when they put some inarticulate Negro in front of the cameras.

Now, I have been accused, mostly by white people, of looking for racism. I qualify that because brothas and sistas know, you ain't gotta look for racism, it will find you. And every time Cletus or Cephus or JoJo or Bonnequa makes it onto the evening news, it's a reminder to me that even though *Newsweek* magazine says this is a great time to be black, it's not for all of us. Every time one of them stands up before a camera ending sentences with prepositions and splitting infinitives, it's a reminder that there are still brothas without jobs who have the time to stand on the corner and watch things happen and then be interviewed on the news at two o'clock in the afternoon. It's a reminder that even though some Johnnys can read, not all of them can.

My friends and I often play the Don't-let-him/her-be-black game when we watch the news. If you're not familiar with it, this is how it works. You're in your house eating your dinner and watching the news and hear a story about something heinous. You stop eating, fork in midair when the reporter says they have an eyewitness or the police have a suspect in custody, and you chant in your head, "Don't let him be black, don't let him be black, don't let him be black," until they show the mug shot and the person in custody is, of course, black.

Why is all this a problem? Because people learn most of what they know about other people through television. If we've never met a person of another race or ethnicity, but have seen them depicted on television or in the movies, no matter how much we try to fight it, some of what we retain about them is gleaned from these depictions. We often form our opinions of them based on what we've seen, and that is frightening. Which means every time Cletus looks right into white America's living rooms and says, "Oh, yeah, I seent the whole thang," I cringe because I know there's a segment of the populace that's thinking, "They all talk like that." Just like they'll think we all wear Fubu, are on welfare, and smoke crack.

And no, I am not a paragon of perfect English, far from it. When I'm hanging out with my friends I've been known to split an infinitive or two, but when I'm talking to the good white people of the North Shore, helping them find doctors and schedule appointments, they think they're talking to their next-door neighbor. Why? Because I've learned to flip. That is, flip back and forth between standard and nonstandard English.

Flipping is that little trick that some of us have learned that enables us to navigate the worlds in which we live. At home a mistake is "my bad," and at work it's, "Oh, excuse me." At home an exclamation of disbelief is, "Nigga, shut up!" At work it's, "Are you kidding me?" And yeah, the home talk is spicier and more fun, but I know that stuff won't fly at the office so I don't use it there. And yeah, there are times when worlds collide, and you let a home phrase slip out at work, but it usually only happens once. Because when you get that look from people, that, Nigga-have-you-lost-your-mind? look, you make sure you never make that mistake again.

Maybe that's what they need to teach in schools—a class on flipping. Kids can take English and Flipping, so that the next time there's a fire or a ten-car accident or some other tragedy and the reporter seeks out a witness, Cletus can stand before the red light and say, "Oh yes, I saw the whole thing."

Three Photos

MARK CHILD

> Beowulf is my name. If your lord and
> master, the most renowned son of Halfdane,
> will hear me out and most graciously allow me
> to greet him in person, I am ready and
> willing to report my errand.
>
> *Beowulf*, trans. Seamus Heaney

Dear Riley,

There is something secret about the lives of parents, something their children can't imagine—all that came before they were born. As a child I took the fact of my existence as a foregone conclusion. Of course I never thought of it in those terms. I simply understood that I ate, slept, ran, became easily bored with the luxury of nothing to do, pissed as best I could into the middle of the toilet bowl, and led a life of blessed inevitability. God wanted me here. But God is a trickster, fooling young children into believing the cosmos lined up in a particular way to bring life to them, to bring them into being, to make them sensate. I could just as easily (and more likely) not have been born. The lives my parents led before my brother and I appeared could have turned off at a hundred thousand off ramps and detours before I was conceived. When I first became aware of that long line of decisions made or avoided that eventually joined my father's sperm and my mother's egg, I comforted myself with the idea that even if they hadn't met I would still exist as I was, but with a different name. It wasn't until later, much later than I'll admit here, that I realized how unlikely my birth was. And though I am glad of my existence, I have always believed my father would have been better off taking one of those off ramps, venturing down one of those detours, and I try to imagine ways I can counsel him to go ahead—marry your first love, switch nights working the doors at Kenny Brothers Funeral Home and miss meeting Patsy Deegan, run away from home, just the way your mother did when you were three. Anything, just don't let it turn out the way it did.

The First Photo

My father, Donald Wayne Child, is standing next to a hearse—a long hearse with rounded fenders and strips of chrome running down the middle of the hood and along the sides to give the impression (even to a hearse) of streamlined elegance. It is 1948 or '49. My father is either twenty-one or twenty-two years old, a year or so since his honorable discharge from the U.S. Navy. He is standing in the parking lot behind Kenny Brothers Funeral Home (the heavy black-and-silver window signs in the hearse are clearly seen). There is a food store sign to the far left, and I know that store also served fountain drinks. Donny, as my father was called back then, spent a lot of time there drinking root-beer floats. The old soda jerk in him clinging to what was familiar, and because he was in the big city, what was familiar was also safe. He looks so young I can hardly recognize him as my father, yet if I look at the photo with some concentration I know he is the young man who will become my father.

It's his hands. If you look, he has his left hand on the skinny chrome handle of the driver's door. That's what he did back then, he was a driver for Kenny Brothers on Fifty-fifth. Though it can't be seen in the photo, I know he is wearing a small silver medallion from the Teamster's Union with his chauffeur's license number under one of his lapels. (I found that medallion after he died and kept it as a talisman, a hoped-for shield from the difficulties of trying to find out how to live. I gave that same medallion to a friend when her difficulties became more acute than mine. I told her, "Let it sustain you.") But it is his right hand that tells me this is the man who will love me, who will not know how to express his love except to reach into his pocket and pay for anything he could. Look at the thumb on his right hand. It is hard to see. It is little more than a sliver of light gray in the photo, but look at the two prominent bulges from the joint. This is my father's thumb. The knuckles across the back of his hand, too, show very clearly that this is the hand that never once struck me; this is the hand that plunged itself into the icy waters of dead bodies and embalming fluid to earn its living; this is the hand that would teach me how to shake hands—firmly without letting anybody grab you short—and I think, too, this is the hand that will open the door in the months ahead to let Paddy Deegan, the Democratic precinct captain, and his browbeaten daughter Mary Patricia "Patsy" Deegan into the Kenny Brothers Funeral Home on their round of making the wakes in the neighborhood of Fifty-fifth and Halsted and offering the condolences of the Democratic Party, and all will be lost for him.

There is a story my father told me about the night he met my mother. He almost wasn't there. Back then he was an apprentice embalmer living at the funeral home along with two other guys. One of them was Carl Hix. Carl was a man for whom life could not have held more enjoyment. He smoked, he drank, he screwed, and he was always nursing a hangover. (Years later, when I knew Carl as my "Uncle Carl," the father of five girls living in a rambling, tumble-down Victorian house in Aurora, I could still see the hale-fellow-well-met underneath the weight of so much femininity and begrudged sobriety.) Carl was going to switch nights and work for my dad so he could get the next night off and keep his date with Marilyn (later Carl's wife, mother of his five girls and my "aunt"). But for some reason the switch never happened, and it was my father who greeted the Deegans.

I am suspicious of my father's story. I do not believe it happened that way. There is no explanation of why the switch did not occur. There is also this: my father asked me never to mention it to my mother. She might take it the wrong way. That much I do believe, but why bother to tell me this story in the first place? Was it a self-pitying indulgence on his part, to toy with the idea that he'd almost been able to escape his fate, his unhappy marriage, his cumbersome responsibilities? Did he, too, think, *If only I hadn't been there that night?* Or did it go further back? *If only I'd stayed with Maggie, none of this unhappiness would be here.* Did my father tell me the story of almost missing my mother to warn me about my own decisions? Or was it simply the truth, and there was nothing to be made of it?

In the photograph of my father standing next to the hearse, he doesn't look particularly happy, does he? It is hard to be twenty-one or twenty-two years old and not know whether what the hell you're doing is what you are supposed to be doing, or if it makes any difference anyway.

The Second Photo

I am going backwards now. I thought maybe I'd take the photos randomly, not force any order on them, but the story here is suggesting an order, demanding connective tissue. But this isn't the order I wanted—youngest to oldest—this is backwards. There are too many photographs to choose from, too much that comes later that is important for you to know (the airplanes, Rose's Jump River Tavern, the Atlantic City convention, *Mad Dog and Glory,* the farm), but all of that does not fit in here and I have to resolve myself to telling small bits of his story, resolve myself to the impossibility of the task.

This is Maggie. My father is eighteen years old in this picture. He looks quite happy with his arm around Maggie's slim waist. The photo is a bit overexposed, but you can still see her right hand pulled back to her waist, holding Donny's fingertips. The thing I like best about Maggie is that she is bending her left leg ever so slightly, tipping the angle of her hips downward, into my father, letting him feel the sensualness of her hip bone in his side. This is not the best photo I have of Maggie. There is one where she is sitting on the upturned keel of a rowboat that shows how pretty she was, with a pair of long, lean legs that I cannot help but admire. I am certain my father admired them, too.

On the right edge of this photo is the small corner of a picnic table. I have no idea if this was actually a picnic table, but it suits me to believe it was. Also, there on the ground, by my father's feet is the heavy shadow of someone's head. If I line up the shadow with the bit of the table that is showing I can easily imagine the boyfriend or husband of the woman taking the picture sitting on that table. (I presume it is a woman taking the picture and not a man because I believe the shadow to be a man's head.)

I am guessing that this picture is taken in the park by the river in Henry, Illinois, my father's hometown. It might have been the village green, but I'll stick with the river park. This is one of those set photos, one taken to remember a moment exactly. Perhaps my father is about to ship out to Great Lakes Naval for his induction into the Navy and the end of the war. Maybe he is home on leave before he joins the USS *Hillary Jones* in South Carolina. Maybe this is the picture he carried with him when he went to war. If so, he knew what he was fighting for.

But something happened when he came home from the Pacific. He and Maggie were no more. Is that why he moved to Chicago? Because of a broken heart? Or was he already planning on leaving and he broke her heart? He never said much about it.

I never knew these pictures of Maggie existed until after my father died.

They were part of a scrapbook of his life up until the Navy. The paper is crumbling and yellow, but happily the hundred or so photos in the album were all tipped in and not glued into place so they are holding up well. After I found the photos of this pretty girl my father once loved, I remembered an odd statement he'd made to me after I bungled my first attempt at love at age sixteen. He said, "Just because you can't be with someone doesn't mean you can't love them. I learned that a long time ago."

That was all he said. He was not the kind who elaborated. Later when I found the pictures of this pretty girl and the large valentine's card glued into the scrapbook with the salutation "Loads of Love, Maggie," I figured it must have been her he was talking about. For a moment, then, I found myself staring at this picture of my father with his arm around Maggie's waist, and I wondered if I could have been their child if they had married. I wanted to be their child, and then I realized that, just like my infatuation with Katharine Hepburn's angular beauty, this beautiful young girl was now an old woman, maybe even dead, and I wondered if she or her children (if she had any) ever pulled out this same photograph and wondered about what might have been, instead of what was.

The Third Photo

Now we are closer to the beginning, closer to when nothing had been decided, closer to absolute freedom. I like this photograph. It is one of the felicitous compositions that sometimes happen with amateur photographers. It was a widish lens that took the picture with a relatively slow shutter speed. (My father is the one on the far left and is shaking his fist at the camera, and the motion is a bit blurred.) What I like best is how the corner of the building (a barn?) plays so prominently in the composition. The four boys are off center, and the camera is angled a bit at the barn, running the perspective in a wide V, just as I did in my freshman art classes. But beyond the composition is the subject matter itself. If Henry, Illinois, could have had its own Dead End Kids, these four grubby rats would be them.

Two of the four boys do not have shoes on, my father and the boy across from him, but I imagine the other two are barefoot as well. One of the boys is holding onto a gray and white cat that might be trying to get away, or may be lounging as cats sometimes do. But look at Donny. Look at his face. He looks like he is scolding the person taking the picture, "Hey, leave us alone. Get out of here." And he shakes his fist at them.

I remember what it was like to be playing with the kids on our block, transforming prairies and open fields into World War II battlegrounds, or sneaking into Mr. Martin's garage to swipe a couple of *Playboy* magazines and head for our nearest hideout or fort to look at the pictures and grab our crotch-es. It was hell whenever someone found us, even if we weren't hypnotized by the pendulous breasts of the girls in *Playboy*. It was like some spell had been broken and we were forced to come back from our imaginings and be part of the world where our prairie was mowed down and new houses built, where we stopped building forts because someone said only homos did that, where it would be several more years before we'd get a chance to do something other than look at pictures of naked women. I see the same anger at the intrusion of the photographer in my father's face. Leave us alone. Get out of here. We're *playing!*

But when I came across this picture in the tattered scrapbook, there was something else that my eye fell upon, something else that mattered more to me than the composition, or the connection to my own childhood. It is there in the upper left-hand corner of the picture: a bridge, or a trestle, the road out. It is right there for my father to see. How many times did he play there and not notice it? How many times did he travel on it and not realize what it was? There it is, Dad. Get out of there.

But the picture does not change. Like God, photographs prefer silence to answers. I want to warn my dad and tell him how ugly it gets for him, but he will not listen. Moments, seconds after this picture was taken of him and his three buddies, he goes right back to playing in the dirt (I think they are trying to start a fire by the way the pile of twigs sits in the middle of them). He con-tinues making all of those decisions that will eventually cause me to happen and, I think, how rotten for him that all he got for his troubles were two sons and a wife who didn't know him at all.

Of course, he never thought of it that way. He thought he was blessed. Shows how wrong fathers can be.

My love forever,
Dad

Fault Line

JOHN LOWERY

December, 1978. Smoking weed brought us together. November, 1994. Smoking crack tore us apart.

I need to understand how something so right became something so wrong. So I deconstruct twenty-two years of memories. I thought our love would be more than enough to get us through anything.

December, 1978. I leaned over the banister watching him as he made his way to the second floor. He was smiling with full lips and dimples.

"It's Eric, right?"

"Yah, Eric."

"Come in, Eric. Here, let me take your coat."

Smiling to myself, a sky blue wool coat with an electric blue imitation fur collar? He had to have a great sense of humor.

"Have a seat."

He sat on the sofa, and I went to the stereo and played Donna Summer's orgasmic '70s disco hit, "Love To Love You, Baby."

"John, you know they say Donna Summer is a man; what you say?"

"She's just a big girl with a little girl's voice. She ain't got that kind of voice that can blow you across the floor even when you don't feel like dancing. Not like Patti LaBelle or Chaka Khan. Those sisters got voice."

Eric's head was tilted to one side looking as if he was pondering what I had said.

"I guess you right. When I go out to the clubs, I say I ain't gonna party too hard, just lean back and take everything in, you know, real smooth. Then the D.J. starts to scratching on some Patti or Chaka, and I'm up sweating out the creases that took an hour to iron."

Smiling, he picked up the Donna Summer album cover and said, "Yeah she's a real woman, a *real* big woman."

I sat in the armchair at a right angle to Eric. He scanned the living room, briefly stopping at the milk crate of record albums stacked against the wall, the stereo system, and my poster of Malcolm X hiding the crack in the wall over the mantlepiece.

"You been living here long?"

"No, it's been about three weeks now."

The apartment was clean because there wasn't any shit in it. The vinegary smell of freshly painted walls was still in the air. We were sitting on the sofa and chair that used to be in my mother's den. A small parson's table functioned as my dining table and for rolling weed on.

"So, Eric, where did you meet Tony?"

"At Foster's. You know where it is, near Chicago and State? We met there. Seemed like he knew everyone in the place. Running from stool to stool cracking jokes about the bartender, saying that he *invented* ugly. He had everybody cracking up except the bartender. He bought us drinks but *I* had to order them 'cause the bartender wasn't waiting on him."

Foster's was for the after-work set, men looking for men. They'd be packed in that shoebox crotch-to-crotch and crotch-to-ass, everyone holding a drink and trying not to spill it on anyone.

"Tony got me full on some of that fire weed of yours. John, man, he ran his mouth all night, up until last call."

"I know you ain't lying. Tony will talk you into a coma if you let him. So you liked the weed? Good. I ain't dealing anything big time, just enough to keep a few friends and myself supplied."

"Oh, I know, he told me. I was there when he called you from the club to ask if it was OK if I came by today to get a bag."

Tony, my best friend, had also told me Eric was fine and how he was just my type. Tony didn't have a type. As long as you had the XY chromosome then it was on. Eric was what I liked in a man: dark complexion, full lips, tall, and he had an Afro that must have added three inches to his height. There were other criteria, but this was the basic schema. African love, juju babies. I was tired of those high yellow boys sniffing after me. Usually the light guys wanted the dark guys, and the dark guys wanted the light guys.

"So, Eric, can I ask how old you are?"

"Twenty. I remember you now, John, from the White Heat party. You was dancing with Mad Max, now *that's* a big girl. You dance just like a white boy, all off the beat." He flashed a smile as bright as a preacher's Sunday shirt.

"But you looked kind of cute in those white army fatigues and white sailor's top. I almost didn't get in if it hadn't been for Indigo Blue. Fat Phillip was checking for ID, and I forgot to bring any. Indigo Blue asked if he was the FBI and threatened to beat his fat ass until he forgot his name if he didn't stop holding up the line and let me in. That drag queen, Indigo, doesn't play. Now that's who Donna Summer reminds me of."

"Eric, Tony told me you were seventeen."

"If you know, why you ask? Anyway, I'll be eighteen in a few months."

"No problem, just asking. I can see why Tony would talk to someone who looked like you."

I loved his moustache and goatee. I was twenty years old, and my face was as smooth as his ass.

I lit some incense, rolled two fat joints, and passed one to him. Eric pulled on it hard and long. His eyes were closed. It was turning me on the way his full lips held the joint. I can't stand men with mice lips. I didn't want to gawk so I went to the kitchen to get some soda. When I came back I noticed his long neck. He had an Adam's apple as big as an apple, that bobbed up and down. I got a hard-on watching him as he finished his can in five gulps.

"Want another?"

I got him another soda, lit the joint again, and sat back drinking him in. He was my type of handsome, strong face. Bitch-face men like Prince and Michael Jackson are a turnoff. Now, I also don't want them looking as if they've been in a fight with a pit bull either.

"You live here alone?"

"Yeah, it's just me. I was staying with Tony for a while. He parties a bit too much for me, niggers coming home with him every night, some of them trying to crawl in bed with me. I couldn't get any sleep, getting to work late . . ."

"Where do you work?"

"At the U of I Hospital. I'm the admittance clerk for the OB-GYN ward."

"What's that?"

"Obstetrics and gynecology. You know, for pregnant women and taking care of their female parts."

He smiled impishly.

"What's so funny?"

"Sorry, nothing man. But John, I was just thinking, all that pussy around and you don't want none of it."

He laughed and leaned into the sofa.

"Well I'm glad that amuses your little smart ass."

"John, you'll find out ain't nothing *little* on me."

Blushing, I thought, now that's intriguing.

I was glad I had gotten my hair cut a few days earlier. A close cut and lining always made me feel fresh. My muscles flexed whichever way I moved in my T-shirt and Levis. The running and daily push-ups and sit-ups had paid off. I could tell I had made an impression on Eric, the way he held on to my every word and his eyes wrapped around my body.

I was his first lover. He was my third.

1989.

Eric and I had been lovers for eleven years. Every morning we woke with a joint, left for work with one, and took one to bed every evening.

We worked at a telemarketing agency where, most of the time, lunch consisted of a Diet Coke, a joint, and a vial of coke. Cocaine was the drug of the '80s. On the club scene a line was shared as freely as a joint. Cocaine was the story line for movies and TV. Eric and I kept in step with the time. I was wearing a high top fade haircut as tall as a chimney. Because of a receding hairline that didn't have any plans on coming back, Eric's '70s Afro had morphed into a bald head. I remember when he did it, on a Sunday. I was lying on the bed smoking a joint and watching *60 Minutes* when Eric came out of the bathroom yelling, "Born again!"

He had shaved his head bald and had a lit birthday candle plastered atop it. He looked great, chiseled and modern. Thank God he had the aesthetic sensibilities to do it and had the right head shape.

At the time our only concerns seemed to be snorting coke, smoking weed, and what outfit we were going to wear to the club. *Less is more* had no place in our lives. Everything was over the top: too many gold chains, too much cologne, and coke up our noses every day. Death was also over the top. Our friends were dying from AIDS, some never making it into the '90s. Gary, Bobby, Charles, and my best friend, Tony. During the 1980s and 1990s the disease seared through the minority—and particularly the African American—community like a white-hot laser. By 1998 African Americans, who made up about 12 percent of the population, represented roughly 40 percent of all AIDS cases and 60 percent of newly diagnosed cases. Our friends weren't dying glamorously as did Tom Hank's character in the movie *Philadelphia*. Hanks received an Academy Award for best actor as a lawyer who's fired from his firm when it's discovered he's gay and has AIDS. The people I had known who were dying didn't throw masquerade balls in condominium lofts with loving family around them. They were dying in nursing homes, their churches condemning them, telling them that it was God's wrath, their families nodding in agreement.

The simultaneously envied and desired beautiful black men went to Club LaRay at Halsted and Belmont. You were there to see and be seen. Everyone had diamond-cut cheekbones and body. Body ruled, and LaRay was the place to show it. As the night progressed T-shirts and silk shirts were stuffed in the back of pants pockets. Bodies flexed and glowed, dancing to the sexy '80s house music. He was looking at you, you were looking at the guy behind him, and the guy behind him was looking at himself as he danced in the mirror. The pungent perfume of lust was everywhere: on the dance floor, in the washrooms, in dark corners, and the alley in the back of the club. You were also at LaRay to sell or buy drugs: weed, acid, and the new darling, cocaine.

I was going for our second round of deceptively sweet but lethal Long Island iced teas; as I turned from the bar with our drinks in hand, my lips brushed against this guy's chest hair. I had bumped into a redwood tree. I looked up into his face. It was as if a woman's head had been attached to the body of the Incredible Hulk.

"Sorry, my fault."

He had a small turned-up nose, little cherub lips, and his hair was pulled back in a ponytail. He bent down, his lips against my ear, and said his name was Carlos. I don't know how long we talked but the ice had melted in the drinks. As I was taking in the scene, my eyes landed on Eric standing by the exit door glaring at me with acid eyes. I pressed my way through the mass of bodies to catch him before he could leave.

"John, why were you talking with him? What did you have to talk about that took twenty minutes?"

"Come on now, I know you're not jealous. Eric, you know I ain't about that. I came with you, and I'm leaving with you."

The Relationship.

Eric was sleeping when I came back. I wanted to wake him, but instead I sat at the foot of the bed watching the rhythmic expanding and contracting of his bare chest. The fan in the windowsill blew warm night air into the bedroom. Eric's body glistened with sweat. I wanted him to send me to sleep with the smell and taste of his body. I wanted to hear the deep timbre of his voice murmuring sounds of pleasure that would resonate in every atom of my being. My hands wanted to glide over his body, but I didn't move. He was angry with me for flirting with this big hard-body guy at the club last night. I really wasn't flirting, just sucking up the attention he was paying me. I was being polite. The guy was visiting from New Orleans and just asking me about the club scene here in Chicago. He was a high yellow, green-eyed Creole, definitely not my type. My type had narrowed exclusively to Eric. I sat peering voyeuristically at the intimacy of my lover sleeping.

I wanted to wake him, but pride and my need to be right were stirred up, overpowering my desire to do so.

The room was saturated with the stillness of sleep and the white noise of the fan.

The lamp on the nightstand illuminated Eric's face and torso with an amber light. The rest of him was in gradations of amber. The scrunched sheets formed a sculptural relief around his lower body. The collection of crystal objects on the dresser created prismatic stars under the light. I wanted to wake him but instead decided to draw him. This would be sleep sketch #6 in a collection I had started. I got my sketchpad, and #4b, #3b, #2b, and #2h pencils from the portfolio case leaning against the dresser. I fired up a joint and found my corner at the foot of the bed, spreading the pencils in front of me, and began to render my lover in the light I saw him. I started penciling in his form with the lighter #2h pencil, next molding the sinews of his torso with the soft, dense #2b and #3b hatching in gradation of blacks to grays. I took extra care working his face, wanting to get his thick eyebrows and lashes just right. He had an angular face. Planes are easier to draw in such a face than someone with a full face. I took my time to get the fullness of his lips.

Ears were difficult for me to draw. I usually drew some schematic, cartoon-type ear. Fortunately I only had to draw one. The right side of him was in shadow. He had beautiful feet, long and narrow with a high arch, not like mine. An ant couldn't get under my flat feet. I took my time rendering them, but not too much; I didn't want to gild the lily. Linger too long and all you would have was a portrait of beautiful feet. I scribbled in a few hatch marks for the background, because he was beginning to wake up. I emptied the tin foil of coke onto a small mirror. He looked at me and smiled, and I knew all was forgiven.

Early in 1991. The Crack in Our Relationship.

Curtis introduced us to smoking crack. He stopped by the apartment on his birthday and instead of pulling out his usual gram of coke he threw ten tiny plastic bags onto the coffee table, each containing a rock the size of a tooth. He took a glass pipe from the inside of his jacket pocket. It looked like something from a chemistry lab. Curtis pushed a piece of one of the rocks atop a small screen on the bowl of the pipe. He lit it and hit it, holding the smoke in his jaws. He passed it to me and motioned with his eyes for me to do the same.

I eagerly put the stem of the pipe in my mouth, and he lit it for me. Eric nervously laughed when he saw my jaws expand like Dizzy Gillespie's. I inhaled, instantly feeling warm and freaky all over: my chest, back, and groin. The back of my throat tickled, my heart beat wildly, and my lips tingled and were numb. I handed the pipe to Eric. He lit and hit it a few times, staggered and fell on the sofa. Smiling, I walked over to Eric and sat down on the floor with my back against the sofa and my arm resting on his chest. Curtis walked over with the pipe in his hand and sat down on the floor next to me. He opened his shirt and began to idly rub his chest. Curtis and I had screwed around since high school. He didn't see himself as gay or even bisexual, I guess just something he had occasionally been doing for over fifteen years, and in his mind having fathered a kid on every side of the city proved he wasn't. He passed the pipe to me. I hit it again. The rock hissed and crackled like an old witch. I held the smoke in my lungs as long as I could, releasing a miasma of smoke around us. It had a synthetic smell. I was momentarily paralyzed in euphoric bliss. This was all there was and all that mattered. Eric reached out and touched the back of my neck. Curtis smiled and once again he lit the eternal flame. A spark from within had been ignited.

Smoking.
The pipe would break if it got too hot, then another would have to be made from an empty grain-alcohol bottle. I watched Eric as his eyes narrowed and looked down the stem of the pipe. He pulled deeply, inhaling the smoke, holding it in his lungs as long as he could. He looked around, letting the smoke out of his nose and mouth. His face was taut with intensity. Right then and there I wanted us to be naked, to smell the bitter sweetness under his arms, and warm in the incandescence of his skin, skin that glowed like a new penny. I wanted to see that look of intensity on Eric's face and feel it throughout his body.

It was my turn to hit the pipe. Now everything would be OK. A world of smoke would swirl in the glass bowl of a crack pipe. The opaque white rocks on the saucer were at that moment more precious than diamonds. All the pain of life would be carried away in clouds of smoke. The dust on the mirror wouldn't matter anymore. The plants in the living room I had planned to water would wait because the world was whirling around in the glass bowl of a crack pipe.

Eric and I were sitting on the edge of the bed, watching each other smoke. The phone and doorbell rang but went unanswered. Whenever Eric and I finished smoking we would have sex. The pleasure centers of our brains had been bathed with crack smoke. Everything touched had the potential to bring on orgasm. My lips, groin, chest, and hands would touch him and be touched by him. I hugged a pillow to my chest, my chin resting on it. He was covered in sweat, sweat that would soon be mixed with my sweat. My bare feet touched the wood floor. It felt as if the floor had reached up and touched my feet. I watched Eric as he smoked. I knew how hard to bite his nipples. I knew that running my tongue up his back would make him levitate off the bed.

Crack smoke has the smell of an electrical fire. Eric lit sandalwood incense to mask the odor. I hit the pipe again as I looked around the bedroom. Everything looked interesting and new. I was always searching for something new. Eric's head was covered with beads of sweat that streamed down his face. My eyes followed each drop. I reached out and traced with my finger the veins on top of his hand.

"Hurry up, you've already hit it three or four times. Let it cool before it breaks."

He snatched the lighter from my hand. His eyes were filled with a black fury I found beautiful. I laid the pipe on the bed making a scorch mark on the spread. I could hear the hissing and cracking sounds from the residue left in the bowl. I felt I had the power to will it to cool. My heart quickened as I saw it shatter.

September, 1998.

Dear Eric,

I knew it would eventually come to this. I knew that if I was to continue to stay clean I couldn't live with you. I've stopped arguing with myself as to whether I should leave you. If I don't, I'm sure you will get me high before I can get you clean. Eric, I love you. I've prayed and waited for the time you would decide to stop using. But that time never came. Each time you went into drug rehab I'd think now we can get on with our lives. I believed you when you told me you were tired and were going to get help. Every payday you'd smoke your check up. I'd be angry with you, yet it would break my heart to see you standing in front of the apartment building like a wilted sunflower.

Now you don't even look for a job. I'm tired, tired of adding beads to a necklace of broken promises. I'm not young anymore. I spent that being with you. Most of those twenty-two years were well spent. I was able to surrender all of myself because you always gave me enough of you. But now getting high has become stronger than your love for me. Crack has you around the neck, burrowing its claws into you, tearing out all that is good about you: honor, patience, kindness. Are all memories of you being a lover, a son, a friend erased? Crack has turned you against yourself. I've stopped arguing with you; it's like throwing rocks at the moon.

When I was using it was killing more than my body; it was killing my spirit. Eric, it's been over four years since I sat on that park bench with tears in my eyes and snot running from my nose. I felt like dying. You know that I'm not a religious person. But sitting on that bench I prayed to stop fucking up my life. I was tired of dodging the landlord because of owed rent, tired of borrowing and lying to my family, and tired of crack being the nucleus of our relationship, arguing about it and making up with it.

Just like you, I'd stop for a day, a couple of days, a week, but could never stay stopped. I remember spending all night and all the money trying to get an instant replay of that initial rush. You remember my crawling around in circles for hours, picking up anything that looked like a piece of crack. Coming down meant being wrapped in regret and hating myself. Tired, but unable to sleep.

So, baby, I understand what you're going through. But you're going to have to go inside yourself and grab hold of a power greater than you. I always thought you would have gotten clean before me. Your appetites were never as fierce as mine. Eric, I loved you the first time I saw you. Now I find it painful to love you, seeing you gaunt and wasting away, and knowing that I'm powerless to do anything about it. You see, because my life is so entwined with yours, I want to hold on to you so badly. There is no one else. But I can't go back, and you're not ready to come forward.

Eric, I will always love you,
John

On my own.
When I think I've gotten over him, he'll come around to let me know just how much he still means to me. I get so wrapped up in the illusion that I don't see the crack between us. I stir up what's inside of me for someone who will fade by dawn. Afterwards I'm crumpled up like an old sweater on the floor. Yet I still hold on to memories of when we were lovers. I only see Eric when his ass is dragging. How long will this go on? Maybe this is supposed to happen. I tell myself that I'm getting over him. Yet I look at his picture every day, a smile that was for me and not the camera. I loved him from a boy of seventeen well into his manhood. I loved the hair right off his head.

These are my thoughts as I turn the key to open the door to my apartment. The light falls on the hallway floor before me. I flick on the light by the door and the silence of the living room shouts at me as I push through it. My shoes squeak across the hardwood floor. I can hear bits of plaster falling inside the wall. I welcome the sound to keep me company. The zinnias and carnations in the crystal vase on the dining table look so fine. I found out that zinnias are native to South America. They're also called old maid flowers. The vase looks alive, sending sparkling lights throughout the flowers. I got the vase for twenty-two dollars by sticking a clearance tag on a hundred-dollar vase. I needed something beautiful right then and there. As I look at the flowers I tell myself to buy flowers once a week, but then I remember saying the same thing four months ago. This is the first time I've bought since then. The flowers and I are the only living things in the apartment. Sometimes it feels as if the flowers are the only living things here. This could be a fine apartment. I have a second-floor view of the trees that are budded green in the spring; by summer the leaves have morphed into the greenest of greens. The apartment has the feel of living in a tree house. In the winter the tree branches look like the arms and fingers of old men. The hardwood floors and white walls were the reasons I rented the apartment. White walls give the illusion of a larger space. But lately all this whiteness and hardness feels like being adrift on a glacier. I want to see shades of brown that will warm me like hot chocolate and something forgiving underfoot to walk on. I pick up the Miles Davis CD I left on the coffee table before going to work. Miles was more than ugly. Well, he wasn't really ugly. He just had those big eyes, kind of like the eyes of a lemur. I take the disk out and slide it into the player. His music is beautiful. I listen to his *Kind of Blue* CD every day. I like listening to it while I'm writing. I don't feel much like writing tonight. I just want to listen to the music.

My best friend, Anthony, says, "Write even if you don't feel like it." He says. "The feeling will pass once I get into the writing." I miss Anthony. He's been with the Alabama Shakespeare repertory for the past month. Shakespeare and Alabama, isn't that an oxymoron? Anthony reminds me that Eric isn't oxygen and that I'll be fine. But he's not here tonight to tell me any of this.

I miss Eric: I miss eating mangoes with lime juice on top, listening to the *Kind of Blue* CD over and over on rainy nights like this. Our love was as sweet as pound cake. It's been five years now since I got clean. Eric is still chasing the pipe. I know he can't get clean for anyone but himself. But this crack between us still hurts. There have been times I've just wanted to crawl inside my cap and stay there. And there are moments when I have a measure of acceptance.

This really could be a fine apartment, if we were together.

Miles is blowing on a track titled "So What"; looking at the CD cover, I see that it was recorded in 1959, around the time I was born. It's classic. Shit, I'm classic.

Casting a Spell

GERMANIA SOLÓRZANO

The sound of words is important. Any amateur witch or wizard dabbling in the necromantic arts knows that one cannot conjure up the
dead by simply telling their ghostly souls to, "Hey, c'mere!" Ghosts, since
they no longer have corporeal forms, are mostly made of waves anyway.
Sound waves. They respond to sound. And so if the sound of words, simple
Latin phrases strung together with their lulling syllables and long exhalations,
can call the dead from their graves—what power might sound have on the
humble reader, who is corporeal, by most standards alive, with living
eardrums to experience that sound by? To enchant the reader the spell must be
cast at the very beginning. Thus with *Lolita*, before the book has even opened,
the spell has been cast with the mere name: Lolita. Say it to yourself. Repeat
it ten times into a mirror like that juvenile act of dabbling in auto-hypnosis
where the younguns gather around and repeat "Mary Worth" into the candlelit
mirror, and thus, by the musical, haunting repetition of sound, see various
wonderful horrors. Repeat "Lolita" and see if it does not have any effect on
you. Tell me that it doesn't turn the corners of your mouth up into a little grin,
make you feel slightly happy at the thought of lollipops past? It rolls under the
tongue and then rises to a transluscent peak, a musical high on the *ee* and then

ends on a self-satisfying *ta. Ta-da!* The magic can be that simple.

Now, already successfully primed, ready for the further hypnotic chantings of the spell, the reader opens the book to Part One and reads: "Lolita, light of my life, fire of my loins. My sin, my soul. Lo-lee-ta: the tip of the tongue taking a trip of three steps down the palate to tap, at three, on the teeth. Lo. Lee. Ta." The spell has been cast. Everything beyond this point is a continuation of this initial chant. Everything else is a deepening of the suggestive, hypnotic state. Everything else is a variation on a theme, like a composer may work and rework a musical theme until the theme becomes fully incorporated, woven into the corporeal frame of the listener. So that said listener, who may not have even consciously listened to the composition, may find himself in the check-out line of Wal-Mart, that perfect cornucopia of American culture, protectively hugging his soon-to-be-purchased Beer Nuts, *World of Wrestling* magazine, and *Buns of Steel* video to his chest, and recognize the nameless "tune" in the cleverly packaged Muzak version floating along the ceiling.

Thus the spell of the novel, once begun, must be continued for the duration of the novel. For the novel is not the short superstitious act of throwing salt over one's shoulder to avoid bad luck, an act that can be done almost instinctively with no thought at all and once dutifully done can be forgotten for the universal system of fate to deal with. No. The novel is an involved commitment to enchantment. Throughout the reader's experience of it there must be a constant beating of drums and chanting to maintain the reader's concentration and enthrallment so that once finished—ah, well then—the spell has been sufficiently cast. What effect it will have on the reader after they are done reading the completed work—that is up to Fate to decide.

And that, my inquisitive, budding, young hypnotists, leads to Humbert. All roads lead to Humbert. By telling the story, by casting this enchantment (to enchant, from the Latin *cantare,* to sing) in the first person, Nabokov has created a built-in mesmer in this song, this little ditty of his. For, wouldn't you know it, folks, Humbert-Humbert just so happens to share Nabokov's same lust for language, his fascination with phrases, his delight in de poetry of words.

The sound of Humbert's voice *hums* throughout this spell. One particularly potent passage is, "I saw her lovely indrawn abdomen where my southbound mouth had briefly paused; and those puerile hips on which I had kissed the crenulated imprint left by the band of her shorts—that last mad immortal day behind the 'Roches Roses.'" I ask that you look at this not as a sentence imparting images and meaning, but as notes of music artfully scattered across the page. Feel the rhythm of "indrawn abdomen," "southbound mouth." Sense the "puerile" harkening back—not so long ago—to "paused," and catch your breath. Sound out the clever alliteration in "kissed" and "crenulated." Open your mouth and let it expand enough to fully experience the opened vowel notes in "last mad immortal day." It is a sweet moaning song. A whisper of a song in your ear, the promise of great things.

Even the savage, illiterate, tribal shaman understands this basic principle: the art of the spell lies in the music.

But the music of enchantment does not and should not be a constant drone of lulling tones. Such a thing is useful only for those "relaxation tapes" often hawked in the "music" section of the previously mentioned Wal-Mart. Such a thing may be done purposely to put one to sleep. No. It must be punctuated throughout with variations and explored to its limits if it is to be more than a mere illusionist's trick, a sleight of hand, a circus freak-show trick of sword swallowing.

And so the real enchantment. Ladies and gentlemen, Nabokov created for your entertainment—delight and perhaps horror—a character aptly named Humbert. And this character, Humbert, has his own agenda, his own reasons for telling his story. And our Humbert thinks he is mighty smart, dear readers. Humbert thinks he is the enchanter. Humbert believes himself to be quite the wizard in the ways of weaving a story. Humbert believes he is manipulating his audience with his use of music, his hypnotic hum, his Orpheus's lyre in the lines (his literary allusions). But Humbert is much deceived.

The shaman knows he needs the active participation of the members of his tribe to create the necessary energy for his spell to work, but he never relinquishes control to the tribe. He skillfully creates the necessary environment and tone. He selects the right music to enable the seduction of the minds in his charge.

Nabokov created Humbert so fully that Humbert actually believes he is in charge. What ironic and false modesty he exhibits: "I have no illusions, however. My judges will regard all this as a piece of mummery on the part of a madman with a gross liking for *fruit vert* . . . ," when in fact he is a madman, suffering from an identity crisis. He actually believes that he is the author—when, in fact, it is Nabokov who fabricated this tale. Humbert, poor humming Humbert, is suffering from delusions of grandeur. He is much more accurate than he could possibly know in the next line, "All I know is that while the Haze woman and I went down the steps into the breathless garden, my knees were like reflections of knees in rippling water, my lips were like sand . . . ." Ah, yes Humbert, you are something like a reflection and your lips are definitely *not* made of flesh.

But as I was saying, Humbert is an amazingly real character. For such a spell as conjuring up a soul that never lived one must be open to all and listen to the voices that come—therefore, in the creation of Humbert, Nabokov lets Humbert speak as much as he wants. Nabokov allows him to express as much of himself as he wants. Which, because of Humbert's smug arrogance and his delight at the sound of his own voice, probably turned out to be more than he intended when he set out to write his confession:

> This then is my story. I have reread it. It has bits of marrow sticking to it, and blood, and beautiful bright-green flies. At this or that twist of it I feel my slippery self eluding me, gliding into deeper and darker waters than I care to probe.

Ah, but Nabokov did care to probe, and so there is Humbert in all his fumblings and bumblings.

And so, Humbert's overwhelming fervor pulls us into the book. Even when it is overdone, or perhaps especially when it is overdone, we are sucked into Humbert's mad whirlwind of passion for his nymphet. Listen to the way he abandons all reason and tells us exactly the way he felt when he first saw her:

> I was still walking behind Mrs. Haze through the dining room when, beyond it, there came a sudden burst of greenery—"the piazza," sang out my leader, and then, without the least warning, a blue sea-wave swelled under my heart and from a mat in a pool of sun, half-naked, kneeling, turning about on her knees, there was my Riviera love peering at me over the dark glasses . . . I find it difficult to express with adequate force that flash, that shiver, that impact of passionate recognition. In the course of the sun-shot moment that my glance slithered over the kneeling child…the vacuum of my soul managed to suck in every detail of her bright beauty.

So, though we may be horrified by Humbert's cravings for *fruit vert*, we may actually feel the sea-waves swell in our own chests when he speaks of his Riviera love. In any case we recognize what that feels like, and we are drawn into his mad swooning.

This is a confession. What self-respecting human being with a full brain, not lobotomized, would pass up on reading a confession? Hey, there has to be some incentive for joining the priesthood, right? Faunlets? No. No. I will not go there. The very structure of the confession promises a delightful intimacy, a knowledge of things that no one else knows. And we all want to be in the know, right?

Perhaps the thing that makes a good confession a delight to read is the promise of honesty, hopefully the delivery of it. We know we can never get full honesty. And we are aware that Humbert has his motive, yet we do get his honesty, and the honesty charms us into the novel. Humbert does not always paint himself as the innocent victim of Lolita. He does say she seduced him at The Enchantment Hunter's, but throughout he slides in little jibes at himself which let us know that he is aware of what he has done. He doesn't hide the fact that he is a sexual predator and often uses base, animalistic imagery in reference to himself. This kind of honesty is the real kind we encounter in life. Rarely does anyone come straight out and confess to all their sins, unless they are in the darkness of the confessional or the comfort of their psychiatrist's couch (paying by the hour). And we know that Humbert was not a churchgoing man. And he had a tendency to fabricate in the psychiatrist's office. But in *Lolita*, as far as we know, we are given the truth as Humbert sees it. We get the inside scoop of what it is like to be tormented by nymphets. People do reveal the truth about themselves, especially in little self-deprecating comments they may make, and this is what Nabokov lets Humbert do so well. Humbert tells us that he knows Lolita would let him kiss her, but how does he know that? Well, he goes on, "Perhaps my ape-ear had unconsciously caught some slight change in the rhythm of her respiration." Two days later he has become a strange spider:

> I am like one of those inflated pale spiders you see in old gardens. Sitting in the middle of my luminous web and giving little jerks to this or that strand. *My* web is spread all over the house as I listen from my chair where I sit like a wily wizard. Is Lo in her room? Gently I tug on the silk. She is not...Is she still brushing her teeth . . . ? No. The bathroom door has just slammed, so one has to feel elsewhere about the house for the beautiful warm-colored prey. Let us have a strand of silk descend the stairs . . .

Although there is something truly chilling in the way Nabokov characterizes how the mind of a sexual predator works, in Humbert's careful calculations as to Lo's whereabouts, it is this very chill that keeps us spellbound. It is similar to the spell of a horror film. We are scared, but we like it. We are caught in Humbert's sticky web. He has us by the ears. And we are waiting anxiously for other such confessions to leak out of him. And we do not have to wait long. That's the good thing about Humbert. He delivers. A week later he writes in his diary, "I began creeping up to her . . . ." And creep he does, until he creeps his way into Big Haze's bed and finally into Lolita's.

Humbert is determined to keep the reader's attention. If not by poetry and passion, then by confession, and if not by confession, by science. But what is science anyway if not a more elaborate, methodical form of magic with its hocus-pocus chemicals and magic tricks and abracadabra jargon? If nothing else, Humbert approaches this tale with absolute authority. HE KNOWS OF WHAT HE SPEAKS. He knows it through experience. But he wants us to know that he is not a mere ape; though he is an ape, he is also an *educated* ape. An ape capable of careful observation and learning through this process and so he tells us:

> Now I wish to introduce the following idea. Between the age limits of nine and fourteen there occur maidens who, to certain bewitched travelers, twice or many times older than they, reveal their true nature which is not human, but nymphic (that is, demonic); and these chosen creatures I propose to designate as "nymphets." It will be marked that I substitute time terms for spatial ones. In fact, I would have the reader see "nine" and "fourteen" as the boundaries—the mirrory beaches and rosy rocks—of an enchanted island haunted by those nymphets of mine and surrounded by a vast, misty sea. Between those age limits, are all girl-children nymphets? Of course not. Otherwise, we who are in the know, we lone voyagers, we nympholepts, would have long gone insane.

He has the structure of a scientific hypothesis, but the language of the bewitched transports him to a long-ago time, like I said before, where science and magic were still one and the same, where the scientists spoke of *humours* in the body and believed in bloodletting and demoniac beings. In fact, Humbert's attempt to become the anthropologist and distance himself from his own predicament is peculiar, a bit shocking to the system as you read but also adding to the already quirky character of Humbert. This is a full-fledged human being, full of idiosyncrasies as well as psychoses. This is a man who, while looking back fondly at the memory of viewing his delectable morsel on the porch, can also go into an explanation on the medical causes of acne:

> Marvelous skin—oh, marvelous: tender and tanned, not the least blemish. Sundaes cause acne. The excess of the oily substance called sebum which nourishes the hair follicles of the

skin creates, when too profuse, an irritation that opens the way to infection. But nymphets do not have acne although they gorge themselves on rich food.

And again, while in the midst of rationing and fantasizing a response from Lo, Humbert begins to talk puberty. "The median age of pubescence for girls has been found to be thirteen and nine months in New York and Chicago. The age varies for individuals from ten, or earlier to seventeen. Virginia was not quite fourteen when Harry Edgar proposed to her."

Humbert feels guilt. It is the tormenting impetus of this confession, for he is surely intelligent enough to know that the ladies and gentlemen of the jury will throw his big fat book right back at him after reading it. After he tells us how his lust is consummated, he then tries to sort things out for himself in a paragraph that is pained and ineffective in the struggle to "sort out the portion of hell and the portion of heaven in that strange, awful, maddening world— nymphet love." And then again he launches into history and anthropology, but reaches the guilt, his so called "horror":

> The stipulation of Roman Law, according to which a girl may marry at twelve, was adopted by the Church, and is still pre- served, rather tacitly, in some of the United States . . ." In such stimulating temperate climates [says an old magazine in this prison library] as St. Louis, Chicago, and Cincinnati, girls mature about the end of their twelfth year." Dolorez Haze was born less than three hundred miles from stimulating Cincinnati. I have but followed nature. I am nature's faithful hound. Why then this horror that I cannot shake off?

Science and witchcraft meld in the novel. This is a spell cast by incanta- tions of the musical poetry as well as by the chemical methods of "Papa's Purple Pills." Nabokov takes from both, and we accept them both, our eyes heavy-lidded under his spell and eager to be shown more horrors and marvels.

Really this book is an act of necromancy. It is filled with ghosts. Both main characters are presumably dead when you read this. Thus Nabokov has conjured up the dead for your bizarre pleasure (what freaks you are!) much like Mephistopheles conjured up the great Julius Caesar and Helen of Troy for the delight of decadent Faustus. Ahhh . . . but where is Lolita? Where is she? Nowhere. She is not there. What you have, dear readers, is a flimflam sham. Lolita is dead. And perhaps she never lived. Nabokov cannot tell you about her without breaking the hold that the book has on your imagination. All throughout, Humbert has been humming his own tune of Lolita. His own Humbertzak version of Lolita. The reader gets her character through the eyes of Humbert, whose vision is clouded by the spectacles of obsession.

Even Humbert tells us that he did not *know* Lolita. He only knew his version of her: the nymphet.

From the moment he first lays eyes on her, he describes her in physical terms because that is all he knows, and at the moment, that was all that mattered. "Why does the way she walks—a child, mind you, a mere child!—excite me so abominably? Analyze it. A faint suggestion of turned-in toes. A kind of wiggly looseness below the knee prolonged to the end of each footfall." He watches her on the lawn:

> There my beauty lay on her stomach, showing me, showing the thousand eyes wide open in my eyed blood, her slightly raised shoulder blades, and the bloom along the incurvature of her spine, and the swellings of her tense narrow nates clothed in black, and the seaside of her schoolgirl thighs.

But much later reality sets in. When Humbert finally has his nymphet to himself on the whirlwind tour of tourist traps, he finds that she is not all sweetness and spice:

> A combination of naïveté and deception of charm and vulgarity, of blue sulks and rosy mirth, Lolita, when she chose, could be a most exasperating brat. I was really quite unprepared for her fits of disorganized boredom, intense and vehement griping, her sprawling, droopy, dopey-eyed style. Mentally, I found her to be a disgustingly conventional little girl.

But it isn't until he has completely lost her that Humbert fully realizes that he never really knew her. The novel swells with her absence and his regret:

> And I have still other smothered memories, now unfolding themselves into limbless monsters of pain. Once, in a sunset-ending street of Beardsley, she turned to little Eva Rosen (I was taking both nymphets to a concert and walking behind them so close as almost to touch them with my person), she turned to Eva, and so very serenely and seriously, in answer to something the other had said about its being better to die than hear Milton Pinski, some local schoolboy she knew, talk about

music, my Lolita remarked: "You know, what's so dreadful about dying is that you are completely on your own"; and struck me, as my automaton knees went up and down, that I simply did not know a thing about my darling's mind and that quite possibly, behind the awful juvenile clichés, there was in her a garden and a twilight, and a palace gate—dim and adorable regions which happened to be lucidly and absolutely forbidden to me, in my polluted rags and miserable convulsions.

And who knows if the "nymphet" ever really existed anywhere other than in Humphert's slippery mind? And so throughout the book we have a feel of her haunting the story with her potential and then her absence, much as Humbert feels in the end when he writes:

> Reader! What I heard was but the melody of children at play, nothing but that, and so limpid voices, majestic, and minute, remote and magically near, frank and divinely enigmatic one could hear now and then, as if released, an almost articulate spurt of vivid laughter, of a toy wagon, but it was all really too far for the eye to distinguish any movement in the lightly etched streets. I stood listening to that musical vibration from my lofty slope, to those flashes of separate cries with a kind of demure murmur for background, and then I knew that the hopelessly poignant thing was not Lolita's absence from my side, but the absence of her voice from that concord.

We have listened to that musical vibration in Humbert's unique voice, waiting for the promise of Lolita, the nymphet, to be pulled out of the magician's hat. And every time we think we catch a glimpse of her, we are tricked by mirrors and smoke. And in the end, it is not Humbert who has tricked us, but Nabokov who has enchanted us by channeling Humbert's strange voice and letting it speak on the page. And Lolita remains a bittersweet mystery for Humbert, and for the reader.

Cherry Bomb

KYLE KINANE

This was an overwhelming experience. The secret you can't hide. The moment that you'll always want to remember, until it happens. Then you can't forget it, no matter how hard you try. I don't know why people say they "lost" their virginity. "I lost my virginity in the back seat of a 1972 Nova in Flint, Michigan." "I lost my virginity during the solar eclipse of May, 1995, with the girl that works at the Fotomat." Sounds like they know exactly where their shit went. You don't lose it. It's not car keys. I know, and will always know, where and when I shook hands/curtsied/high-fived my virginity a fond farewell and watched it ride into the sunset of purity.

It was at the Days Inn, Joliet, Tuesday, January 28, 1998, sometime between 1:30 and 4:00 A.M., Central Standard Time.

And her stage name was Crystal.

That evening I was running the Marathon (the gas station, not the race). It was an uneventfully average night. The typical geeks and drunkards stumbling in and out with forgettable faces. Two packs of Marlboro Lights here, a Slim Jim there, directions, thanks. A couple regulars come in, shoot the shit. Dante told me I should get a job as a runner at the stock exchange when he found I was going to school to be a writer. Joe said I could come work at his construction company. Nice fellas at heart, you know, lookin' out for me or whatever. But yeah, that's how the nights went. Normal, regular, plain-old happenings. The (already way too hot to be) sixteen-year-old comes in and tries to buy Virginia Slim Ultra-Lights because she knows she's younger than she looks. I card her. She says she's only got a ticket and then smiles at me, flirty-like. I say it's cool. She gives the wave to her boyfriend. "It's OK, he'll sell them to me. What did you want again?" Bitch. I would've sold 'em to her regardless. I always sold to the kids. If anybody needs 'em, it's the youngsters. Growing up is stressful. What if some young cat was trying to relax while he was studying for an algebra final, or had to stay up all night making his Pinewood Derby car? I wasn't worried; it's not like it was hard to spot the narcs. They'd come in and ask for "one package of cigarettes, please," and I would just point to the sign on the counter top. "Sorry, bud. It's the *law*. And next time, don't talk directly into your shirt collar."

But that fateful Tuesday, a six-foot-three vixen with a Camaro and a misconception that a whole bunch of lip-liner would be a good idea came lanking over into my station. I looked up like I usually did, giving the customers a standard once-over. Maybe I looked at her twice, but probably not.

"Hey, do you have a phone book I could use?'

"Yeah, sure." I tossed it onto the counter and helped the other customers after her.

"Can I use your phone?"

I imagined my manager John's big Samoan face yelling at me for letting customers use the phone. "What the fuck? They're not the ones paying the phone bill, Kyle." She smiled at me, flirty-like. She was skinny. Skinny face, skinny brown hair, skinny lips and nose. And lip-liner. Fat lip-liner.

So she's got the phone cord stretched over the counter while I'm trying to help the customers pacing around her.

"Shit. I need to get shoes for work. Do you know of any place around here?"

Shoes, at this hour? Who goes to work at 9:30 at night and needs a new pair of shoes, *right away?*

"I don't know. The place across the street is closed already, too. Which direction are you heading?"

"Stars Gentlemen's Club, in Franklin Park. Have you ever heard of it?"

Heard of it? *Heard* of it? Marcus and I would sit in the parking lot there just about every other weekend and split a half-pint of Crown Royal. We went there enough that the dancers knew our names. One even got Marcus a birthday card. They made us feel like Norm from *Cheers* when we rolled in there, our throats burning from whiskey. It was nice. A lot of times I just listened to the music. No, honest. I love AC/DC.

Most of the time we'd have a couple of young ladies lounging with us at our table. It was an honest flattery—they knew we were broke and never bought private dances. We just weren't creepy like the other fellas there. We didn't have a wife or kids at home, and we weren't the stalker type. We weren't meatheads who called them "baby" or "sugar tits." Maybe they thought we were a couple of gay guys just going to the strip club for a campy evening of heterosexuality and that I would mockingly imitate a strip-club dance for him when we got back to our townhouse. No way. Marcus would be doing the sexy dance for *me*. What I'm trying to say here is that I have most definitely *heard* of Stars Gentlemen's Club.

"Oh, you mean on Grand Avenue? Yeah, I've been there a couple times."

"Yeah, I need to be there in twenty minutes, and my shoe broke last night."

Bummer.

"Well, I have to go. Thanks for letting me use the phone."

"No problem. Good luck with your shoe fiasco."

She was halfway out the door.

"Oh, thanks. Hey, you should come by the club sometime." She smiled at me, flirty-like. "I'll give you a dance." She stepped into her black and red Camaro and sped off. The guy who was next in line was ogling her the entire time.

"Whooh, imagine havin' them sticks wrapped around ya'." He was drunk.

"Yeah." I agreed with him only to keep the small talk to a minimum. Marcus was sure to agree that a free dance was enough of an excuse to go to the nudie bar on a Tuesday. I called him and we got there about 10:45 p.m. The whiskey was downed, and I felt a bit cocky. Hell, a stripper was going to give me a free dance. Sounded like "I might even get laid," we joked, "if I was into that sort of thing."

Being a twenty-one-year-old virgin, I never really even let the thought of actually having sex with a girl cross my mind. That's the only reason I went for as long as I did. I just never assumed it could happen without some kind of warning or notice, like a nuclear missile landing in your front yard. You're a churchgoing virgin one minute, and the next minute you've got body parts that doctors won't even touch without rubber gloves, mashing together in awkward silence. I was just going to get a dance from this girl, because guys don't lose their virginity to strippers without a film crew around. Just an innocent dance with maybe a little bit of extra-dirty talk, nothing more.

Marcus and I drank beers and talked with the talent. Destiny said that Fat Sal was buying pizza for all the dancers and that he's a fucking weirdo.

Nothing sadder than to see some chump come down with a heavy case of she-likes-me-for-my-company (not my money). This Fat Sal looked like he sold beepers or car-stereo equipment. Jumpsuit, gold rope necklaces, you know what I'm talking about. Probably just barely making the payments on his Cadillac each month. But he spends cash on the ladies. Drinks, dances, unsolicited gifts. We understood when they left our table for his. "Gotta go make some money, guys. I'll be back in a little while." Everyone has bills to pay. So we drank more beers and talked to more of the ladies. Then I saw the girl from the gas station. Her stage name was Crystal, and she danced to "The Lumberjack" by Jackyl. To this day, that is still one of the worst fucking songs I've ever heard. If you gave me the option of listening to that song once a month for the next five years or having my ears implanted with tiny speakers that played nothing but Celine Dion twenty-four hours a day, seven days a week, for the rest of my life, you could be damn sure that when I turned eighty I'd know every last word of "My Heart Will Go On." Jackyl *sucks*.

I flagged her down when she got off stage.

"I didn't think you'd show up." She touched my leg.

"Yeah, well . . . don't have anything to do tomorrow, so . . . what are you drinking?"

"Bud Light."

That one threw me for a loop. Strippers drink screwdrivers and Long Island iced teas. Guys with moustaches drink Bud Light. She laughed a little.

"I owe you a dance, don't I?"

"Oh, I don't care. You don't have to do that, you know . . . ."

She grabbed my arm.

"No, no. I told you I'd give you a dance, so c'mon."

She led me upstairs and into the "private" dance area. It was one long, darkly lit corridor with chairs lined up against the one wall. She sat me down as the next song started and did her thing. It was OK. Lap dances are always awkward. All day at school or work, guys will hope for even just the quickest flash of cleavage. Then they pay thirty bucks to have it shaking in their face and they squirm and look into the girl's eyes instead. The subtly domineering power of a naked breast is not to be reckoned with, I've always said. So Crystal makes me squirm a bit, and then we return to the table and chat about nothing memorable. Marcus stayed quiet most of the time. Figured this one was my ordeal. We hung out, drank a couple more, and Crystal went up to dance again. I got her to dance to AC/DC, thank God. She came back to our table.

"Hey, do you want another dance?" she said between huffs of air (she was a very acrobatic dancer).

"Well, I'd love to, but I'm kind of broke." It was the truth.

"Don't worry about it." She grabbed my arm and dragged me back to the corridor. This time she was quite a bit more animated. I watched her, and she watched to make sure the bouncer wasn't watching. This wasn't the thirty-dollar dance; this wasn't even the *fifty*-dollar dance. This wasn't an employee/customer kind of transaction. This was the director's cut. The "don't let anybody see where you're putting your hands because I'll get fired and you'll get beat up" dance. Things were being rubbed and pawed at and thrust upon. A moisture and odor permeated the room, indicating "too much to be allowed." Down the corridor, there was another "couple." Looking around to make sure I wasn't going to be pummeled, I saw the guy looking our way. You could tell he was thinking, "I'm getting a dance from *her* next time."

Topless dancers tend to wear a lot of bad perfume. My nostrils were topped off with it. Her clammy back was to me as she did the standard lap-dance ass grind, but my hands were not by my side, per regulations. I was crossing the border without proper documentation, sneaking into a foreign country via a pulled-aside G-string, and I was beginning to fall under the impression that this woman wanted to have sexual relations with me.

But why me? This stuff happens to drug dealers and rock stars. Not twenty-one-year-old virgins. She leaned in, her breath heavy of Bud Light and Newports.

"So are we gonna hook up after this?"

No hesitation, no hinting. She just laid it right out there. A woman, an exotic dancer at that, wanting to have sex with me. This was game point. If I lost my virginity to a stripper, that would be the most rock-and-roll thing *ever*, wouldn't it? I didn't even view it as getting laid. It was to be a story, a legend even, that people would tell for years to come, around kegs on backyard porches everywhere. "Yeah, that's Kyle. I heard he's the craziest cat around, even lost his virginity to a stripper. So fucking *cool*." I couldn't answer you today if you asked me why I thought like that. I was just an idiot, I guess. If I said yes to this lady, there was no turning back. I would be signing the papers right then and there. By rightful duty I would have to tear up my Virgin's Club membership and step into manhood. No more flopping around in bars with no worries. I would have to try and be cool from then on out, because sex could be an option at any moment when you're not a virgin anymore. Was I ready to handle all the pressures and responsibilities of being a sexually active young adult? Wouldn't I look like a complete jackass doing it for the first time with someone of her sexual caliber? This girl had a black belt in fucking, and I was still playing around with my foam-covered nunchaku.

She met me at the Citgo down the street because it would "look bad" if I got into her car over there, she said. Marcus let me sit in silence to think over my decision.

"Should I do it?" I bit my thumbnail.

"Why not?" For being older than me, sometimes I wish Marcus had more insight.

"Here she comes."

"All right, dude. Good luck." Neither of us was really gushing with excitement. He gave me a handshake and bid me goodnight as I left his car.

I pulled open the long door to the Camaro, and she was playing a Garth Brooks tape. The petrified feeling of being dropped off at summer camp for the first time came rushing back to me. Why do I have to do this? Why can't things just stay the same? Why can't I just play Legos and drink Capri-Suns forever? Because I was twenty-one. When you're twenty-one you drink beer and you fuck, and that's just the way it goes. I got in.

"So what's up?"

What's up is that you are the one I have chosen to be the recipient of my flower. Prom-night dreams aside, you are the one I will remember forever. The name on my heart, the love of a lifetime that I will never forget.

"I dunno."

To say that conversation made me feel more comfortable with the situation would be a lie. I found out that she does all her own work on her car. And her motorcycle. I found out that she's "already done that tying-up-and-whipping shit" with her ex-husband, the marine. She didn't wear shoes. Not while driving, not while walking around on the frozen January sidewalks. And I didn't have to worry because she brought "protection." We drove for a long time. Couldn't go back to her place because her neighbors knew what she did for a living, and it would "look bad," she said.

There was some serious explaining to do on my part. Did I really think I could pull this off like it happens all the time? Hell, no. I was shivering and sweating all at once. Obviously not enough beer.

"Hey, guess what?"

"Huh?"

"I've never done this before."

"Oh, don't worry."

Judging by her tepid response, she must've thought I was talking about one-night stands.

"No, I mean I've never done *it* before."

"What? You? You're kidding." She thought I was joking. Great.

"No, really. I'm a . . . a virgin."

She did the flirty smile thing again.

"Well, not for long."

Vomit rose up to my throat.

We pulled up to a Days Inn just outside of the middle of nowhere. She said she'd take care of the room because they "knew her there." When a girl says she knows all the people who work at a hotel the next town over, it "looks bad." As she walked into the lobby, I started to dry heave in the car. Obviously too much beer. Obviously.

I would have run. I would've kicked the window out of that shit-box Camaro and just hit the ground with my Adidas burning. I would've run through the snow-covered fields to a farmhouse and banged on the door until the elderly couple who lived there woke up and responded to all the commotion by saying, "My Lord, boy, what happened? You just calm down and tell us what happened," and in between breaths I could spit out the words, "She's . . . she's . . . trying . . . (gasp)...she's trying to fuck me!" and before they could even respond she'd be standing in their doorway with her lip-liner turned down at the corners in a disappointed pout, and she'd say, "Did you really think you could get away?"

I looked down to the left and saw her shoes lying by the brake pedal. And I stayed.

We drove around to the side where the room was. She grabbed her duffel bag and her shoes (she carried her shoes) and popped open the console by the emergency brake. "Can't forget these," she said, grabbing a few rubbers from the compartment. Regardless of what you may think, or what may be the truth, it is my reasoning that she kept condoms in the console of her car for the simple fact that when checking the oil in your engine, you can always slide a few jimmies over the fingers to avoid getting your hands dirty. She certainly did *not* have them in there because she had a lot of anonymous sex with dirty gas-station attendants. No, sir. Not at all. No way.

I followed her up to the room. The cheap décor just enhanced the theme of the whole evening. Green drapes, floral-pattern bedspreads, bland carpeting—it was like they knew we were coming. And to add to my already deep-seated regret, there were two beds. They knew we were coming, and they knew how I felt. The good folks at the Days Inn were saying, "We understand, buddy. Most of the guys she brings here like to fuck and sleep in the same bed, but you're probably going to want some personal time when all this shit's over." I looked around the room for sharp objects to skewer my eyeballs with, but the only things that weren't bolted down were the ashtray, the soap, and the Bible.

She was lying on the bed.

"Rub my feet."

I was sitting on a chair.

Rub those unholy stubs you've been traipsing around the January slop fields with? Are you out of your tiny mind, you sick hillbilly whack job? Then I remembered who I was with, and why, and where.

"OK."

She had turned on the TV, and thank God because at least then there was some noise to muffle out the silence of my bad choice.

I rubbed those rotten tires for a good five minutes, which was apparently enough to "turn her on." She pulled her feet away and turned off the television.

"Take your clothes off."

She said it so sternly and directly, I was afraid of what would happen if I *didn't* get undressed.

"Come here."

I did.

I don't think we kissed at all. We might have, but it's not something that's sticking out much. What I mainly remember is that *certain* parts of my body were most definitely *not* cooperating with my plan to "Seem uninterested, and maybe she'll just take you home." Oh yeah. It was like how dogs get all excited when someone's at the door, whether it's a mailman or a serial killer. It's not like I have eyes down there; a pair of hands (other than my own) is most always going to be a pleasant surprise. My hands just floated around her back, over the dragon tattoos on her shoulder and ass. I contemplated running my fingers through her hair, but the web of Aqua-Net would surely have caused problems. She responded to my southern interest by yanking on it like her hand was stuck. This was fine by me, but she was going to want some attention of her own soon. I knew that was going to be tricky.

I would go down on the fucking Titanic before I went down on this woman. Being just a topless dancer, people saw her feet a hell of a lot more than they saw her pussy, and she couldn't even keep those halfway decent. Besides I don't think she'd be too flattered if I went down on her with a Days Inn shower cap over my face. Kyle-lingus was most certainly out of the question.

She flipped onto her back and pulled me on top of her. Our parts were touching. Some precautionary measures would have to be taken if this was going to go any further.

"I should be wearing one of those, um . . . you know." I couldn't even say the word "condom"; what the hell was I doing in a hotel room with a stripper?

"Oh, yeah." She grabbed one off the nightstand and tossed it to me. I never saw the whole "condom on the banana" demonstration in health class, but I did put one on once just to see what it was like. I ripped open the wrapper and slid that slippery little sucker on.

Then we had sex.

People say they had "rough" sex. Like pushing-and-shoving, hair-grabbing, tossing-around, falling-down-the-stairs sex. I had "rough" sex. Like riding an epileptic bull strapped to a hydrogen bomb falling through the fiery atmosphere of a Catholic hell in July sex. You know it's not the heat that's bad in hell; it's the humidity. And the fact that your soul will burn eternally for losing your marital gift of purity to a stripper.

She said to grab her harder, so I put my quivering fingers around her waist.

She said to push her harder, so I unlocked my hips.

She said to fuck her harder, so I fucked as hard as I thought was socially acceptable in the way of fucking.

She said to make more noise, so I stopped breathing through my nose and let out a few sighs disguised as grunts.

Legs bent in gymnastic-like ways, entangling us. Off the bed, on the bed, on the other bed, the floor, the dresser—we covered every square inch of that room with our sweat. Pushed against the door, pulled into the shower, thrown onto the table in the corner, tossed onto the bed only to be dragged off onto the floor. Bruises and bite marks raised on flesh waiting to stain it. Fingers left red marks around arms and ankles and necks. It was so much that sometimes I even caught myself being a bit physical. A squeeze of the breast, a light slap on the ass-dragon—I was starting to loosen up. My irregular breathing even dissipated a little.

Then we had "rough" sex.

You open yourself up to someone when you have sex. You're letting go and allowing new things to happen, and that person is doing the same with you. It's a time for consensual exploring. Try it like this, do it under here. In its most idealistic form, it is complete and total safety. Crystal, aka Sharon, aka the girl that I was currently sharing reproductive space with, shattered every notion of that. She took my belief, wrapped it around her finger, and shoved it right where it belonged.

Up my ass.

With all of my other naïve delusions about life.

Did I mention this was my first time?

She did it with such ease, such perfect nonchalance—like I wasn't even going to notice. I didn't think it was actually happening at first. I thought maybe I had fallen on a pen. But pens didn't thrust that hard or repeatedly. Of all my expectations and anticipations for the adventure I embarked on that evening, this was the last thing I could've thought would happen. She did it all so effortlessly. *"Come in and I'll give you a free dance." "So, are we gonna hook up tonight?" "Hey, howsabout I put my finger in your butt?"* It was my first time, for Christ's sake! I didn't know if this was like hitting a home run on the first pitch or crashing the first time you ride in an airplane. It didn't *feel* like a home run.

It felt wrong. Wrong in a hotel room with her. Wrong on that night, at that moment. Everything felt wrong. I felt like a cheap date. Buy me a few drinks and do whatever you want to me. That little spark of adventure that kept me hanging on and wondering what would happen next went out. I saw the whole, sticky, greasy reality of it. A kid fucking a stripper in a hotel room on a cold winter night. Cold sex in January. Unromantic, passionless back and forth. From the thin atmosphere over Joliet I saw houses for miles with couples doing the same thing inside—fucking, because that's what happens at night, after work, after Letterman. I saw cars with steam and footprints on the windows. Two kids happy that the seat folds down in Mom's minivan. A guy with his ear up to a dorm-room wall, listening to his roommate knock pictures off the wall with some pre-med, wondering when he was going to "get some." I made some noise.

"Uh, that's enough of that."

She stopped as coolly as she started and continued with the operation, but it was no use. I was cold. I didn't want any more.

"Hey, let's stop."

She looked at me confused.

"Did you come?"

"No. Let's just stop for a while."

She unstraddled me and lay down on the bed next to me.

"Why are you shaking? Are you cold?"

No, I'm not cold; I'm *ravaged.*

"Yes. I think I'm gonna go to sleep. Kinda beat, you know?"

"All right. Are you OK?" She kind of laughed. I didn't share in the novelty.

"Yeah, just tired."

"OK."

She ground her teeth in her sleep. Even when she was unconscious, she was repulsive. The noise was unbearable. I didn't think she was going to have any incisors left in the morning. I lay with my back to her, staring out between the drapes as the black gave way to gray. My clothes were in a pile where she demanded them off. I put them on and sat at the table. She smoked Newport 100s, so that morning I smoked Newport 100s and waited for her to wake up. She rolled over around ten-thirty or so.

With squinty eyes she questioned what I was doing up so early. I whipped up some bullshit about how I had to be at work soon. The shower ran while I smoked more of her cigarettes. She gathered her things and put them in her duffel bag, and we left. I sat in her car quietly as she drove and flipped radio stations.

And I wasn't a virgin anymore.

Fucking cool, I guess.

Fish Camp Gamers

TODD H. DILLS

Jo's is set up against a vacant yard on its left, a textile mill on its right that extends about a half-mile up Main and butts its old dirty brick flush against the grounds of the bleachery where me and Louie used to work.

One day he asked me, "Got five?"

"Five what?"

"I feel like hitting the camp today."

I took it he meant five dollars for a plate of Jo's greasy catfish, though time might, too, have been something to think about. We ride our lunches past the end of the road, sitting and talking of the black girl I let get away—we both let get away. Louie, see, he's white; twenty years down the road and he still can't get out of his thick, shaggy white head the shimmering backs of Dedra's tree-trunk thighs. Every day of the week—for the past two, at least—we've hit the camp for the lunch-hour, gotten wasted on Jo's new liquor license, and talked about this like two old fogeys with nothing on their minds but death. Drunk, yes, and I almost got fired for my inability to hide it. The foreman, super on the shift, I, almost got the can, busted drooling drunk on secretary-to-the-boss Annie's arm. In Oglethorpe's office, I stood over her shoulder on the pretense of borrowing a cup of coffee from their bubbling pot. I stood over her shoulder inquiring into what she was doing and sucked the slightly perfumed scent of her red hair, eyes rolling way back into my head, slimy tendril emerging from the corner of red-brown lips quite unbeknownst to me.

"You drunk bastard! Goddamn no-good monkey bastard!" she screamed, rising to full Amazonic height and flinging the spit quick with her arm, and I laughed, scurried to the door. The Boss later comes out flailing white arms and wringing his hands and launching into a tirade on my horrible performance. I grabbed quick to the post that held the paper rollers in place and smiled a big toothy Uncle Tom at him.

"And you, my goddamned foreman," he said, "drunk. It's a goddamned shame." Oglethorpe could hold a candle to all the filthy-mouthed comedians, Bruce to Murphy to Rock.

Louie sauntered up wagging his head like, *goddamn I can't believe this nigger getting drunk even at work*. That's how it came off—like a promotion plea, but I know it's just Louie swaggering over drunk as me, and I started laughing at the mock-sober look on his big shaggy face, beard like a pirate.

Oglethorpe's eyes lit up at Louie. "Well," he said, "and you, you dago son of a bitch, what the hell do you think about your nigger boss here getting drunk on the job?"

I felt I had to get a word in but couldn't hold back the laugh. My stomach collapsed at it, doubled over, face to knees. Louie's hand had gone up like a kindergartner. "Actually, I'm Irish, sir," he said.

"What the fuck ever, Murphy, I know you're Irish. Goddamn wipe that silly look off your face. You drunk too?" And the boss wheeled around like to leave it alone, shaking his head and muttering, "Goddamned imbeciles," when Louie answered the man with a sly look my way and just one word: "Quite," he said. "Yes, quite." And now we were both bursting, tears springing from ducts and dripping from our overhung faces onto the concrete below.

Boss turned around: I caught a tear-blurred sight of his face in flames like to blaze from anger, and he wheeled again, stormed back and into his office. Could even hear him through the walls—dago this, nigger that—and Annie's protests to him to just leave us be, sweet old lady Annie.

And today. "Sure, I got your five spotted," I eventually told little Louie, little except he's about twice my size.

"Two more for a beer."

"Sure."

"Four for a couple more?"

Louie was pushing it. My wallet had already taken a hit from two weeks of this. Jo'd just got his liquor license so the price of the lunch hour had suddenly doubled for the two of us. But then the little bell rang for the first shift to cut off for lunch, and we sifted out into the sunlight, floated up the road past the textile mill and into the old wooden door at Jo's, the handle rattling in my palm as I pushed the thing open and we sat in out usual spot, against the wall in a booth that looks beaten like it came straight out of a failed pool hall and Jo's had it shoved up against the rear plaster wall not planning on giving it a chance to ever feel at home. The seats are a gaudy red, curved to fit, the table-top a fake Formica thing, white vinyl covering peppered with little gray squiggles and bordered by an aluminum ring.

"Hey, Jo, get a coupla beers over here?"

I say two weeks, though it's more like ten years we've been sitting around here jawing about the girl, Dedra, my then girlfriend, having long since left me for a banking nigger and who probably sits right now on the stoop—the balcony, more like—of a glitzy Charlotte apartment building, sipping quaint on a martini or somesuch. Dedra—the bigger black girl, the little white boy—my now quite large friend Louie—wanted so bad that he sat four hours straight in the hottest sun yet that year, sat on the front step of his walkway from the time he stormed from his second grade classroom, knowing—little Louie—that Dedra would be swinging by here within striking distance, down this sidewalk after being released from her own late high school class. Dedra—tight-butt cutoffs, tree trunk thighs, the sweat of days putting a shine down the round backs, what little Louie wanted, then—

"Wanted it so bad, J., so bad," Louie said repeating the obvious. I slumped back down in my seat, watching Louie's big shaggy head as he did the same. Jo leaned in and wiped the table in a half-hearted circle. Plopped down two cans of High Life. "Bad, bad craving," Louie said. "Damned awful, horrible."

"So young, though, so young."

"Crazy early puberty," Louie pulling back on his can and rising, following Jo back to his spot behind the register, asking for the board, and we trounced through four or five quick checker games in silence, him trouncing me, as always—Louie black, J. red—until my fingers bled from the thinking. "I had pubes when I came out of the hole," said Louie, kinging one of his blacks with the only casualty I've managed to retain this game. "Had a peach-fuzz 'stache at age five. Shaving by seven."

"Torn up at ten by a woman, a girl," I said, then, "You win," sweeping my arm across the board and sending the pieces in a cascading of red and black down to the tile floor. They clattered and bounced, warranting a "What the fuck!" from Jo back behind the register and a genuinely pained expression from Louie. His eyes squinted, corners of his mouth turned down. "Now what the hell'd you go and do that for?" He leaned to his right and out of sight.

I picked up my spoon and began tapping it on the aluminum table's edge. I turned up the beer and downed it. "Hey Jo! How 'bout a couple more here!" I get sick of losing.

Wanted Dedra so bad, Louie, that he'd lost the ability for a time in second grade to beat his little brother at checkers. Came to a point he just had to have it, so he sat there, waiting for Dedra all afternoon, skin rising on his pasty-white face and arms with oozy sunburn welts, out front of his house, one of only two white boys on the block—the other his brother—and I was waiting for her too. After I dropped out, I'd always be there, out front of my house three doors down from Louie, waiting, long as it wasn't a swing-shift week in which case I'd be down at the bleachery watching the paper come rolling gleaming white through the machines and hoping for fire and flood both before a jam. Blazing hot that day. Me and Dedra'd been spending her after-school time going skinny-dipping down at the Dog's Landing. We'd meet here, my place, cruise down in my T-bird, ever since it got hot. The hottest day yet, school almost out, late May. Me and little second-grade Louie tapping our feet and rubbing our shoulders while they baked in the sun, waiting.

I'd be sitting there smoking one last cigarette (she chastised me for the habit, even at seventeen). I'd see her burst round the corner up the road, and I'd flick the butt way back up in the bushes. This particular day the sun seemed so high and bright everything had the air of a school bathroom. The leaves of the trees lining the road washed full-out of color. I puffed my smoke and had been watching little Louie for at least a half hour before I look up the road again, up by where he is, about a half football field farther along the side-walk, and here she comes. (Butt flies, trailing sparks and tendrils of smoke.) Queen Dedra—hips swinging back and forth like the pirate boat at the county fair, the black of those thighs shimmering even in this bland heat-light like the shiny brown catfish strips Jo invariably plops down in front of us.

I watched her coming along, not so much as even distracted by little Louie sitting eagerly there, tongue lolling out, drool threatening to slip out of the corners of his mouth—much like my own state, Louie's. I'm sitting tantalized by the swaying of hips, the sweatshine-glimmer of thighs like the tops of a pair of freshly polished oxfords glowing under a streetlight. She swings this way, catches me looking, and raises a hand fluidly up level with her chest in a sexy wave. Swaying, coming on slow to Louie's spot by the sidewalk. Doesn't even acknowledge him sitting there, and what I see she doesn't even register. That hand is up in a wave, and what I'm seeing is the dive, the forward thrust of Louie's gleaming white face, mouth open, teeth bared and tongue and all of it pitching forward into the back of Dedra's left thigh. It's like I can catch the boy there, in that moment, the boy and his face in a freeze-frame caught the instant before it hits, then plants; Louie's now down on his hands and with his white—I'm up, poised; Dedra ain't registered a thing—his white bare knees and body skidding along the sidewalk like a skittering roach with Dedra's slow swing, the boy's back arching, tongue sliding up the back of the sweat-soaked, deep-black thigh and rising up to the half-moon of her brown bottom I know's got to be poking out of those cutoffs, the tongue pausing and holding there and the little boy's body lurching, exploding forward with more cuts and skids for his baby knees. I take off in a sprint her way just as she finally registers the sensation of baby-man tongue on her butt. The palm of her right hand comes barreling round and catches little Louie hard on the left side of his face. She takes a step. He falls forward, onto the pavement, panting and smiling—

"Game on," Louie said. I popped open the fresh beer and looked coldly up at his face, his pockmarked cheeks, the spotted and shaggy beard, the curly red hair that looks like it hasn't been combed a day in its life. The board was set— Louie black, J. red. "All that time you had her like this," Louie describing hooks with each of his index fingers, fitting them together, pulling. "Had her all tied up and you let her get away." He went on about how like a nigger it was of me to let the house go all to pot after she'd moved in with me, spending nights foreman on the third shift at the bleachery when God knew I wouldn't be taking but a 5 percent cut in pay for a switch to a first-shift line job. "Goddamn knows," he said, "when you had that fine piece of work all locked up in there just waiting for you to come round to please, yes, please her and you know that's the thing, the point of it all. Goddamn!" he banged the edge of the table with a closed fist. Came off a little rough—the checker pieces went flying. That was a cheat, a cheap shot.

"Calm down, boy. See what you done?" I waved my hand, palm up, over the table quick to remind him of his own failures, the old rangy hag Bess he married after he'd dropped out of high school.

"Better than nothing," he said, went on staring at the space above my head like a dead man. Another cheat. I drank my beer. Then: "She's a damn hick," I said. "A red if there ever was."

"Well," he said, draping his big thick arms wide to indicate the table, me, himself.

"Screw it," I said.

Jo plopped down the plates just in time and we ate, checkerboard shoved over into the empty space next to the wall.

We don't talk about what happened next, and if we do it's always the why, never the what or how or when, because, Louie will say, I came running, flying up the walk, with the gleam in my eye of the madman I would later become.

The little boy rose to his feet before I could get him, taking off running across the street and up the other side in the white-hot light. The early puberty put a quickness in his feet that was outstripping even me, ten years his senior. Dedra's eyes went wide as I hurled past her, the black cave of her wide-open mouth leaving a long, thick trail in my periphery, the sound of whatever she yelled descending in garbled pitch, nothing more, and I yelled out to my boys—Dinty and Wes—who I knew were out back of Dinty's smoking on a reefer I'd gotten them earlier. Louie was headed for the back of Mama Theresa's, back to the tunnels through the brambly bushes (the tunnels we'd created oh so long ago, the ones we couldn't fit through anymore). I was yelling this out to the boys, crossing the street to see lanky Dinty, arms and legs pumping, eyes wide and stoned crazy, coming up around the far side of his house. My own feet churned the sidewalk, the road as I crossed it behind Dinty, whose strides were near twice as long; Louie didn't even get so far as Theresa's front yard before Dinty came railing up the walk a pinwheel of fists and knees and caught him in a dive, an expert roll, Louie balanced for an instant midroll on Dinty's massive hand like a palmed grapefruit.

Then he stopped and set the boy flat on his back, smile still spread slow and buttery across his oozing white face. Dinty glared down. Me and Wes shuffled up either side of him. "What the hell do you think you're doing?" I asked, really pissed at the boy then, though later who could be mad at him? He knew what he wanted and went after it.

Why? I would ask him, even if we couldn't kill the smile. I realized later it was *this* that lost her, this act.

A goddamn tasty woman, Dedra. You oughta know, he would say.

Me and Louie both almost up and quit the bleachery two days ago, after the insult of having almost gotten fired for a week straight of coming an hour late back from lunch, that drool incident.

After the house went to shit and slumped slowly away from itself like a scared dog, and I'd lost the car even though here I was foreman, just before Louie quit school and came to work at age sixteen under me at the bleachery, long after it'd become standard protocol for you to find me drunk on the street corner just as soon as at home or work; after I'd come home one day and Dedra just wasn't there—I came to know what lost her. More than a little embarrassing. Left little Louie blistered and bleeding lying puffy-face-up in the hot sun out in front of Theresa's. Thought we'd killed him when, an hour later, we came back and he was still there, blood seeping from the left corner of his mouth and pooling in a red circle on the pavement. Died with a smile on his face.

And so I was looking at a ghost. "How's that fish?" I asked it.

"Same as always."

"Damn good."

We ate slow, method-forking a strip at a time, but soon enough it'd be gone and I'd look at my watch.

"Hey Jo! how 'bout a coupla more beers!"

We headed out a time later after I'd whipped him for once, the last game we'd played. "Ever thought about working here?" Louie said. We were out front of the textile mill, standing slack-shouldered on the sidewalk facing the plant. I envisioned that rangy hag of a wife he's got in there with a towel tied tight around her head, sweating over some boiling weaver machine.

"Nope," I said. "Didn't Bess, though?" It just seemed right.

"Wonder what it's like? Actually, yes. Bess worked here, I think. Once."

"We should get back." Certainly, and we took our sweet time about it, backed up once into Jo's and had another beer apiece, stood at the counter and whacked Jo over the head with talk about his liquor license and how it was turning us into a couple no-good paupers. Rolled up to the bleachery and the gates were locked. We were an hour late. The third lunch shift was on its way out. I recognized boys who worked under me, tried calling out their names, laughed when they didn't respond. Tried to get them to let us in. Laughed when they guardedly swung the doors closed in our faces. "I think this is it, J.," Louie said, pointing up to the building. Here came Oglethorpe.

"You boys goddamn well shoulda been back by now, huh?"

I looked to Louie. He said, "If you're gonna fire us, why don't you go on?" He went on.

I yelled out for Annie a couple times. Didn't work.

Well worth it, though—we each got one of that fat bastard's patent leather wingtips with a gummy spitball through the gate before it was all over.

"Any idea where Dedra might be these days?" Louie said.

"Goddammit, you ain't gonna cry again."

"No. Any idea?"

"Got a vague one," I said.

We jumped into my slightly newer T-bird—compared to the last—and hit I-77 to Charlotte doing ninety before we left the on ramp.

Well worth it—that last game.

"Game on," Louie said. I looked down and there it was, the board all set up and ready to go. "One more," Louie said. "Screw Oglethorpe. Fat pansy bastard." We were fifteen minutes beyond at that point. Five minutes and Louie already had three kings on his plate. Someone told me always answer a cheat with a cheat. So I asked him: "Louie, there's something I never got out of you."

"What's that?"

"I think you well know." His concentration honed, he lighted on a jump and made it. I was down to four reds against his probably double number of blacks there, three of them kings.

"Nossir, I don't," he said.

"What she tasted like. That day."

Louie flinched, eyes glazed over, lips curling half to a smile. I slicked one of his kings off the board, slipped the black into my pantspocket.

"You need another beer?" I asked.

He didn't answer. I made my jump. "Your turn," I said, flicking the casuality down the table where it rattled against the wall. "Jo! Get this man a beer!"

"Goddamn, I think you should know," Louie said.

"Know what?"

"That taste." Louie stared up into the ceiling. He pulled and downed the last of the can in front of him.

"Mmm…" I flicked another of the kings from the table. Jo came over with the beer. "Check this," I said to him, pointing down at the table.

"You red?" Jo asked.

"Of course. Black usually wins, but red might just take it today."

"Good luck."

Louie looked down at the beer and at the table. "You been cheating," he said, flat.

"So tell me, Mr. Murphy, tell me."

"You should know."

"I don't, can't remember." My confession of the day here. Louie suddenly looks me in the eyes, for the first time in a long, long time, I realize. His eyes are deep brown, like mine. Then his head falls back like a limp dick. Way back. I said, "Feeling sick lately. Sick like I wake up aching, can't remember who told me to get up. Or maybe I told myself and forgot it."

"She tasted . . ." he paused, head still back, eyes closed. ". . . tasted . . ."

"Yeah?" I said, pulling the last of his kings from the board and sliding it into my front shirt pocket.

"She tasted…" and now his head pulled slowly upward, level. Deep brown eyes stared strangely from that pasty-white face, that red hair. "She tasted incandescent."

"Incandescent?"

"Yeah, incandescent."

"Incandescent, you mean, like a light bulb?"

"Yeah, like a light bulb."

"Christ, man, are you gonna cry or what? Jo! get *me* another beer!" I jumped the last of all his blacks with a single red, legitimately. He didn't even notice. "Nice game," I said, shot my hand out for a shake. He looked at it, but didn't take it.

Mad Hettie

DEB R. LEWIS

That day's leg of the cycle run ended a couple hours before nightfall, and their fire found welcome in the far-out dark of the last campground before the unbroken woods. A few motorcycles still ripped around the lumpy, bumpy, tree-dotted stretch through the campsite. The young bucks tried to climb different rises, playing king of the mountain up the walls of a nearby washout. The washout grew into a deep ravine, like an unstitched cut in the flesh of the earth, away from where the men would eventually fall, passed out on pills and liquor, or drop face first from raw-dicked exhaustion, so the young bucks went further and further out seeking challenges.

When they circled back, their ripping bikes sent up dust and an engine buzzroar that nearly doused the crackle of the high flames, lifting the raucous free-for-all to a new height. Pie-eyed men stood in small groups drinking beer or whiskey and placing bets on which of two bottoms could take the most men in two-ended fuckings—up the ass and down the throat—before passing out from the tireds or a bad cum-to-air ratio. Beug spied One-Eyed Onely leaned back against a tree-trunk with some friendly little fucker sucking him off. Three or so others had made a kind of love fort in a clump of bushes and would be covered with chigger bites come morning, while Spartacus—known for his ancient Roman-style leather armor, complete with the sky-brushing bristles on the helm—tottered from place to place showering the guys with colorful handfuls of pills.

Beug stood just at the edge of firelight looking loose, buzzed on whiskey but still slightly too serious for twenty-five, his thumbs in his back pockets, jeans soft with war and dust, squinting out as someone on a white bike spun out on one side, catching the cycle's fall with a last-minute kicked-out leg. The rider hooted out his thrill to the others and took off into the dark again. Though the noise of the cycle engines came from all directions and distances, the majority had kicked down for the night; the machines nodded off in quiet, precise rows, chrome gleaming icily when the moon peered between clouds. Beug shivered as the wind hit the sweat under his heavy, leather jacket; a brief chill in the pleasantly warm night made him dread the approaching end of summer.

From the bikes came a jingling man—Vic—stumbling under the weight of some heavy chain. A scarred gash angling out from the outer edge of Vic's eyebrow to the edge of his receding hairline seemed to flicker and pulse with the firelight. He grinned at Beug as he approached, his iron-colored curls wind-twisted and sticking wildly out from his leathering, wind-cut face. "Hey, c'mon. Animal's at it again."

Beug pushed his elbows out once and relaxed. "Lesson time?"

Vic kept walking, stabbed his head toward a beer stash. "Hell-yeah. Grab you a beer and come on."

Beug pulled out a couple beers from an iced bucket sitting on the seat of an overturned picnic table. In the table's hollow sprawled a fallen-out man, naked but still in his biker boots, one meaty hand cupping his balls and his mouth wide open. He must have been the first to nod off—someone had fingerpainted TOILET across his chest with engine grease, and he reeked of beer and piss. *Pig in mud*, Beug thought.

Vic stopped, turned back to find the hold-up, suddenly calling out, "Hey, d'jya *look* at these?"

Beug sauntered up with the wet, cold bottles. "Chains, right?" Since it was Animal they were talking about, he figured they were for a beating.

"Manacles. Wrist size." Vic held the heavy pile of chain out so Beug could notice the ironwork. The cuffs closed with a hex nut and bolt, but Vic could yank those out and use a padlock if he wanted. He beamed as Beug fingered the cuffs, stewing over the possibilities, and when Beug looked up again Vic added, "Fully adjustable. Had 'em made long enough so we'd'n loop 'em over a branch and lock 'em tight."

Beug nodded and they walked on, quiet themselves—Beug carrying the beers, Vic with his new toys—surrounded with far-off laughing and engines running and all different intimate moans and smacks and slaps and glocking noises. A series of four dark figures raced through the bushes. Beug squinted as he asked Vic, "So—where the hell'd you get those?" It looked like a wolf chase, three howlers after some quiet, desperate, and definitely going-to-be-had piece of ass.

Vic bumbled over the uneven ground, turning his face sidelong to the younger fellow as he came to a halt. "Member how me and Minnow had to bust ass to catch up with y'all? Well, that foundry guy fixed 'em up for me." Vic tossed his head to the west where they'd come from. "Said he'd make a collar and some leg irons, and I can get 'em next time through."

Beug nodded at the chains again—it was strange to see Vic humping his own shit—and asked, "So where's your boy?"

Vic nodded toward the bikes. "Sent 'im after Mad Hettie."

Off in the distance, they heard one of the younger guys call out an abrupt, "Jumpin' Jesu—" that rose and fell sharply, punctuated with a "SHIT!" as he spilled, his bike's engine snarling as it went down. They both peered out. Then Beug said, "Sounds like you're gonna have another boy, next time through." If someone really busted up, they'd find out soon enough.

"Eager to please, ain't 'e?" Vic laughed.

"Minnow'll have to learn some Daddy tricks and act like a big boy." Beug took a few steps and Vic dragged along.

"Shit—he's already pissy 'cause I haven't used these on him, and here I am letting Animal use 'em on his own little tribulation. I told that jealous little fucker he best learn to serve and not worry 'bout what's fair. Told 'im I'll tell him what's fair, all right? And to bust his heart a while over my boots, right? To worry a little more about my hard-on and less about his own."

Beug shook his head. "It's hard bringing these boys up right."

"Well, Minnow wadn't in the army or nothing. He just missed The War, so that's part of the problem. No discipline."

They skirted around a clump of young trees and undergrowth to find a second smaller fire and a growing cluster of men in a small clearing. The surrounding trees leaned in such a way as to make any neighboring society seem remote. Animal, a huge man with an equally broad head and whose belly warped his wide black belt—had to be in his early forties—stood smoking a fat cigar that smelled like damp and burnt autumn leaves. The new novice, twenty-two years old—"Mr. Anything" they were calling him—knelt naked and blindfolded at Animal's hip, hands clasped behind his head. Mr. Anything was already half-hard, crouching over to hide it, but Animal bent a little, grabbed a fistful of hair, and pulled him up again, easy as scruffing a wayward kitten, and growled, "Get those knees apart, boy. Don't make me tell you again."

"Yes, sir."

Animal spied the chains and nodded at Vic, the half-smoked cigar pushing his lips into a snarl. Then he leaned down, his thick, black brows tangling over his bullish nose. "What'd you say?"

"Sir, yessir."

Animal pulled up on Anything's hair: "Get up!" He gave the kid a shove against a large tree, keeping a hand on him to "set" him there and told him to stay put.

Vic passed one of the long chains to Animal, then pointed to two trees that seemed about the right distance apart, indicating that he and Animal should throw an end over each of the lowest crotches, then showed the padlocks for hooking them in place. So they each threw an end over like a lazy lasso that hit with a metal-on-wood clatter. Vic waited while Animal pulled Anything over and fitted the cuffs on the kid's wrists and kicked his feet apart so that he went from the shape of a human Y to that of a human X in two blinks of an eye. They pulled the free ends till the chains stretched taut, and instead of tying knots, each stuck a lock in his respective end link, each chain locked to itself in a long loop that kept the novice's arms stretched tight as telegraph cables. Animal gave each one a tug to make sure it was good and fast.

Vic dropped out, taking one of the beers as Beug leaned in and whispered, "Those are some nice chains you got yourself."

"Can't wait to get the whole set," Vic whispered back.

Minnow sidled up behind his topman smiling like a dog as Vic cut him out of the corner of his eyes. If Minnow'd taken much longer with Mad Hettie, he'd've beat the shit out of the boy and let him find his own way back. Vic raised two connected fingers, caught the burly guy's eye, and nodded toward Minnow. Animal jutted a chin out and Minnow started to move forward, but Vic yanked him back, hissing, "Not yet, you sonofabitch—just watch. He'll let you know, and when he does, you go, give it to him, and traipse your ass right back. No *bull*shit."

Animal signaled for Anything's boots, and someone brought them over from the pile of neatly folded clothes and the bedroll. He quickly, gingerly put them on the young man, then proceeded to rope his ankles apart, this time tying them off at the base of the trees, to anchor him spread-eagled facing the crowd. Anything was answering reveille, hard as he was, and there wasn't any hiding it.

"Now, just to be clear," Animal said to his fledgling novice, pulling out the tobacco stump as he sized up the crowd, his face serious, even as he stumped and showcased, "You told me I could do anything I wanted, anything at all, that right?"

The blindfolded man's chest seemed to swell. "Sir, yessir!"

Animal sucked his teeth and nodded, waddling slowly to the kid's other side, the men giving him a wide, wide berth. "When I asked what you wanted from me, you told me, 'You can do anything you want to do to me, Mr. Animal, sir.' That right?"

There was a clear ring this time as young man bellowed, "Sir, yessir!"

Coming up close, Animal put a hand on the boy's ass, giving it a rough little rub. The men on the ends of the great crescent saw the boy's prick visibly jump at the contact. "And when I asked you what you wouldn't allow, you said, 'No limits, Mr. Animal, sir, anything you want. Anything at all.' That right?"

"Sir, *yes*sir!" The kid nodded.

Animal mugged a *holy shit* for the crowd then, having established that anything goes, returned his attention to the pale carcass that had so readily thrown itself into his big meaty paws. Still, the men could hear just about every word Animal said as he frowned up into the boughs of the tree. "Now see, I'm of a mind to use you as my ashtray. You ever been burnt by a cee-gar?"

The kid went shock rigid. "No, sir."

Animal nodded, pacing a little, until he spoke in the kid's other ear. "Really?" He stepped under one of the outstretched arms and pressed his whole body against the kid's back, the hand with the cigar—hot, orange-glowing end out—around the kid's middle. "Now, how come you lay yourself out for old Animal, hmmm?" He eased quietly to the boy's other ear, stage-whispering, "Why you think they call 'im Animal?" then stepped back out between the boy and the crowd.

Beug closed his eyes. He could imagine how the kid must feel. Animal enveloping him like a voice in the fog, Animal's voice coming from all blind directions.

"Your mama know you're out here in the woods," Animal called, "all naked and tied up, playing cowboy and injun with these ol' perverts?"

Beug opened his eyes. Animal had stepped behind the boy again, his free hand rubbed the kid's ass slowly and firmly, until the boy eased back against him, leaning back as much as the bonds allowed as the big man growled into his left ear. "What on earth did you think 'ould happen—you'd get your ass fucked a little bit? Oh, well—that *could* happen."

Animal patted the other asscheek, leaning to the right now. "On the other hand, I could rent your ass out—penny a throw—till I got a hundred dollars in my pocket. These boys is plenty horny lookin' at you." He paused and suddenly the crickets and tree frogs sang clear and free above everything. No one could say when the motorcycles had stopped.

Animal laid a palm across the boy's belly. "And I'll bet don't nobody knows you can guess where you're at."

The kid seemed relaxed, turned on to the talk, loosening against Animal's touch, waxing to it, more pliable all the time. Animal put the cigar back between his lips and pulled out the knife he carried on his belt, and, holding the kid tightly from behind so he couldn't jump, laid it cold and flat against the kid's chest. "What is *that*? *What is* it? Ew-wee, that's cold, ain't it?" Animal traced over the skin lightly with the dull side of the blade, resting the point against a pale nipple, pressing flesh against blade with his thumb. "Oo-oo, sharp! What'll you say? I think it's a knife!"

Beug felt a nudge in his ribs, saw Vic smirking at him, and grinning, nodded back. They watched as the boy started to squirm, then thought better of it, and went still, breathing hard through his nose. Animal traced a line down the flat stomach and into the pubes, leaning heavily now to one side, his massive arm bringing the knife up gently under the kid's ball sac.

Vic and Beug looked at each other, Vic sucking in his cheeks and rolling his eyes. Beug, mouthing, "Vi-car-i-ous," nodded toward Minnow who frowned intently at the unfolding scene. Vic checked his boy, then rolled his eyes and snorted.

"Tell me, now, son," Animal poured out, slow as blackstrap molasses, "did you ever stop to think about the possibilities?"

The kid kept his body rigidly still, all of it, except his hard-*no*-shaking head.

Animal let the knife down, put it away, and pulled the cigar out of his mouth again, exhaling a smoky halo around the boy's head, calling out over his shoulder: "Anything! You promised me complete power over you!" Animal brought the cigar around to hover over the boy's chest, saying, "Well, get ready, boy, 'cause I got me a whole heap of things I want to do to you."

Animal waited, standing very still. There was a long pause until finally the boy broke the quiet. "Sir?"

The hot tip of the cigar quickly touched the boy's chest—long enough for him to jump—then just as quickly came away, Animal rubbing the boy's belly with his other hand.

"Yeah!" he whispered, watching the young body flex and release as the boy eased down off his toes. "Yeah, you're still hard—that's it." Animal laughed softly, pushing the hard lump in the crotch of his jeans against the boy's backside. "I do like a boy who gives himself completely."

He stepped around to the front and nodded to Minnow, who brought up Mad Hettie. There was a sudden stir in the crowd. The hardcocks grinned.

Boys shook their heads in disbelief, jumpy with lightning, thinking—*It ain't me*. The less reliable few imagined someone'd call the cops, landing the whole lot—meaning themselves—in prison. They kept secret contingencies to high-tail it on bike, and if there wasn't time—screw everyone, each for himself—race for the woods on foot.

Animal took the chainsaw—Mad Hettie, a tequila-crazed perversion of the word machete—and raised her high with both hands as he spoke around the butt of his cigar.

"Now, son, I have looked for you all my life: an altruist so selfless, so giving, he don't hold nothing back, but I never had the fortune of anyone to tell me I could do anything I wanted, anything 'thout *bounds*, till you came along. So I just want to thank you, last of all, sweet boy, for offering yourself up as, well—a very *human* sac'rfice—an' allowing this bit o' magnificence we're about right now."

Beug saw the kid, pecker hard, grinning below the blindfold, his lips between his teeth in a blind effort to contain the pour-over pride of having won Animal's words of gratitude. But then Animal took a couple steps back and gave Mad Hettie's cord a terrible, quick pull, and she sang out much like a 'cycle engine, only with a higher, more nasal tone. The smile washed out to a yawp of disbelieving horror as the kid heard what it was.

Animal gave a whoop and someone hollered, "Skin him alive!"

The kid panicked, hanging all his weight forward on the chains, digging in with the balls of his feet, arching his back, flinging himself backward with all his weight. Tightly tied, he got little momentum, but it didn't keep him from trying again and again, working up into a wild foamy frenzy.

"A-HAHAHAHAHahahaha!" Animal crackled. "Buckets of blood for everyone! I'm gonna have me a big old bath in it!"

Beug whooped and yelled out, "Yeah!" and fancied he heard it answered from somewhere around the other end of the crowd's swollen crescent. Had to give it to the tough little bastard, he wasn't crying yet. Most of the others in the Anything clan had cried by this point, started pissing and shitting themselves by now—this'd be something worth remembering.

Animal stepped in closer to the boy, eyeballing him narrowly, keeping the chainsaw out and away, as if trying to decide on which cut to take before getting into the mess of his work. Mad Hettie was heavy, but he held her carefully in one fist while reaching down to wrap his other hand around the boy's meat and give it a rough tug. "Your ears first, then this" he shouted, "—you keep dead still—maybe you live longer, got it? Maybe savor you a while."

Both hands on the saw again, Animal watched how the sweat welled so suddenly on the kid's upper lip and down his ribcage. He admired the musculature as it gave show to the bone below, watched how the kid panted, his dick still hard but looking doubtful now—going down to half-mast as his lips pressed and twisted together in an effort not to shriek.

It was time to break the kid, turn him into human hamburger.

Animal swung the rumbling saw slowly in, watching the kid go deathly still with terror as the buzzing filled his ears and the oily smell of metallic friction bit at his nosehairs. "Keep still. Keeeep still," Animal soothed, "I only want your ears now…"

Keeping his head surprisingly still as the saw came within five inches of his head, Anything howled with terror, mouth yawning with the still-headed terror of a baby bird, spurring a couple of whoops and pockets of nervous laughter as he lost it. His cock shrank as he pissed down his leg, and his legs gave out.

Animal suddenly stopped the saw. The kid hung limp and sobbing from the chains, so hopeless that he did not hear, or hearing, failed to recognize the cessation of the chainsaw's roaring buzz.

Animal lay the silenced Mad Hettie down to sleep at the foot of a tree— on the far side of one of these pillars of this young Solomon, out of the boy's view. He unlashed the ankle ropes and pulled off the boots, feeling the feet for that blue cold of shock. Meanwhile, about half of the men cleared out—being too jazzed up to bother with how the boy came out, all wanting some little scene of their own, even a little hand-job if they could get it.

Animal motioned to Vic and then, on second thought, to Beug as well. They came up, each to a side, and held up the heaving, sobbing, limp-dicked, and trembling kid as Animal loosed the wrist cuffs. They stood quiet, waiting for Animal's mark. Minnow approached, his eye on the chains, wanting to be noticed, and Vic, pointedly ignoring Minnow, breathed, "Hey, where do you want to put him down?"

Animal nodded toward the fire. "Over there. He's in shock. Gotta warm him up."

"Minnow," Vic ordered, "get that bedroll and lay it out on that flat spot by the fire."

Minnow skulked into the shadows, bringing the bedroll out, his hair sticking up noticeably in the firelight, making it look like he had a head full of needle-y meringue-peaks as he unrolled the blankets and smoothed them out. Vic noted the concern now come into Minnow's hands as he felt over the bedding, pulling up a corner and throwing twigs into the fire, and thought maybe his boy wasn't a complete good-for-nothing waste of time after all.

They hauled the clammy, snot-dripping kid over, and Minnow watched as the three masters eased him down. Beug sat behind the pale, limp young man, legs wide, supporting him in a sitting position, his open jacket wrapped around the kid's shoulders like protective wings—his heat against the kid's clammy back. Animal squatted before the boy's huddled legs and carefully lifted off the blindfold, sweat pulling his hair up into boyish spikes. The boy looked very much like a kid with fever—when he peered through slit eyelids, his eyes and expression were fever dull and his lips shivered—though he'd stopped crying now.

"How you doin'?" Animal asked, eyes glinting from the deep creases in his face.

Mr. Anything turned his head and stared out dully at the fire.

Animal ignored the small slight, pulling up one limp hand, then the other, inspecting the raw wrists, feeling the elbows and shoulders, telling him to bend this way, now that, the kid complying in the smallest, dullest of ways.

Animal turned to Vic, who'd silently gestured for Minnow to get the chains down quietly. "Bring that canteen?" Vic nodded to Minnow, and Minnow hustled it over.

Animal took it, wet one of his kerchiefs, and washed the kid down lightly, paying close attention to the wrists before bathing that flat-expressioned face. Wiping the left ear softly then gently taking his damp chin, Animal turned the kid's head away from the fire, watching his eyes pass calmly over his face and seeing the dim spark of wonder behind them, the curiosity regarding what he'd just experienced, the why of it. As the kid stared out into the cool dark, Animal wet the rag again and, holding the kid's chin easily—this was the side he'd threatened with the chainsaw—wiped the right ear and the temple, smoothing back the hair.

That little acorn stayed calm. Tough nut to crack all the way around. The masters nodded to themselves and to one another. Beug eased out from behind the kid and together he, Vic, and Minnow left Animal and his charge alone. For better, for worse, they were bonded now—only the next crucial hours would tell if a trust might build up between them or if the kid would creep uncertainly away, disappearing, his return doubtful, as Animal slumbered. As it later turned out, the kid would be quiet for a few days, afraid of Animal, yet clinging to him.

Beug broke off from the others and headed toward his sleeping bag, alone, musing that the boy just might have the makings of a top somewhere in him, but that would be Animal's call in the long run.

Stalking Nirvana

MARCIA K. BRENNER

Green pistachio shells haphazardly littered the Mexican blanket that covered the ratty backseat of her old yellow Volkswagen. They seemed to emit a fluorescent glow in the dingy gray light of the February afternoon, and Lucy watched them in her droopy rear-view mirror and wondered if they meant something; wondered if they weren't some kind of a sign of what was wrong with her, like someone stranded on a desert island might spell out an SOS on the beach with big, pink conch shells. And there was something wrong with this, wasn't there? Something wrong with sitting here in this cold car, in a pair of long underwear, combat boots, and a resale shop shearling coat with a very Dr. Zhivago matching hat, watching the front door of Joe's apartment across the street each morning for nearly a week, studying the sad locomotive white puffs of her breath in the car. And how exactly had she gotten to this point? Hard work, dedication, lots of free time, and perhaps just a touch of obsession, and that was probably Roger's fault, the bastard.

Lucy had really thought things were going pretty good with Roger. She had been with him almost a month, and she had only picked up on a few things. Him thinking about how much he was going to kick everybody's ass in the office football pool, while they watched the Broncos game, curled up on the sofa at his place. Or him thinking about how he didn't like her using his toothbrush as he kissed her good morning after the first night she slept over. Of course, that kind of hurt, just a little; after all she'd had *his* tongue in her mouth half the night, and here he was worried about his damn toothbrush. But, all in all, still pretty normal thoughts, things Lucy could handle. Of course, she hadn't told him about her. She'd done the honesty thing before, and it hadn't worked; they either freaked or split, or they wanted to take her gambling. One guy forced her to read the stock market report every morning over breakfast and just let him know if she "had any feelings" about anything. And besides, being psychic wasn't like having some sexually transmitted disease; it wasn't like they were going to catch anything if she didn't tell them. Too bad though. She kind of wished it was. She liked to imagine Roger right now, itchy rash all over his crotch.

He had to go to some dental convention in Cleveland. In retrospect, she should have known better than to have dated a dentist; weren't dentists the one who were always leaving their wives and kids for their pretty twenty-year-old hygienists? And as soon as you had a profession that required semiannual stays at out-of-town hotels, didn't you think, for sure, swarms of prostitutes? Maybe it was just her.

But Roger didn't even make it to the hotel. They had taken the train to O'Hare; Lucy had insisted on seeing him off, a sad attempt for those last seconds of physical proximity before he left. They made love at his apartment. No. Scratch that. They had sex. But she was in that state. That state you get into where you honestly start to believe that your skin really does glow in the dark from some kind of precious love venom that lies dormant in your DNA until that perfect soul mate comes along and some sort of chemical reaction occurs, causing you to do things you would think idiotic, or at the very least uncharacteristic, under normal conditions. Like leaving for the airport with no panties on, and only a gauzy, flowered skirt between you and the middle of October, because it seemed romantic. Or letting Roger grab you when you got to the gate, and dip you low, your hair brushing the ground and the blood rushing to your head, kissing you like you were some kind of fluoride treatment he desperately needed to prevent gum disease. And the people all around applauding like it was the lost scene between Bogie and Bergman at the end of *Casablanca*.

She had waited, nose pressed to cold glass, for his plane to disappear down the wet runway, and watched until she thought for sure she had seen it take off and disappear, a distant flashing light into the clouded night sky. Walking in the tiled, subterranean hallway on the way back to the train, Lucy saw her sketchy reflection in the burgundy velvet-backed window of some dormant hotel shop, and felt a rare, fine moment of synchronicity. Everything she had always expected, always hoped she was on the inside was rising up like cream, through her pores, up to the surface of her skin where it was visible. She was sensuous, intelligent, imparting volumes of poetry and complex mathematical equations with just a flick of her wrist or the delicate shift of her walk. Her hair felt thick and heavy, and it no longer *felt* like the eggplant color she had accidentally dyed it a few weeks earlier but instead some otherworldly opalescent mass. She was a character of her own creation, a mythological creature that sits on a mossy rock, lures sailors, and sinks ships with just a whisper of her lips. She could see all of this in the dim window reflection like some enormous magic, except it wasn't magic; it was real.

And then, of course, the bottom fell out, and in that window she no longer saw herself; it was as if someone had just flipped a channel on her optic nerve. It was Roger, looking at himself in the mirror, screwing some ninety-five-pound contortionist stewardess over the blue water-filled toilet in the cramped lavatory of the plane. Lucy could hear the rush of the engines, see how the stewardess still had on her little uniform, her skirt hiked up, her foot dangling a sensible blue pump from its awkward resting place up on Roger's shoulder. Her little hat still pinned and clinging to her tossing blonde coiffure; her name tag said "Tina." From Tina's precarious position over the toilet, Lucy pegged her as a cheerleader in high school. That red vein in Roger's forehead was pulsing like it did, and he was grinning like an idiot at himself in the mirror. This was just time to wonder if Tina left her name tag on so that passengers might remember the appropriate name to call out when they came, and then Lucy was suddenly looking at her own reflection again, standing frozen in the long hall near the airport hotel that led to the trains, listening to the hollow click-clock of hurried feet, passing behind her.

They had no faces, those reflection people. They were anonymous figures: mannequins with hats and bags, and Lucy realized she was one of them too. Her hair was eggplant again, and sprang from her head in corkscrew curls that appeared to be attempting to escape. Her legs were cold. Her lack of underwear no longer felt romantic. She wanted a shower and some thick wool socks. Her reflected skin seemed transparent and sallow, her pale green eyes just dark shadows, like holes in her head. It's just me again, she thought, and after a while she turned and slowly headed back to the trains.

It was cold. The heater in her Volkswagen didn't really work; when she turned it on it would emit a wheezing sound, like an old man laughing and coughing simultaneously and maybe spit out a dried autumn leaf from one of the vents before it sputtered and stopped. She should have dressed better, but she overslept and was afraid she might miss Joe.

Nothing had really happened yet. Joe's place was across the street, two doors down. She tried to keep focused on it through the slightly crystalline windshield. She wished she had a radio, but where hers had been was a hole in the dash, a convenient fit for, say, a peanut-butter sandwich. Come to think of it, she wished she'd brought a sandwich. She'd found the pistachio nuts in a bag under the passenger seat; they were stale and chewy, but she plowed through them anyhow. After all, breakfast was the most important meal of the day, especially when you've got eight hours of stalking ahead of you.

Joe's building was one of a long row of nearly identical graystone two-flats. They lined one side of the block, fronted with carved stone steps leading up to the elevated doors; granite railings looking slightly melted from years of erosion. The other side of the street, where Lucy was parked, hearkened the invasion of the misplaced suburbanites who attempted to become trendy and cool by moving into the artsy, reasonably priced areas of the city, and then drove up rents, spawned commercialism, and totally ruined the place for everyone else. Many of the houses on this side were new, smacking of pale wood, fleshy pink stone, and copper trim that had yet to weather and turn the oxidized green it was supposed to be. But on a day like this, a day where the sun was hidden behind a tarp of dirty white flannel sky, both sides of the street looked tired and asleep; new blended with old. All the windows were like closed eyes, the houses seemed dormant and unoccupied. Wintered trees lined the sidewalks like anorexic chess pieces, leading the way up to the intersection, two blocks up, where stop signs signaled a choreographed waltz between vehicles. Lucy fell into a lull watching them. The distant sound of their engines as they slowed, then accelerated, seemed important somehow; she felt strangely small and insignificant.

Maybe it had started with Roger, her descent into madness. She wasn't the slightest bit psychotic before Roger. But then, she thought, if psychotic people knew they were psychotic, they wouldn't be psychotic in the first place, right?

Roger.

After him it took Lucy a while to trust again. Sure, everybody says that after a breakup, but most people don't have that extra something in the vulnerability department. Lucy's mom called it being "sensitive," as if it called for moisture-enhanced toilet paper. There wasn't any real bonus to being psychic as far as Lucy could tell. She couldn't touch a lottery ticket and pick the winning numbers; she couldn't take a piece of old lace in her hands and find someone's lost grandma. The only thing she seemed to do with skill and precision was to completely and totally spoil any possibility of romance in her life.

Imagine you are on a date. Say he's a big strapping Apollo type, cleft chin, the works. You are both at the dinner table in a better-than-mid-priced restaurant, and he's thrown caution and Emily Post to the wind and placed his elbow on the table, his chin resting on his rather large hand, so as better to stare dreamily into your eyes. He reminds you of Rodin's "The Thinker." Suddenly you realize that your "thinker" is perusing a mental-picture catalog of the wide variety of riding lawnmowers available on the market. Perhaps he seems to be mulling over the wine list, but in fact he is wondering which mower has the most horsepower, and exactly what kind of torque can you get in wet grass? He might reach forward absently across the candlelit table to move an escaping strand of your hair behind your ear. You shiver at the gentleness of his touch, wonder if this tenderness is a sign of how he feels, a sign of how good he is with those hands. You are entirely unaware of how he is thinking that your ears sort of stick out; they remind him of the handles on the red raspberry Kool-Aid mug he had as a kid, and he smiles at this. You smile back, but he doesn't notice because he's figuring those ears will give him something to hold on to when you give him a blow job. Considering the price of dinner, he assumes this is a given. This place ain't cheap; the wine bottles have corks in them. Ahh, romance...

As a child Lucy had accepted the flashes, not really questioning that there was anything unusual about seeing other people's thoughts. She didn't know better. It was hard when you were a kid to understand that there were things that people thought that they would never want to share; it wasn't until she was older that she started to see this, and even now it was kind of confusing. There were so many different ways to tell a truth.

She spent a great deal of time trying to analyze it, the feeling of the flash, the vision, whatever you wanted to call it. In some way, she felt better understanding exactly how it happened to her, as if dissecting it might temper the mystery and surprise, like finding out how to do a magic trick.

It begins with a tingle, in the fingertips, the toes, the blood starting to warm like the way a summer afternoon sunset feels on an upturned face. It's comforting almost, soothing. It pumps through the veins, moves through the tissue, the body, heart, head, moving faster, like spinning, the light circulating through, speeding, faster and brighter, like sun coming out from a solar eclipse. Then painless, blinding whiteness.

When her eyes adjust, she is somewhere else, seeing other people's sights, or their thoughts and feelings—it is sometimes confusing which is reality and which is fantasy—but then the light comes again, erasing everything, and she is back to her own reality, only seeing through her eyes. The whole thing takes only seconds.

But then, her mom would say it only takes seconds for a car accident to happen ("and you should always wear clean underwear or none at all"). She and her mom never really discussed the flashes, but it was understood. Sometimes Lucy thought of it like having a family history of breast cancer or heart disease, or insanity. Her mom knew all about the stuff; she took cabs everywhere so that if she had one of her own flashes she wouldn't have a car accident. It seemed they were two of a kind, except Lucy wouldn't give up driving. Oh, and that thing about the government following her mom around in black vans; that was just plain nuts.

But then, who was the nut here? After all, Lucy was pretty much stalking a guy she had spent exactly one, count 'em, one night with. But what if he was The One? Would she blow the whole relationship just because she was too sensitive? Wasn't this the main problem between men and women in the first place? What if they were pretty much destined to be together as long as one of them worked really hard at it?

But this sitting in the car thing was starting to suck. Why couldn't she have waited until June to get obsessive? Oh, wait. No air-conditioning in the bug. But still, it might be better than this cold. Her toes were starting to get numb, and her neck and throat were cold where the coat stopped. She had to keep moving, had to keep her mind off the cold; if only Joe would come out and go somewhere, dammit.

She quickly pulled her right hand from the warmth of her pocket and reached over sideways, banging her breast into the gear shift on the floor, and contorting her neck to get into the glove compartment. Too bad she didn't keep gloves in the glove compartment; that's what they were for, right? Nope. Nothing in here but a few parking tickets, a three-prong outlet adapter, and a few pens. She was disappointed, hoping for a stick of gum, or a pair of socks, but before she could sit up, she saw a white van pass the bug and pull up in front of Joe's down the street.

She stayed low, leaning over the passenger seat in an uncomfortable half-twist, her breath sounding unnaturally loud. PRIME CABLE was written on the side of the van in blue letters. A chunky guy in a gray shirt and low-slung pants that barely defied gravity hopped out of the driver's side and waddled around to the back of the van. He opened the doors and took out a red toolbox and a large spool of black cable. When he slammed the doors Lucy felt it travel through the frozen asphalt and come up through the seats into her teeth. Something about winter always seemed to make sound travel with more urgency. She wondered if he could hear her breathing, and tried to huff quieter. She wished she hadn't eaten all of the pistachio nuts.

The cable guy walked heavily up the steps to Joe's apartment and pushed a button for the bell. Or maybe it was a buzzer. Lucy wondered which it was; it seemed to her that Joe should have a deep, throaty buzzer—something masculine, yet not overbearing. Sure. As if buzzers could be throaty. Exactly what did she think she was doing anyway? This was ridiculous. It was stupid. Oh, my God. There's Joe.

Indeed Joe was at the door. For a split second he leaned out to hold the door for the cable man. His hair was a bit mussy on top, his face not yet shaven; he wore a blue striped bathrobe, and the beauty of all this made her heart thud up into her throat. Then he disappeared inside with the cable guy and after a few minutes she felt her heartbeat begin to slow and quiet.

If she could just get past those stupid flashes. Other than that one little thing about the punky juvenile sexpot, Joe was perfect. He was an artist; well, he wanted to get back to the whole artistic thing, anyway, but meanwhile he had to work for that furniture production company out in the suburbs. (Pretty far out, too, as she'd followed him to work the last two days and used up nearly a whole tank of gas.) He owned his own place; he had a steady job; he was a grown-up; he had a really great set of abs. And she had kicked those very abs out of her apartment. Lucy sat up in the driver's seat and jammed her hands into her pockets.

"You just don't throw away great abs!" she murmured through chattering teeth, leaning over the steering wheel as if it might provide warmth.

She wondered what was going on inside his place. She had never seen the place. What did it look like? Was it bare, yet clean? Was there an easel in the corner with a painting in progress on it, half-covered with a spattered tarp? Would the cable guy notice it perhaps and make a comment about how he was no art expert, but hey, that looked pretty good, and Joe would nod, uncomfortable with the compliment, and sip hot coffee from a mug, perhaps offering some to the cable guy?

And what about the cable? Was something wrong with Joe's cable? Or was he just getting cable? Maybe it had gone out in the middle of "the big fight," and he and his buddies had to sit in a circle around the blue-screened TV punctuating the silence with the occasional "shit" and "this sucks," all of them tilting back their beers like a Pabst Blue Ribbon version of *Swan Lake*? No, she thought, shaking her head. That was ridiculous. Joe would never drink beer as shitty as Pabst Blue Ribbon.

Maybe he had illegal cable for a while. Being an artist, he would probably know how to fix the wires. He could have slipped out one dark night, after a light rain, snuck into the alley behind his place and shimmied up a telephone pole in just his jeans, his bare chest glistening in the fluorescent alley lights, his abs practically gripping the pole, pulling him up without the aid of his hands, which he used instead to splice the neighbor's cable. Maybe he felt bad about it, though. Maybe his conscience had gotten to him. Maybe he woke up one morning, looked at himself in the mirror, rubbed his scruff of beard growth and decided this wasn't the kind of person he wanted to be. So he unspliced the cables, and called up the cable company to order it.

Lucy hunched over the steering wheel and sighed, picturing Joe shimmying up the pole again.

But, then again, maybe he couldn't get a date. Maybe his idea of a perfect weekend was to stay on the couch and watch the Spice Channel, a beer in one hand, his dick in the other. Maybe he was still thinking about her.

She sighed again and rolled her neck around. It was stiff. Her watch said it was around two, although it seemed no different outside than when she had pulled up at nine that morning. Her butt and the backs of her thighs were numb, either from the cold, or from sitting too long. She wished she had one of those beaded seats that cabbies always had. Her stomach growled, and the sound made her jump. Maybe Joe wasn't going anywhere today. Maybe he was going to stay in all night. Maybe she should just give up for today, and go home and get some Chinese food and a paper and look for a job, since she couldn't pay the phone bill or her credit cards this month. Stalking didn't pay very well, unfortunately.

The moment before Lucy turned the key in her ignition, she cursed herself for not being religious enough to know some prayer, so she could pray to whatever deity watched over the transmissions of old cars.

"Hail…Fahrfugnugen, full of grace," she said, and cranked the key. A high-pitched squeal sawed the air, then cleared its throat and sputtered and chuckled and rumbled steady.

"Hallelujah," she muttered, and crawled off into the afternoon.

Cuerpita Bonita

REBEKAH MARCANO

Daddy always plays guitar at night, and me and Felice jump on his back. Sometimes he gets mad but he is strong, and he can keep playing no matter what. When he comes home from work, we run to the door and Felice sits on one foot, and I sit on the other. And then he walks down the long hallway, keeping his legs straight the whole time. Me and Felice laugh, and we try to press down real hard so he can't walk, but he is so strong.

Then we all go to the kitchen, and he kisses Mommy. Sometimes for a long yucky time. We eat dinner right away, 'cause Daddy's so hungry. Then we help Mommy clear the table. Sometimes she makes dessert like banana bread. That's made from mushy, yucky bananas, but it tastes so yummy when it's done.

Daddy teaches me and Felice how to draw, but I don't like drawing so much. I'd rather do cartwheels on the fluffy, green carpet. When Mommy just vacuums it, it's even fluffier. Felice is older—maybe that's why she's so good at drawing.

I wanna be able to do cartwheels better than these girls that live across the street. They're so dumb. When me and Felice were walking home from school they were making faces at us. And then they made fun of Felice because her hair's so fluffy. It's fluffy like Daddy's.

Daddy lets us pick his hair out with a pick. It's so fun, and when we're all done, the pick will stay in all by itself. It won't even fall. I tried to do that to Mommy's hair, and it slid right out. Her hair is red, and so soft. Daddie's hair is soft too, but fluffy like Felice's. I don't know why the girls are so mean to her, but I'm practicing my cartwheels, and I'm gonna do one with one hand, and those dumb girls are gonna feel so stupid, 'cause they are so stupid.

I don't say stupid things in front of Mommy and Daddy. But sometimes, me and Felice sit outside in the backyard, and we whisper things to each other that Mommy and Daddy don't let us say. It's so fun, and we laugh. I even said, "Fuck." But I think my dad has special powers because he came outside and saw us laughing, and even though he didn't spank me, I think he heard me say it.

Caroline's stupid too. She's Mommy's friend, and I don't like her. She's not pretty like my mommy. She's fat, and her jeans are so tight. I hate looking at her. When she comes over we just play with Daddy. He can do pushups with me and Felice on his back at the same time.

Yeah, my mom is so pretty. She has freckles all over her body. Sometimes, I wish I had red hair and freckles. A boy in my class has bright red hair and freckles, just like Mommy. I think he is so cute. Maybe I'll marry him, and our kids will have red hair and freckles.

Everyone says Felice looks like Daddy and I look like Mommy. Except I don't. Because my hair isn't red, it's blond. And I don't have freckles all over my body like Mommy. I have one freckle on my arm. Just one.

One time I took a marker and drew freckles all over my face. But they didn't look real, and Daddy spanked me 'cause he says I coulda got poisoning.

One time Caroline, Mommy's yucky friend, came over with a bag of presents. And then I liked her, because I like presents.

And there was a pretty brown doll with yarn hair and patent leather shoes just like the ones I want to buy at Sears, but Mommy says no, patent leather scratches too easy. But then stupid Caroline took the doll away and gave me the yellow doll with yellow skin and yellow hair, blue eyes, and an ugly green dress with ugly green gym shoes.

She said Felice looked like the brown doll and I looked like the yellow doll. And I said she looked like a fat doll, and she should buy herself a fat doll. And my mom sent me to my room, but I didn't care.

And I was so mad because Felice wouldn't even trade me dolls. And I said please, trade me the patent leather shoes, because I want patent leather shoes. And she said too bad. And then I took a marker and made freckles all over my doll's face so she would be pretty like Mommy. And Daddy didn't even spank me like I thought. Not for the freckles, and not for calling Caroline a fat doll. He laughed. And I never got in trouble.

I can still smell my grandmother's apartment. The burning incense, left over *arroz con gandules,* sitting in a pot on the stove. *Café con leche* brewing from morning till night. Her apartment smelled of her, breathed her over-dramatic spirit, resembled her gaudy style.

Always in the corners, day or night, was the stick of burning myrrh or sandalwood, tucked neatly between the crack of a window so the ashes would fall on the sill. The incense scared me a little, because it was lit to ward off evil spirits, bought from the Puerto Rican voodoo store, and the thought of evil spirits lingering about her grandiose space, with statues in every corner, six-foot gold mirrors on every wall, crosses and rosary beads tossed about—it didn't seem unlikely. And what if she forgot to light the myrrh incense? What would the spirits do? That wouldn't happen, I was assured. Her rituals were like clockwork. Her energy was boundless. She didn't forget things.

Her day began at a quarter to five in the morning. She'd wake, nude, of course, except the lovely pink rollers neatly tucked in her short, nappy, red do. Her floppy pink flip-flops could be heard throughout the echoing apartment. Flip, flop, flip, flop. And then—boom! On goes the salsa music. And the flip-flopping turns to scampering and sliding, light stomping in rhythmic motions to the beat . . . "OOOOOOPAAA!!" she'd scream, dancing naked, all but the pink flip-flops and matching rollers.

I know this because once I woke to use the bathroom . . . she wasn't embarrassed. "Da body, it is a beautiful thing. Beautiful. Never be ashamed of your body . . . It is a gift. A gift from God . . . Thank God you have a beauti-ful body. Every day . . . Jesus, Jose, Maria, *gracias por mi cuerpa bonita* . . . heeheeheehee . . ."

I suppose that's why at seventy-five her body was smooth and toned. No stretch marks or cellulite. Just a beautiful, slightly stocky, firm, porcelain com-plexion. Head to toe. And her energy, that was from the *café con leche,* of course.

I must have been five the first time I sipped the perfection named *café con leche*, because in my grandmother's culture, that is when you begin drinking the addictive drink. Five, maybe four, right there at the breakfast table with everyone else.

I can hear the music of her favorite band playing, El Gran Combo, and she'd sing along with the lyrics, only louder and faster, and her hips would sway back and forth, as she ran from the kitchen to the dining room with plates full of breakfast food. She'd never let anyone get up and help her, presentation was her forte, hosting her passion.

Between trips to the kitchen and back, she'd lift me up from my seat, wrap my scrawny legs around her waist; my head would fall between her big melon-like breasts. She'd squeeze so tight I wouldn't fall, and I'd fly along with her to the kitchen, laughing all the way. Then she'd sit me on the counter, right next to the brewing coffee beans, so strong and flavorful. She'd pull out the coffee filter, and hand me a handful of cinnamon sticks. "The secret to *mi café* . . . ," she'd whisper. The beans would mix with the cinnamon sticks, and the whole house would fill with the seductive scent of morning pleasure. The milk would boil on the stove, and she'd pour in her other secrets: honey, and a tinge of evaporated milk, the whole time laughing and dancing. And I'd smile because no one else was allowed in the kitchen, and I was learning her secrets, the ones her own daughters begged for, and she'd shrug her shoulders with a "*Yo no se* . . ." She'd pull out her favorite mug, the one shaped like a cat with a curvy tail for a handle, pour in half a cup of steamy, honey-sweetened milk, and half a cup of cinnamon-flavored coffee. Perfect temperature. I'd smile, staring at her from the counter. She'd place the cat mug up to my lips, and I'd sip the sinful morning treat, letting the yumminess travel to my tummy, and make my insides rejoice....MMMMMmmmm. And I'd say, "*Gracias,* Jesus, Jose, Maria, *Para mi café con leche* . . . and let me grow up to dance and have a beautiful body like Abuelita . . ."

Dear Olivia,
It's pretty scary being a freshman in high school, especially going to such a big one, four thousand kids. But at least I have Felice here. She's a junior now, and pretty popular. People come up to me in the hallway all the time, sometimes seniors. Felice knows everyone. And they're all like, "Are you Felice's sister? You guys look just alike."

Then sometimes they'll ask, "You guys look so much alike, but do you have the same father?" That pisses me off. Just 'cause Felice is a little darker and has brown hair. Then when we're on our way to school, people that don't know us will be like, "What nationality are you guys?" Like every day, and at first I liked the attention, but now I'm annoyed. And people are always like, "Felice, why does your sister look so white?" And she's always like, "I dunno."

At my old school, no one cared. So I guess everyone who meets me assumes I'm white. And then they see me with my sister, and they're all like, "OOOhh, what are you? Your sister looks so pretty. Why aren't you tan like her? Do you have the same father?"

And I'm starting to get the idea that it's not cool to be white. And my mom heard me and Felice talking about why I look so white, 'cause people ask literally every day, "Felice, why does your sister look so white?" And my mom started crying, saying we wished we weren't half white. She's so emotional. That's not what we were saying. And Felice and I dyed my hair after what happened on the bus (I'll get to that in a minute), and my mom started crying more, saying, "No one wants to look like me." Literally CRYING!

And then my dad lectured me about how he was the only Puerto Rican kid in an all-white neighborhood . . . blah, blah, blah . . . but they're not the ones getting made fun of. And it's just hair dye.

So anyway, we were on the crowded-ass bus at three o'clock exactly. And I had to squeeze to try and find a seat. And it's cold as fuck. The CTA smells like exhaust fumes, and I can barely breathe.

Felice moves to the back with her friends, and I sit in the middle. The back is too crowded, and we were only gonna be on for a few stops, anyway. So these girls get on from another school, acting all rowdy, trying to be cool. Like ten of 'em, mostly Puerto Rican girls, a couple of black girls.

And they're not even seniors, they're like freshmen or sophomores, but they think they're the shit. As soon as they step on the bus, they start mimicking the white cheerleaders from our school. And Felice's friends are all laughing, and the cheerleaders are all scared.

"White girls can't shake their asses."

"Polish girls can't dress . . . What the hell is she wearin'?"

And I can feel them walking closer, squeezing their way through the crowd, sure not to miss any white girls to make fun of. "A BLL BLLOO BLA SH SA . . ." One girl started pretending to speak Polish, sticking out her tongue, and exaggerating her lips, then peering her long face and staring directly at any white girl in her path.

I felt her inching closer to me, and I could feel my stomach dropping. I wanted to slap her face and pull her hair. She wasn't special. Why did she think she could fuck with everyone? She certainly wasn't funny. "EXCUSE ME . . . EXCUSE ME . . ." She pushed her way closer to the back, her entourage following close behind, laughing at the language she pretended to speak, in the name of Polish. I could hear her smacking her lips, chewing on her gum, and I could feel the stiffness of the white girls around me, holding back words and fists.

I wished I was sitting closer to my sister, my protector, who was six rows too far away. I wished I looked more like my dad. I wished I was back at my old school where no one cared about your ethnic background. I wished she'd just shut the fuck up. Her round face, and too-tight pulled-back hair met me face to face. She was so close, I could taste her spearmint gum, and smell the coconut oil in her hair. Her bright red lipstick was smeared in the center, and her teeth were crooked with a tinge of yellow. All things I didn't need to know about the too-close bitch in my face. All things I wish I could have told her.

"WHAT'S UP, WHITE GIRL? A BLL BLOO BLASHEE...YOU LOOK POL-ISH TOO." The laughter roared out of her circle of girls, with dark curls and too much gel. They looked like my aunts, and grandma, and sister. I had the same ethnic background as them; I just didn't look it.

"Are those little freshmen messing with my little sister?"

The bus grew silent from my sister's powerful voice. There she sat, in the center of the back of the bus. With her big group of senior friends, ready to kick ass. Her long brown curls and golden brown skin commanded them to shut up.

"This is your sister? Damn, she looks straight-up white. Sorry."

Felice was pretty fed up with people asking what we were, and why I looked so white, so she thought maybe if my hair was darker, people would chill out. Who woulda thought Mom would have started crying? And Dad just thinks we exaggerate, and make up stories. He doesn't believe Puerto Rican girls make fun of white girls. Why would we make that up? So anyway, that's high school, and that's why I dyed my hair.

Love,
Arianna

The Admittance

ROSE MARTULA

Lemme tell ya something about rehab—they got the best Tator Tots I
think I've ever come across in my life, and it may be the one place
where you can always find a cigarette. The Tots aren't mushy like how they
were in the high school cafeteria; they're fried to a perfect brown crispness,
greasy enough to get your fill, but not so much that it gets ya sick. And you
can usually count on two fingers who doesn't smoke in the whole damn place,
and that includes the counselors, and because of that, ya got a wide range of
what kind you wanna smoke—wides, unfiltered, menthol, lights, ultra-lights,
cloves, beanies—I'm telling ya, you're good to go. They even tell ya not to try
quitting if you smoke; rather they encourage you to keep puffing. Guess they
don't wanna freak you out any more than you already are; guess they don't
wanna have anybody's head exploding in therapy just because their nicotine
fixes have been cut off, not to mention every other fix cut off for the time
being. And if you're looking to gain weight? No problem, rehab's the place to
be. Your days are full of lounging in pajama bottoms and slippers, sitting in
meetings and chairs all day long, and being fed a full three times a day (and
that's not even counting snacks and the late-night pizzas that are ordered on
weekends). The meals are stocked full of hot dogs and hamburgers, potato

salad and beef enchiladas, and all the milk shakes and perfect Tater Tots you can dream of.

When the driver from the airport dropped me off, oh baby, was I a wreck. I struggled with my suitcases through the heavy, glass-front doors, my arms shaking a bit from the weight of them, and there were two nurses working at the front counter, both of whose heads snapped up, as I heaved myself through the door. One of 'em, the bigger one with the orange hair, smiled one of those smiles that makes ya wish they didn't even bother smiling—all plastic and stretched, that made her look like a vampire going in for the kill. The other one, the skinny one, didn't respond at all, just snapped her head back down to her paperwork as quickly as it had snapped up.

"Over there," the skinny one said without looking up, nodding over to a bright blue couch when I started to make my way towards her. I could feel her eyes raise up again, though, as I walked past her, eyeing my back and shuffling feet. The last of the heroin I had snorted before I got on the plane was in the midst of swallowing me up, making my walk slow, and my steps shaky, and my eyes half-closed. Could feel that skinny bitch's eyes tearing into my back then, into the back of my head, into my hair that was tangled together in blond clumps. For the life of me, no matter how many times I ran my fingers through it, I couldn't seem to get rid of all the knots. Seemed like there was more oil and grease than actual hair on my head. The couch didn't bounce or give at all when I sat my ass down, either. It was one of those kinds that felt like it was made of polyester or some shit, the kind that made your ass itch real bad right through your clothes and everything. I leaned my head up against the back of the couch, scrunching my body down real low, and glanced around the room. It was pleasant enough, I guess, with thick carpeting, and the lovely blue couches spread throughout were there maybe to liven it up a bit. There were big windows everywhere, windows that looked out to sprawling Minnesota woods and a few ponds and not much else. Besides the nurses' station tucked into one side of the room that made the place reminiscent of a hospital waiting area, there wasn't really anything else to bother staring off at, and so I sighed and sprawled out even more, falling into a nod, letting my eyelids flutter around like butterflies. The spaghetti straps to my tank top kept slipping off my shoulders, and I'd lazily pull them up from time to time as I waited. And waited and waited and waited. Felt like I was sitting there the whole goddamned afternoon while the admitting nurses buried their big noses in the files in front of them and cracked jokes to each other and shared a box of Krispy Kreme donuts without ever looking over at me, like I was just another fixture to the room, and maybe more so, like I wasn't even there. I dropped my head down, sinking my chin into my chest, and let my eyes narrow, staring down at the shiny, black leather coat I had worn tied around my waist. I heard kids' voices and laughter down the hallway, and something about the way they laughed made my heart skip a few beats. There were other kids here, kids my age, and I would have to talk and laugh and associate with them and face their questioning stares and open up to them and bum smokes and all that shit. I hadn't socialized with anybody on a normal basis in so long, it seemed. It hit me then that I was terrified. My armpits began to sweat. My heart skipped a few more beats. Even the nods didn't let me escape much. I raised a hand to scratch behind my ear. Again, another laugh floated down through the hallway to me, and my hand shook. Scared like a little bitch I was.

"Hey!" a voice shouted over at me, making me jump. "You asleep?"

I looked over at the skinny nurse in her pastel pink uniform behind the desk who was now staring over at me, her paperwork still spread out in front of her. She had short bangs that cut across the middle of her forehead and one of them nurse's hats that looks like one of them Burger King crowns that you get when you're a kid.

"Nah, I'm all right," I called back to her, sitting up some in the couch. It was sucking my whole body in, that damn couch.

"Well, come on over, I'm ready here," she said looking down again into her paperwork.

Ready for what? To give me a beating? A smack in the face for all my sins? A spanking? A disapproving shake of the finger? What? I pushed myself up groggily with both arms, and one of my shoulders kinda jumped a bit like I'd been zapped with one of those cow prods as I stood up. Damn, I was nervous, twitchy, my skin cold and coming off in clammy sweats. Don't let 'em see ya sweat, old Pops used to say. I shuffled back across the room and sank into the cushioned chair in front of the nurses' desk, facing her. She didn't look at me none. And while she shuffled around a few more folders and shit, I looked down at my coat wrapped around my waist and started untying, retying, untying and retying it over and over. It was sickeningly hot in that room, the air conditioner must have been broke or something 'cause the early June heat from outside seemed to be taking over the place, gulping down the whole front room in one swallow, making the windows drip little beads of perspiration down the glass. But I was cold, man, my bare arms and armpits sweating little waterfalls, and I rubbed my palms together, and they were cold as hell too. I glanced over at the nurse's pink pastel ensemble, at her Pepto Bismol sleeves rolled halfway up to her elbows, and a few beads of sweat dripped down the sides of her face and one off the tip of her nose.

"It's fucking freezing in here," I hissed at her all of a sudden. She musta thought I was crazy for saying it, in that stinking heat, but everything was bothering me about her at that point—her choppy bangs, her skinny face, her yellowing teeth, her Burger King crown hat, her knobby elbows, her slippery skin, her accusing eyes at my back—and fuck it, I just wanted to be mean.

She gave me an even look. "You're withdrawing," she said simply, not mean, not even snappy like I expected or hostile, just calm and simple, kinda like when you ask the dull-eyed librarian where the card catalog is in the library, nothing fancy.

Inside, I exploded. Well, am I supposed to sit here and freeze then, you anorexic bitch? I wanted to scream at her and clutch her neck with my cold fingers and just squeeze, and let her feel the cold of my skin, just shake her and make her feel all numb like me. But rather, I shut up. Something about the way she said it so calmly made me even more scared, made me lose my voice or something, made me want somebody to start comforting me, put an arm around me and tell me not to worry, that it wouldn't be that bad, there wouldn't be too much pain, that I wouldn't get that cold, hell I wouldn't have even minded if she was the one doing it. But there was no one there for ya, now was there?

The skinny nurse sighed as she stood up and leaned over across the desk between us, reached for my arm, and began tapping the crook of my elbow. She stopped then, and opened a drawer, pulling out a needle and glove and a couple of vials. Then she started poking and pinching at my veins again.

"The hell you doing?" I asked, flashing my eyes up at her face.

"Gonna draw some blood," she answered just as evenly as before.

"For what?"

"To see what kind of drugs are in your system."

"Oh." I held still and stared numbly as she raised the needle and carefully pushed it into my skin, and watched it suck up the blood all the way up to the vials that she kept switching and switching. Must have filled up four damn vials. "Why don't you just ask me?"

"I will," she said, sitting down and pulling off the gloves with a rubbery snap. "Now," she said pulling out some papers, grasping a pen, and looking up briefly at my face and then back down at the papers. "Have you used marijuana in the last seven days?"

"Uh, yeah, a bit."

"Cocaine?"

Whoa. My face flushed, felt unnatural to be discussing this shit out loud. I stared at her fingertips.

"Cocaine?" she repeated, sweaty nose still to desk.

"Yes." Last week in my apartment, no, who's apartment? Some girl, some girl with chubby cheeks and tattoos running all along her arms, had an Asian boyfriend with Nike sneakers, small apartment, red carpet, barely room for a bed, in my favorite blue hoody. Another check on the paper.

"Methamphetamine?"

"Yes." I didn't wanna go through this shit with her. When? Five days? Four, maybe? Tearing open pink Baggies in the bathroom at school.

Check.

"Morphine?"

"No," so there.

"Sedatives?"

"Huh?"

"Pills."

"Oh, OK, yeah." To sleep, to sleep, I needed, Natalie's mother, blame her, blame her.

Check.

"Hallucinogenics?"

"Yes." Smoked dust three days ago, had it been three days? Just three? Where, think, who?

Check.

"You want an AIDS test?"

Oh, those bangs of hers are terrible. "Huh?"

"An AIDS test? Have you shared needles?"

"AIDS."

I looked up as a man walked up to the nurses' station then, and leaned one hip against the desk, giving a nod to the heavier nurse with the orange hair. Then he looked over at me. Blue, blue eyes. Didn't look older than twenty-five or so. Sideburns. Nice skin. Wait, what the hell was I thinking? No time for that. I raised my hand up to my knotty hair and tried to smooth it back as nicely as possible.

"Um . . . ," I started to trail off.

"Have you shared needles?" Ouch, I wished she'd lower her goddamned voice. It was piercing. I threw another look over at the man. His eyes didn't waver. He was waiting for me to answer, I think.

"No," I told her.

"Have you had unprotected sex?"

Oh, Jesus. My whole face flushed, including my goddamned ears probably. I didn't even bother to look over at the guy, didn't even wanna. I think her voice had even gone up a level when she said the word *sex*. I looked down and untied and retied the coat around my waist again as coolly and calmly as humanly possible. Boys raced through my head. But there wasn't one I could put a face on. Late nights in the park when you'd let them all grope you and fuck you right there in the open grass during high school. The black boys who'd hit on me in clubs, the Puerto Rican boys out on the city steps, the ones I'd thrown a smile to or an extra second glance, the boys who worked in the parking garage in the summers, and the beds, all the different beds, the ones I had crept into, the ones I only saw once, the ones I saw two or three times, and my own bed, the queen-sized one that had so many pillows and stuffed animals, some had been discarded when company was over. I could count on one hand how many I'd used a condom with. Stupid, stupid, stupid.

"Yes," I answered meekly, lowering my voice and letting strands of hair fall into my face. Could feel all eyes burning all of a sudden, right on me, the man with his hip bone pressed up against the counter and his cool blue eyes, the nurse with the orange hair and her eyes as big as saucers, and the skinny bitch beneath all her choppy bangs and all.

"Yes, you've had unprotected sex?" she repeated, her voice echoing off every wall, couch, and piece of carpet fuzz in that whole damn room.

"Yes." My mouth was dry.

"Yes, you want an AIDS test?" The words stung.

"Yes." I closed my eyes and let my eyeballs roll back. I was tired all of a sudden, so tired.

A moment later and another needle was plunged into the skin and more blood sucked up into the vial, and again she snapped off the rubbery gloves and let out a huge sigh. Seemed like she didn't like her job much—who would, dealing with bitchy, gripy girls like me, and having to draw blood from cold arms like mine?

The nurse closed the folder in front of her once and for all, and then almost immediately, the man standing with his arms crossed, hip bone and all, and those blue blue eyes strode over to me in soft strides and stuck his hand out in my face.

"You Samantha?" he said, peering down at me. His eyes were soft, but he wasn't smiling or nothing. Just looked at me like he was already trying to figure me out or something.

"Yes," my voice was barely audible anymore. I wanted to go home.

"I'm Shane," he said taking my hand and giving me a firm shake. "I'm a counselor over in extended care, in the boys' unit, but I'll be settling you in."

I stood up as he reached for my suitcase, and steadied myself a bit on the counter with both hands. "They separate boys and girls here?" I barely even realized the question had come out of my mouth by the time it did. But the thought of being locked up with fifty other girls, straight-up girls and nothing else, young girls who were all addicts for that matter, for thirty goddamned days in the middle of goddamned Minnesota and in the middle of the goddamned summer didn't exactly get my fire going, to say the least.

"No, they're mixed in your unit, in primary," he said lifting up my suitcase, and throwing me a look that basically said to me, why you care, ya little slut? "But with cases we think are more serious we send 'em on to extended care for three months, down the hallway. And that's where we separate the sexes. Just 'cause it's easier to focus that way."

"Oh," I said numbly. I didn't care, really, maybe I was just trying to distract myself. I heard that laughter and those voices from down the hallway again, and my heart raced. I took a step and wobbled a bit on my feet, had to stop and waver and take a big breath. Could literally feel the color draining from my face. Felt like I was gonna be sick. Wanted to lean over across the nurses' station and vomit in their laps. My fingers felt like little blocks of ice.

"I'll explain as much as I can about the rules and regulations once I show you to your room," I heard Shane say, but I couldn't see too well no more. Just the blur of his back and his closely shaved head and not much else. He stopped, though, once he realized I wasn't behind him or beside him, and looked back at me holding myself up by the counter, trying my best not to ralph or collapse on the ground in a heap or anything.

"You want a wheelchair?" His voice traveled over to me, through all the blur and tears at the corners of my eyes and heroin fog and blaring sunshine that was coming in through the windows, every word echoing around that room in circles, it seemed.

"A what?!" I snapped out at him even though I had heard him crystal clear.

"A wheelchair," he repeated.

"Fuck that. No thank you, I'll walk." Didn't need no goddamned wheelchair. I was eighteen years old, for christ's sake, I wasn't that bad off, dammit. My life was beginning. Wheelchairs were for old fogies; wheelchairs were for when you were sick, when you were sick, sick.

"You don't have to be embarrassed," he said.

"Nah, really, I'm straight," I said rubbing my eyes to clear them and then began to walk, moving each foot carefully, trying not to let my knees tremble too much. Don't show 'em your fear, don't show 'em your fear. I wanted to walk on my own; I had to walk on my own, to show 'em, just to show 'em I didn't need 'em.

Shane slowed down his walk then and fell into line with me as we made our way past the nurses' station and down one of the hallways. "Need an arm?" he offered.

"Nope," I said matter-of-factly, pulling my arm into my side even though he didn't reach for it, but just in case he did.

"This'll be your temporary room, just for a couple of days," he was saying as we came to a room at the end of the hallway with a big steel door and silver door handle. "Just until you're through detoxing, we like to keep new patients separated from the rest of the unit."

"What, so I don't bother them with all my screams?" I tried to joke, tried to smile, but I didn't. Just frowned sullenly at the floor as he opened the door and looked at me.

"You'll be all right," he said before holding the door open for me. Something about the way he said that made my heart skip, but in a good way, and made me get that kinda tingly feeling. In another situation, god, in another situation, in a better situation, in a normal situation, where I wasn't a patient, where he wasn't a counselor, where I wasn't so sick, so depressed, so bitter, but so sick most of all, I woulda kicked it to him, and he woulda done the same, I knew he would have.

The room was just like a hospital room—the linoleum floor cold and yellow and ugly, a bathroom that was just as cold and smelled like piss, two twin beds with blankets and sheets so tightly tucked into the corners it made my own head hurt, and curtains the color of runny snot. Metal handrails ran alongside the bed—the kind that you steady yourself on when you're old or sick—but no TV, no phone, nothing. If I wasn't cold enough, I got even colder the minute I stepped into that room; shivers went tearing down my spine, I swear. Bad memories in the hospital with my stomach, bad food that tasted like mush and IVs stuck in my wrists and those terrible robes that didn't close in the back and my hair all matted and greasy and the dirt and sweat that became part of my skin. I wanted to go home.

"Not all rooms are like this," Shane said as if reading my thoughts, and he heaved the suitcase up on top of one of the beds. "Only the detox rooms are this hospitalish. You'll see, the regular ones are like hotel rooms—big as hell and much nicer; some of 'em even got balconies."

"Oh…good," was all I could manage to say and promptly threw myself down across one of the beds, the one the suitcase wasn't on, and rolled over, sprawling myself out holding my stomach. I was starting to get real depressed, that black cloud hovering over my head now, fogging up my eyes, and seeping its way into the creases of my skin. Felt like I'd never been so depressed before in all my goddamned life, felt like this was the worst, and nothing even mattered, not even the cute boy beside me.

"I'm gonna have to go through all your things," Shane was saying, and he started to unzip the suitcase, my suitcase. "And anything you're wearing right now. It's just standard, not trying to look at your underwear or nothing."

"'K," I muttered staring up at the ceiling. I didn't even care really, didn't feel violated or degraded or nothing like he might have thought I would. I bet some kids resisted, threw temper tantrums and shit, but we weren't to be trusted. I understood that much at least. Of course I'd brought the drugs with me, of course.

He flipped open the top of the suitcase, and began unfolding a couple of pairs of pants and going through the pockets. My favorite jeans. The tight ones. Made me look like I even had a bit of an ass. My stomach was starting to flip-flop inside. A cramp was starting in on my right side, a cramp like something awful, like something was biting and chomping, trying to puncture right through my intestines or something.

"How ya doing?" he asked, reaching for another stack of clothes, and then sat himself down on the bed to face my sprawling body.

"Not good," I muttered.

There was a moment of him riffling through the clothes. I always loved that sound, the riffling of fabrics together, of clothes being folded like when I was a kid and our washing machine exploded, and Ma dragged me to the Laundromat with her to keep her company while she washed and dried and folded, and I would sit on one of the dryers, the shake of it making my dangling legs dance, and she would buy me pop and a bag of chips or Twizzlers if I begged.

"Are you pissed?" he asked looking over at me and then looking back down at the clothes.

"Pissed? No." A man not far from my age going through my shorts and a mesh of bras, socks, and underwear now in that dark room. How odd, how funny, and alls I could think about was eating junk food and letting it all get stuck in my teeth and washing it down with pop, pop that sent my teeth into sugar shock, with my mom at the Laundromat and all the fans humming in the corners, and the doors left wide open 'cause it was hot and the thick breeze would blow in my dangling legs and all the mounds of laundry, all separated into darks and whites and socks and pajamas and all.

"You're not mad that you're here?" his voice interrupted me.

"Mad? Nah. It's not jail or nothing."

"You're not mad at your parents for sending you here?"

"Mad at my parents? Nah. I don't blame them." And I didn't, I really didn't.

"No?" he said. I knew he didn't believe me.

"No," I repeated and rolled over again. My stomach was really starting to tear me up. Felt like I was gonna crap in my pants any minute or something, could feel my bowels go all loose and jellylike.

"So you wanna be here, then?"

"Me? No."

"No?"

"No." I was tired of these games, these questions. Alls I could think about was how my stomach was starting to make me double over. Never felt quite like that before.

"Why do you think you're here?"

"'Cause I got caught," I managed to get out. I knew it was the wrong answer, knew it would piss him off somehow, or make his eyebrows get slanted and mush together, make his forehead crinkle up—which it did.

He pulled out a Baggie of weed from my blue hoody then. Fuck, it'd been worth a shot. "Gotta take this," he said holding it up as if I didn't know it had been there. "Lemme see that coat that's on ya."

I slowly untied it from my waist, and weakly tossed it over to him. Just take it, take it all, I thought to myself. Take me while you're at it.

"You been to rehab before?"

"Nah, I went to a methadone clinic once," I said reaching down and scratching my hipbone. "But the doctor was a real prick, and I don't know about that methadone shit." I wanted to know if they were going to give me any drugs to detox or if they were just going to let me lie there and pant and tear at my skin. The cold seemed to be invading every opening in my body, and I wanted to crawl under the stiff blankets and wrap myself in 'em like a cocoon. I was even having a hard time keeping the shake out of my voice by that point.

"You think you have a problem with heroin?"

"Nah." My guts twisting and turning, 'bout ready to explode right there on the bed.

"No?"

"Hell, no." Twisting and turning, tossing and burning.

From the leather coat, he pulled out a bag of dope. I felt like diving for it, wrenching it out of his hands with my teeth, even. But he slipped it into his own pocket, taking what was once mine. "You think they made a mistake sending you here, then?"

"Sure, a mistake, yeah, a mistake." I was through talking shit with him. That was my only bag. I eyed his corduroy pants pocket. Had he put it in that one or the other one? "I got things going for me back home," I added.

"Oh, you got things? What kind of things?"

I ground my teeth together, sending a slight shot of pain to my left jaw. In no mood for games. "I'm getting it together." My eyes dropped down to his pockets again. There was just no way to get at it without putting my hands all over his pants, and the only way to do that, well shit, I'm sure that wasn't allowed. "I got things," I said again.

Now finished going through the suitcase, he brought the lid down and laid my leather coat smoothly on top of it, making that nice riffling noise. Loved that damned noise. "You're lucky not to be locked up," he said, in more of a whisper than anything else.

I blinked once and licked my lips. I wanted him to go and leave me to be sick in the bathroom, cold and shaking, hovering over the toilet, letting the cool tile burn at my ass.

"I'm telling you for your own good, and not to scare you for the wrong reasons, but honestly, you should be scared," he went on. "Statistically, less than four percent of heroin addicts recover. And that's four percent out of one hundred. Never thought it would get this far, huh?"

Was he making fun of me? Mocking me? Another lick of the lips.

"So if you're just in here to buy time, then you might as well get packing. We don't need ya if all you're gonna do is go back to the streets. But I betcha a million dollars if you leave now, you'll go to jail...if you don't die first."

"Million dollars, huh?" Two more licks.

He was silent for a minute with his hands kinda resting on his lap. Maybe he was sore at my attitude, my bitterness, my jokes, whatever—I didn't care. Maybe he was just trying to start a conversation, just trying to be nice. My face started sweating real bad then.

"Your mouth is just throwing it all away," he said real quietly, real calm like that skinny nurse. How was everybody so goddamned calm here? In a place like this? In a situation like this? I wanted him to leave, god, how I wanted him to leave. Sweat started to pour down my cheeks then.

"No, we're not," I said, part of me feeling the obligation of having to define my youth, my entire generation as a whole or something. Had to stick up for something, didn't I? We weren't wasted, we weren't ruined, were we? Another lick. Tasted salt.

"Any time you're using, you're pulling your own trigger. Hell, you've fired a million bullets through your skull already, and none of them has killed you. You're breathing for a reason."

"I'm sick, I'm gonna be sick," I managed to whisper out.

He stood up and kinda towered over me, his face taking up the whole room, it seemed. "I'll get the nurse. She's gonna give you some meds to help you detox."

Another lick and he started to make his way to the door, and once his back was turned, I just let it all go—let the shakes take over and held my stomach real tight, and started to crap in my pants, and let the tears roll, and leaned over the edge of the bed and dry heaved again and again and I ground my teeth even harder and I wished, how I wished I could rip into his damn corduroy pockets right then, and how I wished he would come back and hold me and take care of me, and then maybe we'd run away together, me and those blue eyes, and I needed to make it to the bathroom, 'cause I was going in my pants and it wasn't stopping, but I couldn't move 'cause my head felt like lead, and I was freezing, fucking freezing, grabbed at the blankets to twist them over me and the sweat was starting to make my clothes smell and I licked again, and I called out, and I called out something which I didn't mean to say, which surprised me even though it came out of my mouth, that I didn't even know consciously I was thinking about, but he was the only one in the room, and even though his back was to me, and that back of his looked so cold, so hard, and he was opening the door, it was creaking and squeaking real bad like it needed oil, and I didn't want him to leave, didn't want him to twist that door knob open, but I called out anyway, I said, "I thought I wasn't meant to be at all." And he stopped in his tracks, stopped for a full minute, it felt like, but he didn't turn around, he just stayed with his back to me, and he took a big breath, and he took another, until it looked like his shoulders were heaving, and the smell of shit was making me ill, and I knew he could probably smell it, and I leaned over again to dry heave, and my hair fell in my face, and nothing came out, and I looked over again, with his back still facing me, and his shoulders still heaving up and down like in a rhythm, like in a beat, like in a song, and I could have cried for the rest of my damn life right then, cried and cried 'til my eyes cracked and bled, and that still wouldn't have been enough for all that I was feeling, that still wouldn't have been enough, for what had I come to be on that cold bed? Alone in that frigid room with my suitcase of clothes half-opened and fingered by some man's hands, blue blue eyes, and my stomach pulling at me, ripping and tearing and wanting to come loose of my body, it was not supposed to be like this, it was not.

"Of course you were meant to be," the voice came softly, gently through the room, behind that beautiful back, behind that beautiful shaven head, all the way over to where I lay curled up on the bed. I began to shudder.

Wormfood

JEFF JACOBSON

The Sawyer brothers followed us all the way to the cemetery. As soon as we pulled into the parking lot I knew why we were here. I know I wasn't very quick in figuring a lot of things out, but after watching Fat Ernst kick the shit out of Harry's corpse and drop him into the Dumpster like that, I knew that he was capable of anything now. We were here to dig up Earl. And steal that belt buckle.

Earl had been buried in the Lutheran, Methodist, and Baptist cemetery. The Catholic cemetery was on the other side of the river, closer to town. And the Mormons had their own exclusive plot of land up north, near their church or temple or whatever the hell they wanted to call it. I guess people who didn't like to associate much while they were alive sure as hell didn't want to lie next to each other when they were dead. They might end up in the wrong heaven or something. The graveyard waited patiently at the end of Route 11, surrounded by walnut orchards.

When Fat Ernst stopped the Cadillac I realized he *had* been thinking ahead when he took Harry's submersible pump. Only about twenty yards of walnut trees lay between the orchard and the cemetery. Of course, when they had originally started burying folks out here, the river was still a ways off, but over

160   Hair Trigger 24

the years the river had gradually changed its course, carrying away the dark, heavy soil bit by bit, creeping closer to the graveyard.

And now the whole place was under about six inches of water.

Junior pulled in next to us, nose of the truck pointing towards the graves. "Leave your lights on," Fat Ernst called out. I looked out over the acre of headstones rising out of the black water. It looked as though someone had started building a bridge, pouring very neat, orderly rows of various concrete supports and foundations across a swamp. I opened the door and stepped out, feeling the water instantly trickle over the tops of Grandpa's boots and soak into my socks. I couldn't remember the last time my feet had been truly dry. Junior and Bert climbed out of the truck and joined Fat Ernst and me in front of the Cadillac, bathed in the harsh glare of the headlights. "If I would've known we were coming out here, I would've brought some flowers for Pop," Junior said.

"We're going to visit Pop?" Bert asked.

Fat Ernst ignored him and asked, "You got your shovels?"

"Yep."

"Well, go get 'em and let's get to work. We're not here for a goddamn picnic."

"Hold on," Junior said, crossing his arms. "We ain't moving until we know why we're here."

"Yeah," Bert said, nodding. He tried to cross his arms as well, but with his right arm still in a cast, it didn't work so well. Fat Ernst smiled. "You ever seen Earl Johnson's belt buckle? The one made of gold? With a shitload of diamonds all over it?"

"No," Junior said. A moment of silence. Then he smiled back. "But I heard about it."

"Well, I just happen to know that his dumbshit brother Lester decided that Earl should be wearing it when they put him in the ground."

Junior looked astonished. "You mean to tell me, that they...they buried it with Earl?"

"That's what I'm telling you."

"Holy shit."

"Holy shit," Bert echoed. I still didn't think he knew quite what was happening. His eyes were wandering around on their own accord again, and I wondered if he'd been taking his horse tranquilizers.

"So it's out there, just stuck in the ground with Earl?" Junior gestured at the headstones.

"You got it."

"I'll be damned. Wait a minute—suppose we go get it. How are we gonna split it up? Doesn't make much sense to break it in half."

"No, that don't make much sense at all. You gotta think ahead. See, I'm gonna take it down to Sacramento first thing in the morning, take it in to a pawn shop, trade it in for some hard cash. You'll have your share by noon tomorrow, no later."

"Well hell's bells, let's go get it."

"Now you're talking." Fat Ernst glanced at me. "Go grab a shovel, boy. Time for you to earn those wages." It started to rain, softly at first. I heard it hitting the leaves of the walnut trees and tiny splashes began to hit the water all around us. Then it started coming down hard. Within seconds, all of us were soaked to the skin. The rain put out Fat Ernst's cigar. He tried lighting it several times, but no luck. Undaunted, he simply twisted the ashes off and chewed on the end. He spit, and still smiling, said, "Told you I had a plan."

Bert started out into the cemetery first, carrying a Coleman lantern that Fat Ernst had also thoughtfully brought along. It gave me a beacon to follow, as I stumbled along behind him, carrying two shovels and a crowbar. Junior was next, carrying the sump pump, plastic tube looped around his shoulders, and trailing a long, heavy-duty extension cord plugged into the generator in the back of the truck. Fat Ernst brought up the rear, wheezing and panting as all of us splashed through the graveyard. Immediately, I felt the mud grab hold of Grandpa's boots as if it was alive and had a mind of its own. With each step, I sank a little farther and farther into the soft soil, until the water was almost up to my knees.

I wondered how we would find Earl's grave, seeing that they hadn't had time to engrave a headstone or erect one of those giant monoliths that rich people seemed to like so much. Everything was completely covered with water, so we couldn't even spot the freshly dug dirt. But as it turned out, it wasn't hard to spot the grave at all. The canopy, used to cover the grave and the mourners during the services when it rained, was still up, waiting down in the far corner of the graveyard, in the Johnson family plot.

As the four of us struggled across the cemetery, shuffling through the mud and floodwater, I realized that Grandpa was buried in here somewhere. Mom and Dad were with both of her parents on the other side of the river, in the Catholic cemetery. I stopped a moment, looking around. I used to know where Grandpa's grave was located; I'd been coming out here at least once or twice a month with Grandma, but now, in the darkness and rain and mud, I couldn't find my bearings. All the headstones looked alike, just rows of stone slabs rising out of a black swamp. Our shadows, cast by the headlights, danced and flitted over the stones and mud, looking as if giant ravens flew about, jumping and swirling from one headstone to the next.

So I stopped looking for Grandpa's grave and just concentrated on the job at hand. Just get the job done and get out; this had become my new mantra. Just get it over with and get home.

The Johnson family had their own corner of the cemetery, even had a wicked little spiked fence around it to keep out the undesirables. We carefully straddled the fence and climbed onto a wide concrete slab that had been poured over the top of Earl and Lester's parents. Once on top of the slab, we rested for a moment, staring into the dark water under the canopy. Oddly enough, while Junior and Bert and me fought to catch our breath, panting and bent over, bracing our hands on our knees, Fat Ernst seemed the least tired of all of us. I had never seen him with that much energy. He paced the length of the slab, maybe seven, eight feet at the most, chewing on his wet cigar and slapping his hands together. "All right, then, gentlemen. Let's get to it. There's at least ten, maybe fifteen thousand bucks down there waiting for us. All we gotta do is dig down six goddamn feet and grab it. That's it. Easiest goddamn money you ever made. Come on, let's move it."

"You start digging, then," Junior said, still catching his breath.

"You know I got a heart condition. So quit your bitching and get to work."

Junior picked up both shovels, tossed one to me, and we got to work. The beginning was the hardest. We just kind of stabbed the shovels blindly into the water, wrenching great, dipping piles of sludge out of the mud and slopping it over to the side. Eventually, Junior and I built up a sort of wide, low wall around the area where we guessed the grave was. Fat Ernst carefully lowered the submersible pump into the water and plugged it into the extension cord. Junior adjusted the plastic hose so the water was pumped out over the little dyke we had built. I was hoping for a break while the grave was being drained, but Fat Ernst wasn't in a break kind of mood.

More sludge was pried out of the hole. I dug until my back and arms were screaming for relief; blisters rose up on my palms almost instantly, breaking and oozing from the rough wooden handle and the silt. But we kept at it, settling into a ragged rhythm of digging and lifting. Bert got tired of holding the lantern high, so he just set it at the edge of the concrete slab and sat there like an emaciated gargoyle. He hummed the theme to *Hawaii Five-O* for a few minutes, but Fat Ernst slapped him in the back of the head and that shut him up. Fat Ernst didn't say much, either, but he kept pacing back and forth, almost mincing along in the rain as if he was being forced into some formal dance but had to take a leak really bad.

We kept digging, excavating a square hole roughly six feet wide and six feet long. The pump died when we were about four feet down; the motor started in with this hiccuping whine for a while, then simply stopped. There was only mud coming out of the end of the plastic hose at that point anyway. Junior unplugged the pump and threw it out of the grave. Fat Ernst ignored it. We kept going, lifting out shovelfuls of mud that had the consistency of wet concrete and slapping it over the dam around the hole, until I couldn't feel my arms anymore, couldn't feel my hands, and the only thing I could hear was the sucking, squelching sounds as each bite was taken out of the earth and splashed over the wall.

It wasn't too long after the mud strangled and killed the pump that Junior's shovel hit something solid. He pulled it out, tried again. The blade sunk into the muck nearly up to the handle, and this time, there was no mistaking the sound, like a baseball bat cracking a rock under water. I stabbed my own shovel into the mud and sure enough, felt the tingling jolt up my dead arms as it connected with something solid.

"That's it," Fat Ernst whispered in a tight voice. "That. Is. Mother. Fucking. It."

Without a word, Junior and I kept going, holding the shovels sideways as we scraped the mud off the top of the object, flinging the loads away in looping, uneven arcs out into the rain and the darkness. Soon, we had scraped enough of the mud away to find the size and shape of the thing.

It was a coffin all right, no doubt about that. The top was slightly curved, just rounded enough that Junior and I kept slipping on it as we carved into the wet soil packed around it. About three feet of the coffin extended into the hole, the rest was buried under the south wall. We had been close, but we hadn't dug down directly on top of the whole thing. It looked like we had found the top end, because I could see the seam where the lid was cut in half, in case you felt like lifting it up and taking a good close look at the corpse during the funeral. Fat Ernst had to wake Bert up by slapping him in the back of the head again. But once he was awake, even Bert could see that we were getting close now, and he took his job serious, kneeling at the top of the dyke, holding the lantern out over the hole, above our heads. We dug out a narrow trench around the sides of the coffin, so we could stand next to it.

"All right, then," Junior said finally. He stuck his shovel into the mud and left it there. "Gimme that crowbar."

Fat Ernst thrust the three-foot bar into the hole, nearly crunching my skull in the process. "Do it. Pop that bitch open."

"Oh, that's what I'm gonna do all right," Junior said in a velvet, seductive voice as he felt along the edges of the coffin. "Gonna pop your sweet little cherry like a virgin cunt on prom night. That's right, baby. Spread you open wide, get me a taste."

I backed into the far corner, giving Junior some space as he got romantic with the coffin. He found a spot he liked, along the side and near the grooved seam along the top. He took the crowbar and jammed it up under the overhanging lip on the side, then wrenched it down in a rushed, savage motion. The wedged tip snapped clean out of the groove and flipped up and popped Junior in the nose. He went back against the side of the pit, landing hard, and before he had even blurbled out "Mudderfugger," blood started gushing out of his flattened nostrils as if somebody had cranked open a faucet.

"Shake it off," Fat Ernst commanded.

Junior didn't do much except make fists, little grabbing motions in the air in front of his face, and blink rapidly.

"That must hurt like hell," I said.

"Popped your cherry," Bert said, and I guess that struck him as particularly funny, because he started giggling uncontrollably, and the lantern started to shake, throwing our huge shadows around the hole like lurching giants.

"Come on, come on," Fat Ernst said. "We're almost there. Close enough to taste it. Quit fucking around."

Junior blinked a few more times and shook his head, spraying blood all over the place. He tried wiping it away from his mouth, then gave up and grabbed the crowbar again. With a tremendous, "YOU FUCKING FUCK!" he raised the crowbar above his head and brought it down on the coffin with all his strength. The impact left a slight dent and a hollow boom, but that was all. This pissed Junior off even more, and he attacked the coffin in ferocious spasms, flailing away at it like an old blind woman trying to kill a rattlesnake with her cane.

Finally, he gave up, exhausted and spent. Blood was still running freely from his nose, but Junior ignored it and just stared at the coffin like he was trying to scare it into opening. "We need a hammer," he said, swallowing blood. "Or an axe. Something."

"You mean to tell me that you can't break into a little box?" Fat Ernst roared. "What the fuck is wrong with you? Christ on a stick, boy, I woulda thought you were tougher than that."

Junior spit flecks of blood onto the muddy surface of the coffin. "Why don't you come on down here, find out how tough I am. I'll jam this fucking crowbar up your ass, cocksucker."

"You watch your mouth and just get that fucking thing open."

Junior muttered, "Asshole," under his breath and wiped away some of the blood on his face. He bent over the coffin, inspecting the dents and grooves that he had inflicted on the lid. Sliding his finger along the seam where the lid was cut in half, he found a small notch, a chip broken out of the surface. "There we go," he whispered. "Found your little virgin cunt—that's right baby."

He caressed the notch, then gently worked the blade of the crowbar into the narrow space. "Hold this," Junior said to me, indicating the bar. He held it upright, directly in the center of the lid, and I got the impression that he was about to stake a vampire. I did what I was told, firmly grabbing the cold steel, holding it snug into the little chipped space. If I had realized what Junior was planning, I probably wouldn't have been so quick to grab the damn thing, because he stepped back and grabbed my shovel. He said simply, "Watch it," then brought it up over his head in a wide swinging arc and smashed the blade flat down on top of the crowbar.

The blade connected with the curved top of the crowbar in a tiny burst of sparks and stinging chips of metal. The jolt vibrated up my arm into my chest, and it felt as though I had grabbed hold of an electric fence. I'm lucky I didn't let go, and managed to keep the crowbar in an upright position, because the second blow came so quickly. I stepped as far away from the coffin as I could, holding the crowbar at arm's length. Junior kept whipping the shovel over his head and swinging it down, like he was working on a railroad, driving iron spikes into solid rock.

After about five or six blows, my hand went numb. It took a few seconds to realize that I wasn't even holding onto the crowbar anymore, yet it was staying upright. Junior had managed to pound it almost an inch into the seam in the coffin lid. He kept at it, bringing the shovel down and grunting every time it smashed into the crowbar. Before long, the shovel blade, not exactly designed to be a hammer, was mangled beyond repair. Junior hit the crowbar one more time, driving it even deeper into the coffin, then casually tossed the shovel up out of the grave at Fat Ernst. Fat Ernst caught it neatly and pitched it into the darkness where it landed with a splash.

"Alright cunt, spread 'em wide for Daddy," Junior said as he straddled the coffin, crowbar between his legs, and grabbed the bar with both hands. "You like it, don't you?" he hissed at the casket. "You like my big, hard dick, don't you? DON'T YOU!" He screamed this last part out as he wrenched the crowbar forward, then back. It gave a little, but didn't move much. I was hoping it might slip out and smack him like last time, but no such luck. The bar had been sunk too deeply into the lid. "Suck it, bitch!" Junior choked out, shaking the crowbar with all his strength. But apparently the coffin was determined to stay a virgin, and the lid held together.

"Archie, get over here. Give me a hand," Junior said. "Get up on top there." I climbed on top of the casket and grabbed the crowbar, just under Junior's muddy fists. "Now when I say when, you push towards me, then we'll go back towards you, got it?" I nodded. "OK, WHEN!" I braced my boots against the mud behind me and pushed like a madman. I was really hoping the whole thing would pop out, driving it straight into Junior's forehead this time. But it held. "Back," Junior cried, and I pulled, leaning on it, hanging as much weight as I could off the bar. Still no luck.

"OH, YOU FUCKING WHORE! YOU KNOW YOU WANT IT! ALL YOU CUNTS WANT IT!" Junior kept screaming, but I guess the coffin wasn't in the mood for sweet talk. That crowbar didn't budge. Finally, Junior climbed up on top of the casket, shoving me away in the process and started kicking at the bar. It wobbled a little, but that was all.

Junior looked up. Fat Ernst was smart enough to keep his mouth shut. After a moment, Junior said, "Bert, get your ass down here." He looked at me disgusted. "Unlike the Amazing Human Noodle over here, I need somebody with a little weight, a little fucking strength down here." I shrugged.

"You got it," Bert said, and slid feet first into the grave. Junior hopped off the coffin and told me to get back up there. "But this time, sit down, put your back against the wall there and push at it with your feet. Me and Bert'll pull." He positioned Bert at the head of the coffin and stood next to him. I braced my boots against the crowbar, sliding them up under the curve, spread my arms, put my hands flat against the dripping mud behind me and got ready to push. Bert wrapped his left hand around over the curve, over my boots. Then Junior encircled Bert's hand with both of his fists, interlocking his fingers together. "Now, when I give the signal, we're gonna pop this old girl's cherry open so wide she'll need a dildo the size of a fucking tree trunk just to get off." He winked. "And that's a promise."

Maybe it was Bert. Maybe it was my legs, strong from riding Grandma's bike. Maybe the coffin finally just succumbed to Junior's romance. I don't know. But whatever it was, when Junior shrieked, almost in ecstasy, "NOW!" I kicked out as hard as I could, and they jerked backwards on that crowbar. I heard a deep, satisfying crack. The crowbar suddenly flopped over towards the Sawyer brothers, and they tumbled into the mire at the bottom of the grave. I looked down to see a long, ragged crack running between my legs, up towards my ass. This made me vaguely uncomfortable, and I scooted off the top of the coffin right quick.

"That's right, whore. You want it, don't you?" Junior said as he jammed the crowbar back into the crack. "You want it soooooo bad." Another few quick tugs and the crack started to split open even wider. He yanked the crowbar away and jabbed at the opening, chipping away at the surface. After several seconds of this, the thick blade suddenly plunged through the lid, sinking nearly half of the crowbar's length into the crack.

"Yes!" Fat Ernst shouted, clenching both fists.

And suddenly, everything became real, the buckle was close now, close

Jeff Jacobson   167

enough to touch, close enough to smell, close enough to taste. All of our aches and pains and blisters, the rain, the mud, all of it faded into the background, became unimportant. Only one thing mattered now. Junior worked the crowbar around in the crack, slamming it back and forth like a man desperately trying to churn smooth butter out of cheese. The opening got wider and he worked the crowbar down the coffin, trying to crack the lid in half lengthwise.

Then it happened. The whole lid just split right in half. The bottom half wouldn't open much because at least three feet of the coffin was still buried under the wall, but Junior pried open the top half enough that he could force his fingers inside and pull. It swung open with a groan from the mud-caked hinges, but it was open now, by God, a quarter of the lid pried up and waiting.

Nobody said anything. Fat Ernst lowered the lantern down into the hole and Junior grabbed it, held it over the open part of the coffin. Bert stood at the head and I stepped closer, joining Junior along the side of the casket. Junior tilted the lantern sideways to get light into the ruptured coffin. "Huh," he said. "I guess these things leak."

The coffin was full of black water.

"Who gives a fuck?" Fat Ernst hissed down at us, on his knees at the edge of the dyke. His hands kept fluttering around, as if he was a puppeteer, and could control us by manipulating the strings. It didn't work, though, nobody in the grave moved. "Holy fuck, just reach in there and grab it!"

"I ain't sticking my hand in there." I thought this was one of the most intelligent things Junior had ever said.

Fat Ernst nearly had a fit. "If I woulda known that I hired a bunch of pussies…Just reach in there and grab it!" he shouted, high and shrill, with one pudgy finger stabbing violently towards the coffin. "Hey, boy!" The stabbing finger found me. "You. You reach in there and grab it. Do it, and . . . and I'll double your share."

Well, there was no way I was going to stick my hand in there. Fuck that. But before I could say anything, Bert giggled, said, "No big deal," and reached into the black water. His eyes rolled back and crossed as he felt around inside the flooded coffin. "Good job there, Bert. Glad at least one of you has a set of balls," Fat Ernst shouted happily. "Keep going, boy, you'll know when you find it."

Bert pulled his hand out of the coffin, and we all tensed. But he merely inspected a glob of fatty tissue curled in his palm. He rolled it between his thumb and forefinger, sniffed it, decided it wasn't important and flung it away. Then, without hesitation, he plunged his arm back in there, concentration etched into his face.

"Find anything?" Junior asked.

Bert shook his head. "Old Earl didn't make it in here in one piece, did he?" he called up at Fat Ernst.

"No, no, he didn't," Fat Ernst said good naturedly. "Thanks to you knuckleheads, he ended up in the ditch." He chuckled. "He wasn't exactly in the best of shape when they fished him out."

I couldn't help myself and asked, "What's it feel like, Bert?"

He thought hard for a moment, the tip of his tongue sticking out of the corner of his mouth, like a pink, blind animal that's cautiously testing the wind before venturing out of its burrow. "Gooshy," he said finally. He pulled his arm out one more time, but this time he was clutching a black cowboy boot full of water. He tipped the boot up, pouring the water into the grave. "He's…he's all mixed up."

"You just keep going there, Bert. It's in there. I know it."

Bert jammed his arm back into the water, felt around for a minute, then reached in deeper, until he was practically bent over double, water up to his shoulder. He grunted, trying to push his arm farther. His eyes narrowed. "I think I got it!" Bert pulled his arm out of the coffin and sure enough, that gold and diamond belt buckle was clutched in his left hand.

But it was the worms that caught my attention.

Two of them, both as plump as Fat Ernst's cigars, hanging off of his forearm, twisting and undulating, slowly chewing the soft flesh up near the elbow. I don't think Bert actually felt the worms on his skin until he saw them, but when he finally did see them, he freaked. He shrieked, scrambled backwards, kicking away from the coffin, and dropped the buckle into the mud. Junior went after him, trying to help.

"Get the fucking buckle!" Fat Ernst screamed.

While Junior was busy pinning Bert's left arm in the mud and grabbing at the worms, I scuttled over and managed to grab the buckle, a heavy goddamn thing, before Bert's kicking legs drove it even deeper into the muck.

"Oh, thank Christ!" Fat Ernst breathed. "Give it to me." He reached out towards me, leaning closer.

"Little fuckers!" Junior hissed through clenched teeth, a squirming worm between his fingers. He flicked it into the mud and stomped on it.

"Give it to me!" Fat Ernst was really reaching now, still on his knees but leaning way over the edge, stretching his arm out to me. I turned to him, it was an automatic response, like those dogs that started drooling at the sound of a bell, and was holding the buckle out to him when the sound stopped me. At first, I wasn't sure what it was, a deep groaning noise that seemed to come from far away. But then I saw the bulging wall and suddenly understood. I whipped around and had just scrambled up onto the coffin when the whole west side of the grave collapsed, Junior yanking Bert out of the way, Fat Ernst riding the crumbling wall of mud all the way down.

Then a tidal wave of water exploded into the grave and I found myself clawing and kicking at the mud, fighting my way to the east wall. The water swirled and surged up underneath me, lifting me towards the canopy. I kicked out even harder, thrashing and fighting the quicksand muck. Somehow, I managed to grab hold of the dyke and pulled myself out of the rushing, boiling water.

I rolled down the other side, and got twisted around. In the darkness under the canopy, I wasn't sure where I was at first, whether the grave was behind me or in front of me. There was just water. The lantern had been at the bottom of the grave, and was long gone. But then I felt something, looked down, and could just make out a few tired glints from the buckle still clutched in my right hand.

By then, my eyes were starting to get used to the darkness, and I could barely see the canopy, and the surging water where the open grave had been. I heard someone coughing on the other side of the canopy. "Holy Jesus," I heard Fat Ernst say weakly. He coughed again, spitting into the water. I saw his shadow wearily climb onto a faint gray shape in the night—the slab.

I'd been too close to that lantern for too long, and as a result, couldn't see much of anything for a few minutes. But everything was getting clearer now, my night vision was kicking back in. I saw Junior's back as he crawled out of the water and onto the slab. He rolled around on his stomach and peered back into the water. "Bert!" he called out.

I heard vomiting off to my right. Junior scrambled over to that end of the slab and reached out, grabbing Bert by his hair. Fat Ernst suddenly sat up and shouted, "Who's got the buckle? Oh sweet Jesus, one of you fucks please tell me you've got it." Junior pulled Bert onto the slab, pounding on his brother's back. Bert kept vomiting, and I wondered how he'd managed to swallow that much mud.

"Oh fuck, oh fuckohfuck," Fat Ernst started weeping. "Please, please tell me somebody got it."

Bert suddenly jerked, screaming, "It's still there, it's in my fucking arm!" He clawed at his left elbow with his right arm.

"I've got it," I called out. What else could I do? There wasn't much point in keeping the buckle for myself; I had no idea what to do with it. If I gave it to Fat Ernst, at least I had the possibility of getting some cash out of it.

"I've got you, you little fuck," Bert answered. He was holding something in his right hand, peering at it, and I guessed he had managed to pull the worm out of his arm.

"I've got the buckle," I called out again.

"You do? Oh, thank Christ. Give it here. Hurry!"

"Not yet. I want to make a deal first."

"What kind of fucking deal? Just bring it over here, and we'll talk."

"I want a bigger share. Five hundred bucks. That's fair. If this thing's worth ten, fifteen grand, then you can pay me five hundred easy. If you don't think that's fair, then I'll just toss it back into the grave, and you can fight those fucking worms for it." That may have been the longest speech I ever made to Fat Ernst.

"Don't you fucking dare. You stinking . . . all right. Fuck, all right. Five hundred. Just bring it here."

I edged around the grave, staying outside of the canopy. The last thing I needed to do was to fall back into that quicksand nightmare. As I reached the stone slab, Bert whispered quietly, "Oh, shit." He started shaking his right arm, making little whimpering noises.

"What? What is it?" Junior asked.

"I…I think that fucking worm just crawled up my cast," Bert whined. "Oh shit, yes, yes, it fucking did. OH SHIT!" he shrieked, clawing madly at the white plaster.

"Hold on," Junior said, grabbing Bert's arm and taking a closer look.

Fat Ernst sidled over to me, hand out. "OK, boy, you made your point. Five hundred. I won't forget, I promise. Just give it to me."

I handed it over. He smiled and slipped the buckle inside his shirt.

Junior said, "I can't see shit, Bert. You sure it went in there?"

Bert nodded and started to cry, snot running down his muddy face.

"Gentlemen, I suggest we get the hell out of this fucking cemetery. I'm going to clean up, and then I'll head to Sacramento in the morning," Fat Ernst said, drawing himself up to his full height. He nodded, "You fellas did a good job here."

Junior gently wiped Bert's face with the tail of his shirt. "Come on, Bert, let's go home. Get you some more tranquilizers." Then he wiped away some of the blood on his own face.

We splashed back through the long shadows of the headstones thrown by the headlights, abandoning the pump, the shovels, and the lantern. The rain was still coming down hard, but it felt good as the water slowly washed away the mud and grit off my skin. Fat Ernst didn't say anything, just took off immediately, roaring away back through the walnut orchards. Junior helped Bert into the truck and paused long enough to reel the extension cord back in. Then they too were gone, leaving me alone in the darkness and rain.

But I didn't mind walking home. Like I said, the rain felt good on my skin. Clean, somehow. And as I walked, I had plenty of time to think about those goddamn worms.

The Wall

CYNTHIA LITTS

I got home ten minutes early, traffic actually moving for a change. My wife, Eleanor, was in the first room, the living room, her back to me. As soon as I shut our heavy oak front door behind me with a muffled thud, her thin arms flung up and over her head like she was making a quick snow angel. That's when I noticed the wall of furniture stretching across our huge living room right in front of her. It stood stacked all the way up to the cathedral ceiling, and the only way to get around to the back of the room or to anywhere else in the house was a foot-wide aisle Eleanor left on the side where the hallway met the room. You could say the wall of stuff looked a bit out of place, as if someone dropped Mount Everest on my driveway. I saw something start to fall within the wall just above her head and rushed behind her, reached up past her hands, her wedding ring clicking against mine, to hold our oldest piece of furniture—a hunter green love seat—in its place, *its place* now being perched at a forty-five degree angle on top of the bedroom TV and the partially dismantled jungle gym of the cedar patio furniture.

"We're really doing this?" I exhaled on the back of her head. I admit I had forgotten about her idea right after she told me this morning. *We'll split everything ourselves*, she had said, swinging both her forearms—palms up—down and up like a pair of bobbing hammers just to emphasize every word, *we'll save money on lawyers, just take turns picking what we want the most.* This wasn't the first time she'd had these hare-brained ideas, but not about separating, and this was the first time she had actually followed through. I had figured she was mad because I left my wet towel on the bathroom floor. But now I sensed things were getting serious.

"Why?" I asked, both this morning and now, and instead of answering she just started humming the theme to *Three's Company.* I still stood with my hands above my head, holding the loveseat in place, so I shoved it more securely into the pile, where I felt it sink in against something soft and unseen further inside the pile. We had a lot of stuff. I felt my chest push against Eleanor's shoulder blades and my chin settle on the top of her head, her long individual black hair strands tickling my nose. "Think I'd do this for my health?" she asked. She tilted her head back so I could see the kidney-shaped freckle at her left temple, her short eyelashes, the slope of her nose, the glossy corners of her lips. She kissed my neck where my throat and jaw meet, her mouth warm and soft, then started humming again, her whole head vibrating against my neck; I stepped away and looked back up at the wall.

A lot more than furniture sat in there. "Where are the kids?" I expected at school still, or with friends. Then at least they wouldn't have to see us like this. The wall loomed like a giant, threatening to fall over on us. Its sides stood steep, compact and deep. I imagined it was hollow inside, and if I could find the entrance I could live comfortably in it like an Eskimo in an igloo.

Everything either one of us owned was tucked in somewhere. Clothes still on hangers, boxes and boxes of little unicorn figurines and *Precious Moments*, a video rack, some books that were thrown off bookcases and lying awkwardly near the bottom of the wall, a few half-open against the bindings of others, towels still folded on top of the books but wedged underneath the oak nightstand, cream curtains covering an old drum set, the drumsticks pitching the curtains into a teepee. If I were to squint, it would look like a giant's patchwork quilt, filled with patches of odd color—only with no obvious pattern—crumpled and thrown on the floor.

I ducked my head into the hallway and looked down the hall, then into the kitchen. The rest of the house seemed freshly built, not yet lived in. All the lights were off, as if the electricity wasn't turned on yet, and the sunlight poured red into the large front windows, casting stark grid shadows and fiery colors against the opposite wall of the hallway.

"In here somewhere," she told me. I had forgotten what question she was answering. Eleanor waved her arm and pointed to a spot in the wall, and I noticed she had on all her jewelry. *All* her jewelry, and it's all good expensive shit, mind you; I bought most of it myself. She was cheating. I knew I should say something. Shouldn't we, like, start out naked or something? I thought. To make it even? I just had the clothes on my back, but here she was giving herself a head start. Her wrists jangled with a pound of bracelets, gold, silver, or twinkling with diamonds; her pierced earlobes hung low with the weight of a half-dozen earrings strung through single holes, and hidden under her T-shirt must've been all her necklaces, for around her neck, bulging against her collar-bone, I could see what looked like a frayed rope noose.

I looked where she pointed, spotted movement in the wall, and the teenaged manicured hand of our eldest weaved out between the legs of a folding chair and into a little wood box and pulled out the spare keys to the brand-new BMW. I cringed.

"Who goes first?" I asked.

"Well." She stood slumped and looked at me hard. "You do realize, of course, a gentleman would let the lady go first."

The corner of my mouth raised into an involuntary smirk at her sarcasm. I loved it, had always loved it when she pushed on with that sharp tongue of hers. Then I frowned at her. This was, after all, serious business. Don't laugh it up with the enemy, I told myself. I swept my eyes over the whole wall, looking for the elegant groom and bride figures that had graced our wedding cake. They at least *looked* like a gentleman and a lady. "Well, neither of those around, I guess we'll have to flip a coin."

I put my hand to my face to pull the corners of my mouth down. It wasn't funny; this was, after all, war. No fraternizing. This was no person standing before me, this was an object for contempt. I stood in the most military and unemotional way I could.

I had a nickel in my khaki pants, and I tossed it into the air, holding it between my thumb and forefinger and, using my whole arm, drew my hand up my torso, keeping it close to my body, up past my head, and opened my fingers with an audible *pop*.

The coin hit the top of the ceiling, scraped off a fingernail-sized chip of peach paint in the center of the high slope, leaving barely a mark on the ceiling, for the ceiling underneath the paint was the same color. The nickel somersaulted back down my palm, the curl of peach paint spiraling down behind it like a willow leaf, almost getting snagged by a purple feather duster poking out of the wall. I closed my fist tight.

"Call it."

"Tails."

I opened my coin hand against the back of my other hand. The coin seemed partially stuck to my skin as I lifted one hand off. The nickel sat upright on top of a vein for three seconds before flopping onto its side.

"Sorry, hon. Heads it is." I smiled.

"Cheater. You know if your hands weren't so clammy it would've been tails." Eleanor shifted her weight to thrust a sweatpant-clad hip out into a pout, then crossed her arms in front of her. The front of her T-shirt pushed itself forward and swelled into two perfectly rounded flesh distractions. I sighed. Would I ever see those again? Oh, were I a piece of cotton coating her body, those slight muscles under pale flesh that was always warm to the touch.

"Fine," I inhaled and drew my eyes towards the ceiling, noting the almost invisible pockmark where the paint had chipped off. "You go ahead and go first." I watched her scoot sideways past the new wall, snagging her sleeve momentarily on a long blue wooden planter filled with marigolds. It had been in the backyard. She pivoted in the block of space next to the wall that was still kind of living room but almost hallway, then disappeared to the other side of our wall of stuff. This wall was the snow fort children would build for snowball fights, only me and my adversary shared the same one in this case. Her side was apparently the back of the living room and so, apparently, mine was the front. We would each form our own piles.

I barely sat down on my side, a narrow sidewalk-width aisle, when I heard a clink-clunk, like something of thin metal striking wood. The wall didn't seem to get any smaller. I wondered what she took first. She must have had a plan. I pictured her in the darkness caused by the shadow of the wall where she sat with a list, put a line through the first obtained item with the same kind of smirk she always got when she had just gotten away with something. Maybe even a little evil giggle. I noticed the whole house seemed very quiet. "El?" I asked.

"OK." Her voice sounded strained and breathy, like she'd just won a marathon. "Yeah, you go ahead."

What did I want? I shrugged. Nothing really appealed to me anymore. My heart sank; what I wanted wasn't in the wall, but just beyond it. I studied the wall; I knew there was something important, vital to my well-being. Something I must take, at all costs, just to live on. I just couldn't think of what it was. It was like I'd just raced to the airport to catch a flight, only to forget my ticket at home. What did I need to survive in this world without Eleanor?

I took my coffee mug and looked at the brown dried stains at the bottom, like a tobacco-stained smiley face. "Your turn." I placed my new possession carefully on the staple-scarred wood floor that had been freshly revealed since our beige carpeting lay rolled like a giant sleeping bag pushed against the clear glass of our aquarium tucked in the wall. I sat where the wide-screen TV used to sit, just to the side of the front door. There were no windows directly behind me, but windows just to the right illuminated the entire wall except for the section just in front of me.

A *ca-chunk* from the other side. The wall shifted, but remained the same size. I heard her call my turn. Now what? I saw something shiny and blue sticking out like a dead man's tongue, a silken pair of her panties, and took those, carefully working them out from between a video, *Young Frankenstein,* and a book, *The Sound and the Fury,* by tugging gently first on the waistband, then on the crotch. It was kind of like flossing a whale's teeth with, well, women's underwear. I held them hooked on my pinkie finger. Wouldn't it have made sense to just put what belonged to *both* of us in there? Then I noticed I had bought these for her, years ago during that cutesy newlywed phase when we'd talk baby talk to each other in grocery stores and restaurants. My stomach lurched. These panties were partly mine (not that I'd ever wear them), in a way a part of us. Was there anything we owned individually? I had brought the collection of books, but she's the one who read them, she had brought that ugly love seat, but it was my favorite place to sit lately. The kids? I looked for my son and daughter and saw my son at least, six feet up the wall, sitting in an open, upright footlocker, with a cordless phone affixed to the left side of his face, asking someone for the answers to math homework. Half the genes were Eleanor's. At least half.

I looked at my cup with a sudden pride. *My* cup and mine alone. In a bold navy blue font, all caps, the mug told me, "SILVERSTEIN AND MASTERSON: LOOKING OUT FOR YOU." I got it at work, at *my* job. Of course there was something unseen about the outside ridge that made it dribble hot coffee down my shirt every morning. But it wasn't like it was a bad cup.

Eleanor did the dishes, has always washed this, so in a way, it's hers too. I rolled my eyes, that at least explained the smiley stain. I scanned the wall, looking for something exclusively mine, but everything had *Eleanor* etched into it. My desk, right in front of me, had carved into the soft pine on one of its front legs her name. I looked closer, brushing a paisley scarf out of the way; my name, *Anthony* had been etched first, then over mine hers was gouged in bold letters. The aquarium held glimmering scratches forming her name over something else written in pencil.

Her turn, but this time I was certain she took out something big; the wall started to lower down an inch or so. I took an apple one turn, then a work shirt, then my mountain-climbing harness, then a bag of peppermint candies, then my grappling iron. With her turns the wall shrank quickly, and the room grew hotter each time the wall moved, as if her body radiated some sort of sun-heat as she struggled with everything big, heavy, and expensive that was becoming hers. I started to sweat and took off my work clothes, putting them into my pile but wondering if they should count as a turn, but then I figured she had all her jewelry on. I wasn't bitter. I waited for her battle cry of "You go!" which sounded more like a cheap car than a command coming out of her mouth.

Then I noticed the only thing I could possibly want, at the top—a picture of us. I could at least own the memories once she was gone from me. I saw it in a pewter frame, propped up against a pile of papers I knew came from our safe deposit box: birth certificates, insurance papers, bonds, marriage certificate. She could have them, including the birth certificate with my name on it, even that didn't really belong to me anymore. Even from down on the floor, I knew her name was on it somewhere, tainting it as it sat between papers about and touched by her.

I strapped my mountain-climbing harness on over my gray boxers and graying T-shirt (she had done the laundry too), tossed a grappling iron, its three metal talons gleaming, up and barely over the wall, the nylon rope trailing behind like a yellow snake. The hooks struck our jukebox and latched into its golden hard plastic casing with a penetrating squeal as I tugged at the rope. I chuckled. Hell, she could have the jukebox now too.

I climbed my way up gingerly, pulling myself hand-over-hand by the rope. I was barefoot and gaining awkward footholds on the back of a kitchen chair, the top of a computer monitor, a bulletin board with thumb tacks still in it, a CD rack shaped like a climbing lizard with its tongue sticking out like mine probably was, and a partially-thawed pot roast still in cellophane, which squished a little under my heel. And then I was at the top.

I straddled the jukebox and grasped the picture. It was of the four of us on our last vacation. My arm was around her sunburned shoulder, the two kids in front: smiling gap-toothed boy who looked just like a boy version of Eleanor, and a teenage girl, lipstick too bright a shade of red and her grin so wide you could see her neon green gum clamped between her molars. This was happiness. Both kids were still in the pile, I remembered. I wondered if I should take one of them next, but if everything else was marked *Eleanor*, they had it tattooed all over them since birth.

Eleanor's hair had changed already from this picture, taken just a few months ago. She's since straightened out the waves that curled towards me in the photo. We were both smiling too. This picture was mine, it had to be. But in the corner, almost covered by the frame, someone had scraped *Eleanor* into the colored finish of the photo. I looked around from my perch and noticed I could see all the way down the hallway and into the kitchen, the shadows not stark anymore since everything was starting to get dark. And I could see Eleanor too.

She sat cross-legged on the floor where, if it were yesterday, the sofa would sit covering a tomato-sauce stain left by our daughter when she was a three-year-old attempting to master the art of eating mostaccioli. Eleanor's head bowed down as if in prayer, or more likely because of the weight of her earrings. But she was looking at the clipboard in her hands. The clipboard held a list which had some things crossed off in green marker. She looked up at the wall, but not far up enough to see me, her face pale against her dark hair, her eyes glittering in the gray darkness as she searched for something, probably the next item on her list. Maybe she'd go for the kids. I looked at the items she had already obtained: the armoire, the car, the washing machine, the bed, and the stereo system. It was actually two piles she was forming, one on either side of her. They were all boxing her in, with only a foot of space between where the wall ended and the piles began. The car was on its side, its greasy underbelly facing me.

My pile paled in comparison. I put the tainted photo down and its frame clanked against my still-embedded grappling iron.

She looked up at the sound, at me, then suddenly jumped up and leaped to the shorter pile, to the bed, and stood in front of it, wedged between wall and pile, with her arms crossed in front of her chest like a bouncer, but she stared at me wide-eyed, panic in her open-mouthed face. Something on the bed caught my eye. Two shallow scorched star-shaped metal cups—almost like cookie cutters—sat joined by a small hinge at one end, with long wooden handles attached to the other ends. It looked foreign, but familiar. It reminded me of my mother in that vague way that the swirl of cream into coffee in the morning reminds you of a dream you had the night before, not enough to remember the dream itself, just that it had been dreamt. It looked like a doubled magic wand with a star at the end, the kind children would carry on Halloween in one hand, while holding a pillowcase of treats in the other. *Eleanor* was etched nowhere on it. But it might soon be.

"My pizzelle iron! That's mine!" And it was. My mother had given it to me in her will. My mother's dying wish, years before I had even met Eleanor, had been for me to own her precious cookie-maker. Probably out of spite; Momma knew I'd never use it, I don't make cookies, Italian or not. I remembered Momma standing in the kitchen, holding the pizzelle iron, though I knew it only from her stance, since her wide, apron-encased rear blocked my sight. The white, late-morning sunlight poured in generously through the open window, and the promise of fresh cookies wasn't in anything Momma said, but in the scent of anise wafting through the air.

Eleanor smiled, not very widely, and it never actually reached her eyes. "I picked it first. Mine now." Her smile shrank back, disappeared completely, and I knew it wasn't coincidence that she had selected the one thing of mine that had never been hers. And then I knew that *that* was why she wanted it. I knew she had taken it first, had placed it within easy reach when she built the wall so her first and most important move in this pile game we played would take this one thing that was solely me and not us. She only wanted us to split so she could get her greedy hands on my pizzelle iron.

Something in my chest grew suddenly hot, like my insides were melting, and I knew I should give up on this, let her have it. I sensed if I did let her keep it, or even engrave her name, we could go back to sharing the rest. Had I been withholding my pizzelle on purpose?

"I want it back," I said instead, through clenched teeth. I leapt off the jukebox, grabbing the picture to use as a weapon against her if need be, and shouting a Tarzan war cry.

The grappling iron was still hooked into the jukebox. I got stuck part way down, almost on top of her; the rope had apparently hooked on something on my side of the wall, shortening it considerably. I hung, my feet tapping the wall gently behind me, just above her crouched body as she anxiously stepped back from me, blocked by the living room wall behind her, our wall in front, her piles on each side and my body above. Her mouth worked like there was a bug inside.

My arms stretched out to get my balance, like I was body surfing. I kicked my feet, trying to swim down towards her. My harness still kept me hanging horizontally.

She slipped just under me onto the bed and out of reach. "What's it worth to you?" She smiled and picked up my pizzelle iron, dangling it in front of me like it was a carrot and I was the donkey.

"What do you want for it?" I tried to sound casual, even while knowing the front of my boxers was probably hanging open.

"Everything."

"What do you mean everything?"

Eleanor swept her hand to the wall like Vanna White on a perky night. I knew she meant everything already in my pile too. I'd miss my mug, but I'd be getting the better end of the deal. Everything else was hers anyway.

"OK," I said, handing her the picture. I felt a hundred pounds lighter.

She unclipped the harness and let me drop gently onto her floor with a slap, then she kissed me on the cheek like a good little boy. I took the pizzelle iron from her hands like I was being given the key to the city and cradled it like I would a crying child. I stole some bits of flour, anise, powdered sugar and vanilla from the wall, Eleanor allowed me that much, and I slid past one of her piles into her kitchen to mix me up some batter for a couple cookies, humming to myself as she moved each piece of our wall to her own personal pile. The pizzelle was crisper than my mother made, some would call it burnt, but it tasted of pure sweetness.

Papp's Tavern

DENNIS FOLEY

The front door's open when we get to Papp's Tavern, and the Hamm's sign above the door is lit up like a movie star's teeth. The front windows are covered over with a blue paint that you can't see through, not even if you tried starin' through it for ten years. Dad pushes through the front door and sits down at his stool. That's right, "his" stool.

He's a regular at Papp's, and all the regulars mark their stools. Mom says Dad and the others are like dogs that way. I jump up on the stool next to Dad, set my mitt and ball on top of the bar, and look around. Mr. Dunleavy, Mr. O'Brien, and Mr. Sheehy are already in the bar. They give my dad a wave. He waves back. None of them brought their kids with today. When they do, we kids usually get into some good wrestling matches. None of us mind rollin' around the bar floor in the beer puddles and dirt. And the barmen love it. It's like they're bettin' on the winner. I look around some more. Mr. Lassandrello isn't here. Good. No problems today.

Mr. Papp sets a bottle of Old Style, an empty 8-ounce shorty glass, and a shot of whiskey in front of my dad. It's V.O. Whiskey. I know my letters from school, and that's the kinda whiskey my dad likes.

"Thanks, Fred." My father downs the shot. He pours his beer into the shorty and looks at me. I smile a stupid smile and twist back and forth on my stool. "Hey, Fred, you forgot the kid."

"Righhhhhht," Mr. Papp says. He grabs a small bottle of Pepsi from the cooler, cracks off the cap, and sets it in front of me. Mr. Papp places both hands on the bar top and stoops down to my eye level. "How's young Master Timothy doing today. Sir?" he says in a Fancy-Dan kinda voice. My dad snorts out a laugh and finishes his shorty. Mr. Papp watches him fill his glass. "Can I do it to 'im, Jack?" My dad slurps more from the shorty. "Can I?" Mr. Papp again asks. My father nods his head. Mr. Papp stands straight up, a wide smile on his face. He's tall and skinny and the white apron he's wearin' over his white shirt matches the white of his teeth and makes him look like a huge glow-in-the-dark toy. I know what's comin'. We play this game every Saturday. Sometimes, Mr. Papp asks for my dad's permission, and sometimes he don't. Mr. Papp digs his right index-finger into his right eye and plucks it from its socket. He sets the glass eye on the bar top next to me. "Don't go getting into any trouble now, Master Timothy," he says in that same Fancy-Dan kinda way. "I'll be watching you." I can stare at that fake eyeball all day long. I know it isn't real. What I can't do, though, is look at the empty eye socket on Mr. Papp's face. I looked at it once, just once. It was red and raw and kinda dark, like someone stuffed some half-cooked hamburger meat in there. I threw up when I looked that time, and that made my dad and the other barmen laugh their butts off. I learned to wait until Mr. Papp had enough time to slip the black patch over his eye. I usually count to twenty-five. Sometimes my dad whispers, "He put the patch on." Today I count to twenty-five, and when I look up Mr. Papp is standing in front of Mr. Dunleavy, and the patch is in place.

"The Pirate." That's what my mom calls Mr. Papp. She doesn't care much for him. "The Pirate steals food from the mouths of the young," she says, "and turns it into whiskey for their fathers to drink and forget." I've been coming to Papp's Tavern with my dad for about a year now. I know why I'm here. I might only be eight years old, but I'm not as dumb as you might think. Actually, my mom told me why I hafta go with my dad. She says things to me that I don't think she says to my brothers. "Just stay with him, be with him, and that way he won't forget any of us." I'm a permanent reminder for my dad that he has a wife and kids who need things, like food, at home. I am here to remind him that he better have some money in his pocket when we leave Mr. Papp.

Whenever Mom asks me what goes on at Papp's, I always lie. "Nuthin'," I tell her and then I keep on lyin' by tellin' her that I don't like the place much at all. Truth is, those are major lies 'cause I like everything about Papp's Tavern.

Mr. Papp's place always smells like stale beer no matter how many times he drags that old mop of his across the wooden floor. I love that smell. The mirror behind the bar goes on forever. No matter where I'm at in the bar, I can always find my freckled face starin' back at me. I like to watch smoke fly outta the mouths of the drinking men and climb to the tin ceiling where it hangs like a buncha dirty clouds. You should see Mr. Papp clean the shorty glasses and shot glasses. He runs hot water through 'em, shoves a towel inside 'em, and smushes the towel around 'til the glasses are both dry and clean. It only takes Mr. Papp five seconds to clean and dry a glass. I timed him before. Once the glasses are clean, Mr. Papp sets 'em back on the bar top where they stand in line and wait their turn to be used again.

Now I know I'm a munchkin but still I feel like one of the guys when I'm at Papp's. The other men always make a point to say hello to me, pinch my cheek, pat me on the back, or say somethin' about my red hair. My dad lets me drink Pepsi 'til my belly's set to burst, I get to play the bowling-ball machine, and I get to see a few good fights, too. The best was when Mr. Sheehy and Mr. Everett got into it. Mr. Everett's a little guy with a pointy red beard. He looks like the Lucky Charms leprechaun. And Mr. Sheehy's as big as John Wayne. Anyway, Mr. Sheehy was pounding the stuffins outta Mr. Everett. He knocked him to the floor at least three times. Mr. Everett wouldn't quit, though. He kept wipin' the blood from his mouth and gettin' back on his feet. When he was on the ground the last time, Mr. Sheehy said in his thick brogue, "Listen, ya little squirt, just stay down there like the dog ya are." The bar men all laughed. Mr. Sheehy took his eyes offa Mr. Everett and laughed with all the others. That was a big mistake. From his knees, Mr. Everett slammed his fist into Mr. Sheehy's crotch. "Ooohh," all the bar men said at the same time. And that made me think of David and Goliath, the Bible guys that we were studying in school at the time. Well, Goliath grabbed his marbles and fell with a big thud to the floor. He stayed there a good, long while, with his hands in his pants, fixing himself in all the right places. About an hour later though, the two men were drinking together, and Mr. Sheehy even thanked Mr. Everett for sockin' him in the jewels. He said, "Actually, Everett, it should be me Missus who should be thankin' ya. You've found an effective means of birth control for the Irish." I didn't quite know what that meant at the time, but I do know that enemies don't stay enemies very long at Papp's.

Mostly, though, I like being at Papp's 'cause I get to be with my dad, all by myself. Most times he doesn't say much to me, but sometimes he answers my questions. He talks to me about the Cubs a bunch. They're his favorite team. But he's not much help when I hit him with my homework questions. "Ask yer mother" is what he says then. Either way, I really don't care. I just wanna be with him. I like watchin' my dad wipe the beer foam from his mouth after taking a long gulp from his shorty. He likes to shoot cigarette smoke at the ceiling, too. Sometimes, when he knows I'm watchin', he'll blow little chunks of smoke from his mouth that form perfect tiny rings that could fit around your finger. The rings grow and grow as they rise, and they always fall apart just before they get a chance to bang into the ceiling. Mom doesn't like what Dad does with his cigarette ashes, though. Ashtrays are everywhere at Papp's, but my father has no use for 'em. When he drinks, he sits with his back pushed into the back support and his right leg crossed over his left. He always flicks his ashes into the cuff of his right pants leg, and he always wears cuffed pants. My mom's the one who gets stuck cleaning those cuffed pants.

My older brothers used to come with my dad to the tavern, but they don't come anymore. I don't know why. Whenever I ask them why, they never answer. I think they're stupid. They're missin' out on a lot. I think ya get kinda stupid sometimes when ya get older. Sometimes I even get to come with my dad on Wednesdays. Those are his two big days, Saturdays and Wednesdays, but Saturday is definitely the biggest.

Dad drinks lotsa shots and beers as the day passes. He smokes and joins in manly chitchat, too. The day goes along smoothly, mostly 'cause Mr. Lassandrello doesn't show up. Thank God for that. This Saturday ends like most other Saturdays. At 5:00, Mr. Papp tells us to go home. He knows our schedule.

"I'll be taking me eye back now, Master Timothy," Mr. Papp says. "You've been a fine wee lad, today. Now, get goin' before the real master throws your supper out the window." Mr. Papp grabs his eye from the bar top as my dad and I head out the door. I don't watch him stuff it back in place. Mr. Papp's right. It is indeed suppertime. Ah yes, Saturday suppertime. Stew night. I'm ready for it. I flip the ball into the sky over and over again as we walk home, catching it each time with my mitt. Sometimes, I don't get to toss the ball on the walk home, but my dad doesn't need to lean on me tonight.

Fred

DAR HADDIX

The very first week I worked night reception at Pleasant Manor, I let one of them escape. It was a miserable night, freezing cold with rain pouring down, and I hadn't even wanted to come in at all, but this was a good job and I wanted to keep it, *bad*. I didn't want to be one of those girls working at Burger Hut for $5.32 an hour, coming home with grease burns on my fingers. After I got my degree I could do whatever the hell I wanted, like get a job someplace where it never fell below fifty degrees.

It was cold in the front office too, and I drank about a gallon of coffee like a fool, *knowing* it was impossible for me to go to the bathroom with an army of Alzheimer's patients ready to run out the door. Besides, this wasn't some government-funded dump, this was a ritzy place, a private Jewish nursing home on Chicago's North Shore, and they didn't tolerate any crap. What if some paranoid relative popped in unexpectedly, accused me of negligence, and got me fired? But I had to go, *had to*, and I was only in the bathroom for thirty seconds, but blind, fat old Fred managed to stagger past the motion detector without setting it off. God knows why he did it, he didn't have anywhere to go, but he went anyway, straight out the door to the street, which like most busy streets in the suburbs was practically a highway. The nurses had been bullshitting at the other end of the hall all night, a hundred feet away, too lazy to come watch the door for a second so the old geezers couldn't run off, and how was I supposed to hold it for four hours? I wasn't a goddamn coffee machine, dispensing a cup or two of liquid whenever I chose.

I had been back at my desk for a half hour, trying to finish an essay on Tolstoy for Russian Lit, when the doorbell rang. I stood up, peering into the outer lobby through the narrow window next to the office, and saw a middle-aged couple in matching London Fog trench coats half-dragging Fred through the front door. God, he looked terrible, like he'd just been mugged and thrown into a ditch, and it was all my fault. Shirt and double-knit pants muddy and soaking wet, thin white hair sticking up around his bald spot, bad eye spinning in his head like a blue marble, the other one looking everywhere and nowhere. The only thing I could think of at that moment was the cover of a certain book I'd seen. It was black and written on it in capital letters two inches high was the title: YOU ARE GOING TO PRISON.

"Oh my god, oh my god," I whimpered and ran back and forth in my little shoebox office as the husband, who was a pretty big guy, yanked open one of the double doors to the main lobby, and the wife held the door and gnawed on her lower lip as the guy carefully guided Fred in.

"Easy does it, fella." But there was no easy doing anything with Fred, and he tripped over the doorjamb.

"Jesus H. Christ!" I screeched, and the woman screamed, too, as Fred collapsed, lurching across the lobby like Frankenstein. He took two big bow-legged steps and grabbed onto a branch of the potted tree in the corner to keep himself from falling, but the tree was way too skinny, and as he dragged it down I heard him suck in air as the top flattened him like a flyswatter. The roots came right out of the pot, flinging clods into the air, and the rest of the dirt scattered across the lobby.

The couple had ducked into opposite corners to avoid the tree and I thought they'd leave, but they insisted on helping me haul Fred up, each gripping one of his arms at the shoulder, me helping the wife hold up her end while I screamed for the nurse, listening for the squeak-squeak of clunky rubber-soled shoes as one of them ran down here to take control of this mess.

"We saw him walking down the road, walking like he was drunk—then he fell—we saw the sign and thought he belonged here," the woman went on and on. Her mascara was running, and her red lipstick was smeared across her mouth like someone had slapped her. She was about four feet nine inches with a big butt, and I wanted to spin her around and punt her out the door like a football. I didn't want to hear anything she was saying, any of it. What difference would it make?

"Hold him," I said, and ran out into the hall. Not one of those bitches had moved! "RITA!" I screamed this time, singling one out so she left the herd and came running, but with a sour look on her face. I looked back into the lobby at the couple and saw the wife with both hands on Fred's chest bracing him against the wall. The husband was kneeling in the dirt and gripping Fred's ankle with both hands the way a doctor would. Great, I thought, another injury to add to the list. The wife was built like a bulldog, with more than enough strength to hold Fred up, but she was really digging her heels into the rug, pressing him against the wall, and I hoped she had the sense to give him room to breathe.

"Rachel, it's useless; I can't get it, he won't move." The husband let go of Fred's ankle, sat back and yanked a bobby pin out of his hair, and I saw the yarmulke stuck under Fred's big black clodhopper, and if he wore a yarmulke that meant he was Jewish and I was really screwed. I looked behind me at the tree Fred had just killed, at the huge hole in my nylons, tried to wipe some of Fred's mud off my dress and thought, oh yeah, this must look REAL good. *One* hysterical scream should've been quite enough to get the whole bunch up here, and this couple, this *Jewish* couple, who has just rescued a senile *Jewish* escapee from a *Jewish* nursing home because of its brand-new, incompetent, *non*-Jewish receptionist—has to see this shit. I knew it would be in all the papers tomorrow, and my ass would be out of a job; the nurses would gang up and somehow convince Edie, my boss, it was all my fault.

Rita stalked up, cheap earrings jangling, stethoscope and reddish-brown hair bouncing off her scrubs with every step, and seized Fred by his unwilling, eighty-three-year-old arm. She looked like a little policewoman trying to steer some nut toward the paddy wagon.

"Thanks," she snapped, supporting Fred as he tottered away down the hall drooling and left the couple standing there with me, their drenched career clothing adding water to the puddle Fred had left in the middle of the green lobby carpet. The husband picked up his soggy yarmulke with two fingers and wrapped it in tissues; then they both turned toward me like confused little kids. What the hell could I say? They actually seemed like nice, reasonable people. Maybe I could explain myself, tell them how I was a brilliant, dedicated student and played rummy with Fred all the time, which was a big lie.

But I was too freaked out to lie. "I—I," I stuttered, and then suddenly Rita was back in the doorway behind them without Fred; God knows where she'd stashed him. In a flash, she glared, pointed at the couple, and put a finger up against her lips.

"Thanks," I repeated briskly to the couple, taking Rita's cue as she ducked behind the counter at the nurses' station like someone was shooting at her, and hustled the rescue squad out to their car. The woman turned and looked at me.

"He reminds me of my Uncle Moishe. It would have been terrible, him to die alone on a night like this." I saw that she hadn't been thinking along the lines of a lawsuit at all, but I wasn't taking any chances.

"Yes, it's a bad night, terrible," I said firmly, giving her a little push toward the Lexus. It must've been nice and warm in there—the windows were all steamed up. "You should be getting home."

Rita jumped out as soon as I got back inside.

"Thank God you're not an idiot. If you'd said anything to them, we'd all be screwed."

I stopped sobbing for a second. "*We* would?" I noticed for the first time how gray her roots were.

"Hell, yes, we would! I'd be holding my kid's *bar mitzvah* at a rest stop on the highway if I lost this job, God forbid."

"So is he dead?" Marie got right to the point, scrubbing pea soup off her pink smock with dry, then wet, towels, until there was nothing but a damp spot. The fat little corkscrew curls all over her head wagged like fingers as she worked.

"No, actually, Rita said he was going to be fine." We were hanging out, leaning against the high beige wall of the nurses' station and talking about what had happened to Fred last week, even though I didn't want to talk about it, let alone think about it, because it made me feel sick whenever I did, and it only fine-tuned the already stomach-turning nightmares I was having. If you mention something like that to people, they always speculate on what could've happened and add fuel to the fire. See, if I dreamt that I came to work and found Fred rotting like roadkill on the side of the road Monday, Tuesday, and Wednesday night, and I brought up the incident on Thursday morning, Thursday night I'd find him again, but this time he'd open his eyes and sit up, pus would come out of his eyeballs, I'd run to my car, the car wouldn't start, then I'd hear a thump and look in my rearview mirror to see that he had jumped up on the trunk of my car so he could drag me out and eat my brain, et cetera, et cetera.

I thought the dreams would stop if Rita told me once and for all that Fred was all right. I wanted to be waiting with flowers and a big bowl of chocolate pudding when they brought him back, but she'd already dragged me outside the other day while she had a cigarette and told me to leave it alone.

"Forget about it! He'll be there for a few days, then he'll come back. They know he don't have any family asking how he's doing, and it's gonna look funny if I keep calling. All nurses talk, and if they talk, they're gonna get suspicious, and then there's gonna be a phone call and a whole bunch of trouble. They'll be like, 'How did he get the tar on his pants? How did he get all wet and muddy? Was he outside?' Trust me, hon, I know ya feel bad, but it's not worth it." It was true, no one was going to pay my rent but me, and that was a fact, so I better keep a job that's going to pay it.

But today those things weren't on my mind. It was Saturday; the place was dead; my boss wasn't there to invent something for me to do; it was a beautiful spring morning, and I wasn't going to jail. Who the hell wouldn't feel perked up just knowing that?

Beatrice glared at us from where she sat belted into her wheelchair, her big black eyes narrowed, tensing her bony body like a German shepherd poised for attack. Chunks of chin-length stringy gray hair swung like ropes as she swiveled her head on her neck, picking at the sores on the back of her hands left over from her latest IVs and watching us talk.

"Nah, they just sent Fred to the ER for observation to play it safe. They found a big knot on the back of his head and don't want to take any chances. She said he could've died in his sleep from concussion—you know with that crazy eye, they can't tell if one pupil is bigger than the other. Fred's gonna be just fine." The more I said it, the more I believed it and the better I felt, so I said it again. "Fred's gonna be just fine."

"That's good. He *do* get on my nerves, but least only thing he do is smear his shit on de wall sometimes. Now, *this one*," Marie snarled jokingly, pointing at Bea to piss her off, "I going to kill."

Marie picked Bea's bowl up off the tile from where it had landed after she slapped it out of Marie's hand. Bea growled, baring her dentures and tightening her little claws on the wheelchair handles. With those big black eyes, she looked like a rabid squirrel. Marie rolled her eyes, leaned over, and peeled Bea's bread-and-butter off the floor. She dangled it in front of Bea.

"You would eat this ef you was in Haiti, crazy woman." Marie was from Haiti and said *Haiti* the way Hawaiians say *Hawaii*, her voice catching in the middle of the word. This was a Jewish home, but there were just as many Haitians working here as Jews, and they were all related somehow, everyone someone's uncle or second cousin. The patients would talk Yiddish, the nurses would talk Yinglish, the Haitians would talk Creole; the Haitians were Catholic, the Jews were Jewish; the Haitians went to church, the Jews went to temple. I didn't go to anything except school, and the only way my boyfriend celebrated his Jewishness was by not eating ham, which he hated anyway.

"Do you know what de government do to crazy people in Haiti?" Marie smiled in her sneaky way as she fanned her wet shirt with a newspaper. I knew what kind of story this would be, and she had the right look to tell that kind of story, too. She had a bony face with tiny features that hardly moved, like a mask, and liked to talk about zombies and funerals and ghosts. So I shook my head no—I didn't know what Haiti did to crazy people—and prayed that the phone wouldn't ring. I had quickly learned to put everything on hold if at all possible to hear Marie tell one of her stories.

"Dey let them all loose in this big field, miles and miles of field, with a big tall fence around it."

"All the crazy people together, in one field? With one fence? Even the criminals? It's an electric fence, right?"

Marie leaned over and shrieked with laughter. It ricocheted off all the hard, shiny walls and tiles in the hallway. Two old couples, playing bridge in the corner of the sunny atrium off to the right, turned around in their wheelchairs and glared past the hanging plants and potted palms at us. One of them, Phil, who had been an Amoco exec for years and went into Edie's office at least once a week to tell her we should all be fired, slapped the table with his spotty hand and barked, "Hey! Keep it down out there! We're trying to concentrate!"

Marie ignored him. "No-o, honey, it ain't no electric fence. Crazy people don't know no better than that. Dey just keep on walking back to grab de fence, get a shock, fall down, and go at de fence again. Ef de whole fence was electric they'd all be dead! No-o, honey, it's just a tall fence like people build around parks for kids, but taller. There's just one little wire on top that's hot, and that's only for de ones that even have de brain to climb de fence. Most a them don't care nothing about that. They outside already. All day dey just walk round in that field, and if dey come to the fence . . . ."

She made her face blank and started marching in place, hands raised to eye level, fingers clinging to an imaginary chain link fence cutting across her path. It was hilarious but so unimaginable—the idea of keeping people in the equivalent of a giant dog kennel—that it gave me the creeps.

"Oh yes, dey just keep on like that until someone come to get them, when de sun go down or they have to eat something. De people outside come up to de fence and look at de crazy people inside. You hear this, crazy woman? Ef you go to Haiti they stick your ass in de crazy field."

Beatrice flew into a frenzy, screaming, stringy gray hair flying as she clawed the air between her and Marie. I started to calm Bea down, but Marie put her hand on my arm and stopped me.

"Leave her alone. It's good for her blood."

Phil slammed his cards down on the table and rolled off, burning rubber, to find one of the other nurses and tell her Marie needed to be fired.

"Ugh! Ugh!" Bea was still at it, struggling like hell to get out of her wheelchair, using her skinny arms to bang her bony hips against the seat belt for a few minutes until she fell back, panting and muttering. She was thin as a stick except for her fat swollen ankles, and those cheap skimpy cotton dusters her son bought her only came down to her knees and showed you she was liver-spotted from head to toe. She'd only been there for three weeks, but we all knew she was a case. She liked to throw things: bingo chips, silverware, finger paints, anything within reach, and once she got started it was hard to stop her. She would refuse to eat for days, or fight her neighbor for what was on their plate. She would deliberately piss all over whatever nurse's aide was unlucky enough to change her diaper. But sometimes she would wake up in the middle of the night, crying and screaming, until someone came and read something to her, anything would do, but you couldn't stop till she curled up into a little ball and fell back asleep.

"My sister and I, we weren't in the Holocaust, the camps, if that's what you're thinking," her sister Yeddi had said to me one Saturday morning as I stood frozen next to the coffeemaker, riveted by the sound of the last of Bea's shrill, terrified screams before she wore herself out. Yeddi liked to come see Bea in the morning. She was tiny like Bea, and had the same huge, black eyes, haunted eyes.

"The way Bea screams, you would think it, but we got out, thank God. Bea and I, we weren't there because my *imma*—my mother—put us in the little room my father had built behind the bedroom wall when we heard about the Nazis, how they were putting all the Jews on the trains. She put us there. There wasn't time for her to get in there with us. Then the soldiers were in the house. My mother was very good-looking. My father, he found her when he came home, in the living room. She was already dead by then, but Bea and I, we were still in the little room, afraid to come out—we heard everything they did to her." She looked at the floor. "I almost went out to help her, and Bea had to keep me in there, cover my mouth so I wouldn't scream, cover my head so I wouldn't hear. She heard everything they did to her, everything. I wish I could do more for her now, but Art says it won't be long."

I knew that Bea's husband David, who she had been married to for fifty years, had only died a month or so ago, too, from what Yeddi had said.

"A good man, the best. Always kind to me. He brought me kosher food in the hospital. The ambulance took me to Resurrection; they had no idea what to feed me. They couldn't move me; I had to stay until it was safe to move me."

"Were you that sick?"

"Was I that sick? I wasn't sick, I was mugged. He didn't like that I wanted to keep my purse. My spine was fractured."

I saw Bea's wedding picture once. She could've been a movie star, but not with three kids to feed and a busy doctor for a husband. Still, Bea was mean as hell and, frankly, it was hard to remember she was human most of the time. Today, though, I noticed how she was shivering uncontrollably. I crept behind her and eased her arms back into her grimy tan sweater, expecting a fight, but she smiled up at me and patted my arm as I buttoned it up.

"Look at that *schwartzer* hair! Just like my daughter, you are." I patted her bony knee, and it was cold as ice. No nylons. She didn't even have any socks on, just those cheap white plastic shoes.

"I'll be right back, Marie. Answer the phone if it rings, OK?" I went halfway down the hall to Bea's room and checked her dresser. Three pairs of underwear and not even one pair of socks, and her sleazy son Arthur always flashed his three diamond rings at me whenever he stopped by—both pinky rings and his wedding ring. I was mad as hell.

"Marie, do you know that Bea doesn't have one single pair of socks and only three pairs of ratty underwear besides the one that's on her ass? She came in here wearing a ring with a two-carat rock in it, and I know Arthur practically cut her finger off trying to steal it. Why doesn't that cheap asshole buy her something warmer than those dollar-store dusters? She's only got that one sweater? What the hell, did he already spend all of her money? And why doesn't Yeddi do something? Doesn't she give a shit, either? God, no wonder Bea's always pissed off."

Marie shook her head. We looked with pity at gnarly old Bea, who had fallen asleep with her mouth open.

"Yeddi do what she can, honey, but she just too old to fight that Arthur. You don't even know the worst of it," Marie said, looking around and lowering her voice. "I hear him say that he's not gonna spend one more penny on this old lady 'cause she about to die anyway. 'Course he took that ring and sell it for himself. That was her wedding ring, too."

I was shocked. "You actually heard him say that? But it wouldn't take more than twenty bucks to fix her up. He could go to Kmart with a twenty and get her socks, underwear, nylons, and maybe another sweater. Hell, *I'll* go *for* him. And you know what else? You know, I make up all the new patients' files, and from what I read about Bea, I know she's not dying. Not soon, anyway."

Marie nodded. "This woman in one of de most expensive nursing homes around only because her husband, God bless him, got them some good insurance, *and* she got a sister and two other kids making sure she OK. Ef it was just up to Arthur?" Marie just shook her head. "Yeddi pretty old too, and I hope she keep coming, 'cause Bea just gonna dry up ef no one come to see her. She been busy for her whole life, she need something to do, someone to see. She going crazy, just sitting around de whole day. Yes, she just gonna dry up slow, like a plant that don't get water. Least, ef you get run over by a car like Fred, it over with quick."

I had noticed Bea was short on diapers, so I ran back to the office to get some. I dug around in the box until I had five, but I wish something would've told me to settle for four, because when I stood up there was that scumbag Arthur stinking up the lobby with one of his disgusting colognes. He owned about twelve, but everything smelled like piss once it touched his skin. I hated him, but oh, was I glad to run into him today, and I gave him a big smile.

"Oh, HI, ARTHUR, come to see BEA? Look, she's RIGHT AROUND THE CORNER, IN THE ATRIUM."

Arthur cringed and ducked into the office like the coward he was. He never came to see her, but he came to pick up Bea's itemized bill, and complain about it, like clockwork. If the doctor hadn't stepped in, Bea would've been eating one meal a day and crapping in a towel, not a disposable diaper.

"Oh, no, no, it would only upset her, seeing me now! We never got along, and with her out of her mind like she is? Impossible. But how are *you*, my dear?"

Arthur looked just like he always did, greasy and repulsive. He had a few wet black hairs combed over the entire width of his scalp to cover his bald spot. He had dandruff caught in his bushy black eyebrows, and he sold commercial real estate. He was very good at it, so good, in fact, that he was convinced it made up for his personality and appearance. He harassed me regularly, and today was no different.

"Are you not a woman? Am I not a man? We should take advantage of this good fortune, meeting each other in this cold cruel world. Come on, baby, let's have lunch tomorrow." He took a card out of his wallet and flung it dramatically on the desk. He had perfected this trick so if I was sitting down, the card would land directly in front of me on my desk, right side up. A flake of his dandruff floated down to rest next to the card. Plus he was staring at my legs again, the way he always did. I covered my thighs with Bea's diapers, wanting to vomit in the wastebasket.

"Arthur, I told you, I'm involved with someone. And I know you're married."

"I should lie to you? Of course not! I'm married, yes, but she'll never find out. Married? Ha! We're practically divorced!" He waved his arms around like he was acting in a soap opera.

When I handed him back his card he deliberately brushed his hot, dry fingers against mine. I jerked my hand away, and the card fell on the floor. How dare that swine touch me!

I dropped the diapers and yelled, "Look, I'm practically married. And by the way, *he's* Jewish." A small muscle in his forehead twitched, but then he smirked and gave a little bow. He had an aggravating way of smirking at me and saying, *Maybe next time*, every time I rejected him, but he didn't say it this time. He was looking at my legs, and as he moved closer to me, I saw he was sweating like a pig. I jumped behind the desk, but he could still see my legs. It was sickening seeing him sweat like that. Why didn't he take off his coat? He pressed himself against the desk, sweating, and through his pants I saw the huge, nauseating outline of an erection.

"Such beautiful legs. Such sheer panty hose." His voice sounded different, kind of hoarse. I realized I knew that voice.

"Panty hose? *Panty hose*? It's you that's been calling here, isn't it? Isn't it?" I was out of my chair, jumping up and down. He fell back from the desk. His erection withered instantly.

"What? What is this?"

"*Panty. Hose.* I know you're not deaf. You're the one that's been calling here every month saying you're doing a survey on panty hose for some bull-shit research group. And every time, after you ask whether we wear sheer toe or reinforced, you drop the phone, and groan like some farm animal, and then you never call back. That's what the other girls said. And I thought they were crazy, and then last week I got a call from the pantyhose man, and I knew his voice sounded familiar! It was you!"

He stood there, shaking, his comb-over spiky and disheveled like he'd been in a fight. "I? It wasn't! I'd never! My God, what am I hearing! What are you telling me! Calling me!" He slammed through the double doors. Then he came back, hands held palms up in a pleading gesture.

"Can't we discuss this over lunch? You have such beautiful legs . . . ."

I pointed at the door. "Maybe next time." At least I'd figured out why Bea didn't have any panty hose.

The very next day, as she was getting ready to leave, I asked Edie about Arthur. She was the administrator, the big boss, but she was also thin and vain and one of the worst gossips I ever met. She didn't even dye her hair just to show that even with her gray bob she could still pass for thirty-nine. She'd grown to like me in the past few weeks so I knew she could lay the straight truth on me, especially if a creature like Arthur was involved. Recently, Edie had interviewed a morbidly obese woman with a purple birthmark sprawling across one side of her face like a flapjack. After the interview, Edie escorted the woman all the way out the front door, like she was afraid she'd try and graze on the plants in the hallway, then ran back into our office and watched her waddle to her car.

"Damn it," she sighed, turning to look at me as if I could help, "She's got ten years' experience with Kraft Foods and can type 103 words a minute. She'd make me a hell of a secretary—if she didn't look like a walking pustule."

"Edie, you know Arthur, Arthur Meyer?"

She reached up and took her coat off the back of her door. "Arthur? The one that smells so good, with the gorgeous comb-over?"

"Yeah, that one. I mean, it looks so *natural*, parting your hair half an inch above your left ear." We cackled together, but then I got serious. "Listen, Edie, I think someone needs to talk to Arthur. Tell him to get Bea some decent clothes. All her underwear looks like a dog's been chewing it."

"Talk to Arthur? The self-proclaimed genius? As if that would do any good! If God himself tried to tell Arthur something, that *schmedrich'd* cut him off with 'Trust me! I know about these things!' Thinks he's a genius. Genius-schmenius! I've got his number." Edie started stomping around. "His own mother! Should at least make sure she has some decent underwear, for God's sake."

It looked like I'd pushed just the right button to get her going, but I wanted to make sure she stayed focused, that she didn't just drive to the health club and aerobicize all this anger out of her system like she usually did. I'd had a bad dream about Bea last night, just like the ones I'd had about Fred, and I was scared. "Edie, you will talk to him tomorrow, won't you? Listen, Edie, he's been telling everyone that Bea's going to die soon."

"Will I talk to him? Yes. Will it do any good? No." Then she was looking at me and yelling, but I knew she wasn't yelling at me.

"Talk to him? I'd like to choke him! A son like him, no mother deserves. Her husband must've been a fool to do what he did, giving Arthur control over Bea's affairs, and not Yeddi. So what if Arthur's the son and Yeddi's the sister? So what?"

"Calm down, Edie! Everyone'll hear you!" I held up my hands but she just kept screaming, like she'd reached some kind of breaking point.

"Then the husband dies, and how does her son comfort her? He steals her wedding ring to pay for his drugs, because his wife knows about the drugs and watches the money! Allergies, he says, that's why he sniffles all the time! What a joke! I hear him in the bathroom! I know!"

I wished I'd never brought up Arthur, just sat at the computer, typed the stupid flyer for Spring Fest and kept my mouth shut. Then all of a sudden she stopped yelling and sat down in the chair across from me like she'd worn herself out.

"The money for Bea's clothes? He uses it for his drugs, too. The others live too far away, they don't know what he does, the wife doesn't care, and he orders Yeddi around like a dog, tells her, stay home! Says Bea is tired enough, she won't last long, what the hell are you hanging around here for? Yeddi's no fool, she's got eyes, but the bastard scares her half to death. I even heard him tell her, you don't listen to me you won't see your sister at all, and Yeddi crying like her heart would break! He'd deny it, but I hear the pig when he uses my phone, when a line's free to listen in on." Edie'd worked in these places for twenty years, as iron-clad as they come, but she really looked shaken up. She looked like she needed to get drunk and forget about all this. She looked like she needed to quit this job.

"You think I'm crazy, but I've seen this happen a hundred times. Arthur isn't the first. All that's keeping Bea going is seeing Yeddi. She's too confused to focus on anything else, and the less she sees Yeddi, the worse she'll get. You understand? It's like not letting her eat. It'll be slow. She'll just . . . ."

"Dry up," I finished.

"Dry up. Exactly. You know, people always think it's worse to die alone, without your family. How about dying alone *with* a family? Hell, half these patients don't even recognize their families. I'll tell you right now, family doesn't matter. The only thing that matters is that you go quick and peaceful, like Fred did, in his sleep. Quick."

She jumped up, grabbed her briefcase and coat, and escaped, slamming the door open. I sat frozen in front of the computer, forgetting all about Arthur, even forgetting about Bea. There was no one to ask, but the words still came out as a question.

"Fred? Fred died?"

Meditation Mirrors

FELICIA SWANSON

Today was the first day that felt like fall. When we came out of the windowless kitchen for morning chapel, the front hall was flooded in the bright clean light of autumn, triangles of blue and red reflecting off the glossy floor through the stained-glass windows. And everyone was smiling, glad to greet the day, gliding gracefully through the cool air. I was practically joyful when mistress Josephine assigned us to work in the garden the entire day since an early frost was expected and the crops needed to be taken in. There was color everywhere: the sun was a pale, comforting gold in a sky pure blue, like the Blessed Virgin's gown. Over the fields hung a low mist, wet against our shoes and hems. It felt good to kneel in the thick dirt, pulling up the bright vegetables, hefting bushel baskets, lugging them back and forth, and I felt glad to be alive, inspired the way only a cool day can inspire you after a relentless summer. We worked vigorously alongside the professed sisters, who led us in psalms and prayers. Harvesting the herbs was my favorite—all the intense scents of oregano and basil and rosemary. At noon, I scarfed up my dinner, eager to get back out to the garden in the afternoon, which was warmer, but not sweltering as it had been for three months.

When the bells rang at three, I was standing, holding a basket of healthy carrots, and I saw the doors of the school open and a flood of uniformed children swarm out. It was at that moment that I was hit with a wave of memories so strong I couldn't move. I saw myself among them, in my old life, younger, running out of school, free from responsibility for just a little while. In my mind I traced my old route home, through the ravine where the early yellow leaves were already falling, past the street with newly built, identical one-story homes, to my street, in the older part of town, with two stories and porches in various states of repair. I usually arrived home first, my brothers lingering behind with their friends, Sam and my dad at work. The house was always quiet when I opened the door, Peter still down for his nap. Mama knitting in her bedroom chair, as she liked to do in the afternoons. I would enter very quietly, not ready to disturb Mama yet, and wander peacefully through the house, enjoying the few moments of privacy before chores. If I felt like it, I would start my homework then, but usually I just sat at the clean dining-room table and listened to the stillness.

For the rest of the day, every step I took was mirrored in my mind by what I would be doing if I were at home. My body was dressed in black, hauling bushel baskets, my lips reciting prayers, but in my mind I was at the clothesline in the backyard, watching hummingbirds fly backwards to the sugar water Dad put out for them under the awning, as I unpinned the various sizes of pants and shirts and folded them into the basket. During recreation time my body went with the others down to the cemetery, where Carolyn had decided she liked to go and the rest of us followed, and as they discussed the next day, our first day of class at the college, I was standing at the kitchen counter, slicing vegetables for the pot roast, which we always had for supper on Mondays. The newspaper arrived, and while the meat was cooking Mama would sit at the table and skim through it, reading aloud to me the important news and the strange stories from page eight. When we sat down to supper in the refectory, I could hardly eat anything. Sister Josephine left the table for a moment to go to the kitchen, and Debbie exchanged her empty plate for mine, and she finished my meal. On Mondays Dad only worked one shift, and he and Sam would arrive home together, and we would all gather around the table. On a day like this everyone would be in a good mood, ready to share whatever happened to them that day, which always evolved into some kind of lengthy, hilarious story from somebody, usually my dad.

Afterwards, Mama would tell me to go ahead and start my homework, she could take care of the dishes, and the boys would race outside to play since the sun didn't go down until late. Sam would sit in front of the radio, drawing; Dad would doze in his chair with the newspaper spread across his lap. Mama wouldn't wake him until everyone else had been bathed and put to bed, and then I would watch them go off to their room, books spread around me at the table. I wouldn't mind my insomnia on a day like this one, the night just cool enough to give me plenty of energy to keep going, to read one more page, to follow one more train of thought.

Somewhere there was a normal routine going on, just as it did when I was in it. But there was no way I could return to it now; they wouldn't even recognize me.

After supper mistress Josephine led us in a silent single-file line down to the basement and into a hollow, sunken room which roared with racket as soon as she opened the door. From the high ceiling, yellow beams of fluorescent light beat down on all the machinery. It was like entering a giant kitchen, humid and sweltering from the various pots cooking. The dust and mold kicked up by our shoes clumping across the filthy floor would have glittered in sunlight; instead, it hung like a heavy blanket in the sick yellow light, weighed down by stale cigarette smoke and the stench of thick oil. Next to one wall sat a filing cabinet, a cot, and a desk with a small radio, a duct-taped coat hanger for an antenna. The red light flickered as the static reception wavered. On the opposite side of the room, a white partition was arranged to conceal whatever was behind it.

Mistress Josephine led us into a line facing the partition, and halted Jeanette six feet from the curtain. She looked us over and then disappeared behind it. The loud boiler room swallowed us up. Along the opposite wall, above the partition, thick panels of wood, painted black, covered what must have once been windows, preventing the last dusky light from coming through. Under the windows a walkway reached the boiler which clanked and sputtered breathlessly behind the curtain, whistling thick steam into the air, which already seemed ten degrees hotter than when we entered.

The harsh yellow fluorescents made mistress Josephine's face ghoulish when she came around the partition to retrieve Jeanette from the front of the line. Jeanette obediently followed, disappearing behind the white shade.

We whispered loudly to each other over the noise, but no one knew what was going on. I felt my stomach begin to churn, my heart speed up, and that odd clenching I had been having lately in my chest, almost like I would choke on air. But none of the other girls looked upset or concerned. The next one in line examined her fingernails blandly, like a man would, pushing back the cuticles. Others coughed on the stale air, stood casually with their weight on one hip, gazing around at the mechanical excess. Behind me I could hear giggling over the whir and sputter. Their nonchalance unnerved me even more.

I watched the curtain for Jeanette's return, my dress feeling heavier as it absorbed my sweat and the steam around me. Finally they reemerged, mistress

Josephine guiding my roommate by her elbow. I held my breath. Jeanette looked strange, shocked, a little shaky, but pretty much the same physically, her white veil and black dress in order. She didn't look at any of us as she walked past out the door, presumably back to the cell.

The nail picker was summoned behind the curtain next. I was completely silent, listening, but I could hear nothing over the clamor. Images began to fill my mind: a thick slab of granite like in a morgue, scalpels and silver tools for experiments. Methods of torture they employed in barbaric countries like the Soviet Union and China. Wild dogs that would tear you apart on command.

There was some commotion behind me, and I turned to see one of the girls race out of the room. "She said she felt sick," Carolyn shouted to us so we could all hear. "It's not that bad. What can they do to us?"

The nail picker came out and followed Jeanette's lead, eyes down, back to the room. I tried to pray to keep my mind focused, but I couldn't concentrate. I told myself it was going to be all right, that mistress Josephine wasn't going to do anything to me, why would she, what would she do? But the others weren't worried, and if something really horrible was going to happen we would know, we would have heard, the others would be just as nervous as I was.

I stepped up to be next and felt the wave of nausea pass through me. I needed to sit down, but everyone would wonder what was wrong with me. You didn't just sit down in line. They would think I was overreacting. The clanging and hissing grew steadily in intensity until my ears muted the raucous banging, and all I could hear was the loud, steady thump of my heart in my head, in my throat, between my legs.

Mistress Josephine looked at me and nodded. My feet led me behind the partition, and the first thing I saw was the boiler: enormous, sweating, sputtering, like an angry pressure cooker that's been ignored for too long. Humid clouds emanated from the boiler onto the sister in front of it, standing with her back to me, bending over a table. In the center stood a wooden stool; I sat down without being told to. I didn't notice the clumps of multi-colored hair around the base like abandoned Christmas presents beneath a tree.

There was a large mirror, propped up against the railing of the walkway. It was the first time I had seen my reflection in three weeks. Staring back at me was a person I did not know. Her face was covered in faint red blotches, growing in size and number as I watched them, splotching her cheeks like countries on a map, clustered at the chin and along the jaw line. The oceans between the countries were scaly, reptilian, and in the sickly yellow light her skin looked ill with jaundice. Black circles like bruises ringed the bloodshot eyes, and her lips were white and chapped. This person was old, haggard. Her jaw moved back and forth of its own will, as if her teeth were trying to fit together, grinding themselves into puzzle pieces.

The sister appeared in the mirror, empty-handed. She had a large, flat dark mole under her nose, just above the right side of her mouth. Her wide blue eyes met the anxious gaze of the sickly girl, and she looked away, embarrassed. This reaction frightened the girl even more, her teeth grinding faster. Carefully, as if she were removing stitches, the sister took the two bobby pins from the girl's temples and the two from the back of her head and removed the veil, handing it to the girl to hold in her lap. She pulled the elastic from the nape of her neck and thick auburn waves fell just past her shoulder. With the veil off, the girl almost looked like me.

The sister disappeared from the mirror and reappeared in a moment, holding a pair of shears. She grasped a thick strand of the girl's hair the size of a celery stalk, and snipped it a few inches from the base. She continued separating stalks of hair, clipping them randomly, without any consideration for evenness or form. She left a numb scarecrow in the chair, and this time when she reappeared she held a small electric razor. Standing behind the girl she clicked the switch; it emitted a low hum. When the blade touched the girl's scalp, at her right temple, she winced and the razor snagged. The barber placed her left hand firmly on her shoulder to steady the girl, and in one agonizingly slow arc she curved the razor over her ear, pulling it away at the nape. She drew another stripe next to the first one, revealing tiny red bumps scattered everywhere on the pale white surface. The girl wrung the veil in her lap, looking as though she ached to touch her scalp, which was covered in bright red blemishes. Stripe after stripe was shaved away, falling unceremoniously to the ground, and the scarecrow gradually took on an alien quality, not only unfamiliar to me, but to this entire world.

The girl brought the veil to her mouth and bit down on it, clenching it between her molars as the barber trimmed around her ears and made sure there were no stray bits. She looked hideous, with a lopsided, pimpled head and withered face. The hazel eyes stared back at me as if they weren't attached to anything. No brain, no feeling, no person at all.

The barber wrapped a new veil around my head and secured it in the back with a thick pin. Mistress Josephine watched the entire thing. At my conference with her that afternoon I asked if she thought I would make a good nun, and after scrutinizing my face, she told me, "Maybe, when you are older. But for now, you have too much pride. Life experience will take that out of you."

When I passed by her to go back to my room, I glimpsed her face for one second, and I'm certain her lips were curved upward in a grin.

And then suddenly she tears off my veil and pushes down the partition, exposing me to the rest of the girls. When their black animal eyes narrow in on me, I scream, and try to raise the curtain again, because if they can't see me, they can't hurt me. But it's too late—they're all trampling the horizontal curtain, coming straight for me, and then they're upon me, scratching at me with their claws, scraping off layers and layers of my scalp and throwing handfuls of my head in a pile on the ground. Someone shines a bright flashlight on me, and when I look up it's Annie, telling me to get up, it's time to prepare breakfast.

When I opened my eyes there was Annie's face, her face so large beneath her bald head, staring at me in horror. And then I saw the blood—in light brown splotches all over the pillow and sheets. I sat up and looked down—my nightgown was stained, too. She looked at my bed and at me, her eyes drifting up to my scalp. "I'll get mistress Josephine," she said.

"Cover your head," Carolyn told her, handing over her veil to Annie. After she was gone Carolyn hovered beneath my bed, her hands tremulously reaching up for my face, but resting on my thigh instead. Jeanette remained in the far corner, watching me anxiously. When Annie returned with mistress Josephine she took one look at me and told me to go to the infirmary. "Make sure you're on the bus at 8:30," she added, and I went out with a towel over my head, eyes lowered.

"Sister James, RN" it said on the door, and when I entered the sister at the desk looked up from her reading. Her wide blue eyes and flat dark mole caused me to take a step back; it was the barber. Immediately she rushed over to me and took me in her arms. "I'm sorry," she said. "I'm sorry. I'm so sorry." She pressed me tightly to her. I kept my body tight and rigid—I wanted to run as fast as possible away from her. She kept repeating how sorry she was, and then she released me and wiped her face across her sleeve, still holding me with one hand.

"Come inside and I'll clean you up," she told me, taking me into the second room. She pushed back a curtain and sat me down on one of the beds. I let her take my head in her warm hands and examine my scalp. Her hands were gentle and purposeful, as they had been the night before. Then she grasped my hands and held them out. Caked blood dried under and around the edges of my fingernails. "I'll put some astringent on it and some ointment. Does it hurt?" I shook my head no. "Good. The scratches look deep but they should heal in a couple days." While she worked I kept my eyes low, looking around at the empty beds and tables of bottles and metal instruments. When she finished she dragged a chair over and sat across from me.

"How do you feel?"

I printed the word *fine* on my notepad and handed it to her.

She took the pad and glanced at it, then asked me again, in a softer voice, "Really—how do you feel?"

I reached out for my notepad but she held it in her lap. I wasn't going to plead with her. I shook my head and looked down.

"I am your superior," she stated, her voice suddenly sharp. "Speak your answer aloud to me."

"I told you it doesn't hurt," I said to the floor.

"I mean inside."

I didn't think about my answer; as soon as my mouth opened I broke down into heaving sobs. It was the first time I had cried since the cemetery, and my loss of control embarrassed me even more. She handed me a box of tissues and sat beside me on the bed, put her arm around my shoulders while my sobs subsided. "I know, I know," she said. "It's very hard at first. There is so much to get used to, you never know what's coming next. The first month is the hardest. It gets easier. You start to make friends, you become a family, the convent becomes your home. Lots of girls have trouble adjusting at first. Just out of high school is too young, I think. My first month I was so homesick, I cried myself to sleep every night. But it gets easier. It really does."

She waited for me to say something, as if her story was going to make me feel any better. When I didn't say anything and didn't look at her, she asked, "Do you want to talk about it?"

I did. I wanted to scream at her that I couldn't understand how she could be so sympathetic when she participated in the mutilation. I wanted to shove her arm off me, push her down to the ground, kick her in the stomach, rip off her habit, and tear her hair out in handfuls.

And I'm not sorry. I know I should be, but I'm not. For that instant I saw fistfuls of thick hair, and I wanted to see her face in agony. As soon as the image flashed in my mind I flushed with shame. I had never wished harm on anyone like that before. I pushed the image away, and the only thing I said was, "School starts today."

She sighed and nodded her head. "Yes—that can add to your anxiety."

She asked if I wanted to stay and lie down, that she would request mistress Josephine to excuse me from class if I wasn't feeling up to it. But mistress Josephine had already told me to be on the bus, and going to school was better than lying on a cot in the infirmary all day, alone with the barber. So she brought out yet another veil and wrapped it gently around my head, securing it in the back. She didn't ask me what happened to my other two veils; I couldn't tell her, anyway.

I was late and everyone was already seated two by two and waiting nervously, holding small canvas bags on their laps. As I passed down the aisle, they peeked at me from under hooded eyes. Carolyn had probably told them I scratched my scalp bloody in my sleep. I sat in the back, patting the veil Sister James promised me she secured tightly to my head to make sure none of the wounds showed.

When we arrived at the sprawling, first-floor community college, mistress Josephine passed out our class schedules. I stared at mine as if it belonged to someone else: Calculus, Richards, 9-10:50. Survey of Russian Literature, Kiel, 12-1:50. Early Childhood Development, Harris, 2-3:50.

I wasn't surprised when Mistress Josephine led us inside and right to our classroom door. It was closed. "You're late," she told us, looking us over. "Sit in the back seats—they're reserved for you. Stick together. The bus will be waiting to pick you up in front at 4:00. Pay attention."

She opened the door and we filed in, Jeanette taking the first brave step. A sea of countless heads all turned at once to take us in, and Jeanette stumbled, as if she didn't want to go on. We stopped, unable to move ahead to the empty back rows, raised up like in an arena. The sea became individual faces, faces of men and women my age, individual eyes all staring at us. I patted my head to make sure the veil was in place. The professor on the small platform to our right turned away from the blackboard and pushed his thick, dark-framed glasses up his nose. "Oh yes," he said, smiling at us, "go ahead and take the seats at the back. We're just getting started." We paraded past them, shuffled into the rows in age order, and quickly got seated. The others pulled out notebooks and pens. I bit my lip. Tears sprung to my eyes. It's stupid to cry about not having a notebook. I should have thought of it before I left. When the girl next to me saw me copying equations from the board in the small notepad with the little half pencil, she offered me some of her paper, but I shook my head.

Someone behind me passed a note over my shoulder. *I have an extra lunch for you*—was scrawled in Annie's hand.

I'm not hungry, I wrote back.

But you didn't eat breakfast.

I'm fine.

You look very upset. We'll talk at lunch. I put the note in my pocket. I couldn't even think of food. I wouldn't turn around to look at her.

I continued copying the equations in small, cramped print so I would have enough paper to last me all day. I was having a hard time paying attention. My hand grew too tight to grip the small pencil, and I had no idea what I was writing down, anyway. The morning was hot and humid, and the room soon became stifling despite the open windows. I could feel my scalp sweating, and I fidgeted with the veil to make sure it covered my head completely. As soon as class was over we filed out in canonical order into the crowded hallway. I slipped away from the group. Annie would want to talk to me and try to make me eat. I didn't have anything to say to her. A current of people was coming at me, flowing in the same direction as the other novices. I made my way past and climbed the stairs out of the wave of students up to the third floor, where it was quiet and dim. All of the classroom doors were closed, and when I peered inside the windows, they were empty of people. My footsteps bounced off the walls. I found a bathroom and went inside.

There was faded paper from grocery bags over the windows, *Okey's Grocery* printed on them in red block letters. The sunlight pouring through the windows tinted the room a warm, soft brown. A row of sinks stood to my left, across from the stalls. I went to the mirror over the sinks to examine my head. A splotch of blood had seeped through the front of my veil. Immediately I tore it off, causing the sore to start bleeding again. I pulled some paper towels from the dispenser and ran them under cold water, then blotted at the stain, but it only spread further in a pink mass. I turned the water on full blast and held the veil under the stream, but by this point it looked like a bloodied rag. I couldn't wear a rag on my head, and I couldn't go without one, either. Pleading with the only person present, I looked at the bald woman in the mirror and shook my head in disbelief: "This isn't happening!" The mirror was old and cracked along the bottom, with tan water stains streaking down from it. But the eyes that met mine were real, attached to a real brain and a real person. They still had bruised circles under them, the lips were still chapped, and the acne had spread from the scalp to the forehead, inflamed by the veil, but it was me. Those were my eyes. I shut off the water and stared at my reflection.

At the time, a part of me wondered what God must have thought, if he by chance looked down on this alien girl in an abandoned bathroom, talking to herself in the mirror. He was probably uninterested, at most slightly amused by the whole thing. There was something defiant about it, talking to my reflection, as if I were praying to myself instead of God.

My voice emerged stilted, unused. "I can't do this. This is not what I signed up for." The reflection nodded her agreement. "Those girls think I'm hideous. I'm nothing like them at all. They're not my sisters. They're never going to be my family . . . ." I took a deep breath and my face clouded over in anger. "I wanted to go to school. But this isn't what I expected. I didn't even get to choose my classes." Spurred on by the intent eyes and agreeing nods across from me, I looked around for something to throw. I reached into my pocket for the pad of paper, intending to hurl it at the bagged windows. My fingers found the veil from the night before and pulled it out. It was wrinkled but unstained. I looked back at the reflection and started to laugh, a strange sort of triumphant laugh.

I hadn't planned on returning to class. I wanted to stay in the quiet bathroom until four o'clock, but I washed my scalp and then secured the veil at the back my head until it looked all right. Then the bell rang again, so I went to the room on my schedule. The other girls were already there. They stared at me when I came in, but this time I ignored them completely. I knew Annie was trying to get my attention, but I wouldn't look at her. It wasn't anyone's business where I had been. I wasn't a sheep; I didn't need to stay with the flock.

The class was smaller than the last one—only a handful of students weren't wearing veils, and we sat at desks like in high school. A young woman sat on the edge of the desk, observing all of us without smiling. She wore a plain long black skirt and an ordinary white sweater, but her face was exquisite, with full dark lips, very high, broad cheekbones, and dark, piercing eyes that were slanted up and circled in dark kohl eyeliner. Her thick dark hair was tied back in a bun.

"My name is Professor Kiel," she spoke to us in a rounded tone, her mouth carefully enunciating each word. She continued to perch on the edge of the desk and talked as if we were having a casual conversation. "This class is called Introduction to Russian literature. We will be concentrating mostly on the Russian writers of the nineteenth century—Tolstoy, Dostoevsky, Gogol, Turgenev . . . ."

"She's a Russian," I heard someone whisper. I didn't even realize the lecture had started or that students around me were taking notes. I looked back to the instructor. I had never seen a Russian before. I had imagined them as enormous giants, with tree trunks for legs, and loud voices that always yelled. This woman looked more like an exotic princess, educated, refined. I couldn't take my eyes from her.

I listened and didn't bother to take notes, and when the bell rang I was surprised that two hours had gone by so quickly. We filed out and down the hall to the next classroom, where an older woman stood at the board writing an outline. This class had even more students than the morning class, all girls, and we tromped up the steps all the way to the back rows again. She started her lecture with the psychology of the primary school student, and with the hot afternoon sun pouring in through the windows, everyone was yawning, their heads drooping. The girls on either side of me both had their eyes closed, one of them bobbing her head into her chest now and again. I think I was the only one listening at all. The instructor noticed everyone was nodding off and started to ask us questions. I knew nothing about child psychology, but the answers seemed fairly obvious. I was one of the only people to raise my hand, but she ignored me every time, asking one of the regular students instead. She didn't even look at the back rows where I sat.

I tuned the instructor out, too angry to nod off. I stared around the room, which had obviously belonged to this teacher for some time. Posters from plays hung on the walls. Her desk was cluttered with papers and knickknacks, and on the edge sat a blue ceramic duck, its back opening up into a candy dish filled with peppermints.

When it was finally four o'clock, we filed into line and waited for the regular students to make their way out first. As we proceeded out of class, falling into our regular order, I lingered until the end. I couldn't help myself. That ceramic duck sat on the corner of the desk all period, and all I could concentrate on were the peppermints inside. And it would be so wrong to take one; it would be a sin to take one and slip it into my pocket. Someone might see me, and I'd have to confess it in front of everyone. But I couldn't help myself. I don't think I wanted to stop. I think I wanted to sin, and that's a worse sin if you mean to do it.

As we marched out, all the regular students went first, racing to meet their friends, talking loudly, followed by us, slowly and silently marching out. I hung back until the end, and right at the moment I passed the desk, like a spy on a stealth mission, my hand swiftly swiped one of the peppermints in one swoop and stuffed it into my pocket next to the pad of paper. I didn't look around me, and I never stopped walking. It was the first time I had ever stolen anything.

Letting Go

SARA A. KLEYNENBERG

"Oh, wait," said Mitchell, a neighbor kid from up the street, looking up at me. "You're the one whose mom is dying."

We had just reached the barn, the sliding doors on both ends wide open, a few horses munching on the hay in the grates. Birds flew overhead and perched on the timbers in the eaves, cooing and twittering, flapping wings and building nests. Cats napped in the sun, and because it was the middle of the day, the usual scamper of mice from below the boards couldn't be heard.

After Mitchell spoke, my cousin Jo hit him and yelled at him, and when I looked around, he was heading back toward the fence, his head bent and cowed, and Jo had a grim set to her face. But before I looked around, the world had stopped moving, the barn tilted, odd because none of the animals moved. But I know I felt a certain lurch, and the sun fade and fall, and the air grow tight and close and thick. The dust off the ground silted above me, and the horses all seemed twenty feet tall, the barn immense and growing, and me small and shuffling in the dirt, my flip-flops melting into the ground. I held my breath, and I felt my heartbeat in my neck, my face bulging and small sparkles of darkness along my eyelids. When I took a breath, the barn and horses went back to normal size, the sparkles left, and the dust settled down. Mitchell was walking away.

"Junie, he didn't mean that," Jo was saying to me, her honey loop of pony-tail twirling in her hand. "He's a stupid boy and says really dumb things and never knows what he is talking about, never. You ignore him, and I'm going to ignore him, and he can't come over ever again, ever." She stopped and turned toward where Mitchell was walking away.

"YOU CAN'T COME BACK HERE EVER AGAIN!" she yelled to him, and than turned back to me.

She stared up at me with wide blue eyes and teeth biting her lips, and I knew she was waiting for me to say something. I cleared my head, wiped my hands on my shorts, and said, "Are those kittens still in the barn? The ones from last time?"

A grin broke out on her face, and she grabbed my hand and pulled me inside, talking about how much bigger they had gotten and how the mama cat was still really protective, but would probably let us hold them, and we walked into the barn. But part of me had frozen up and was slowing, chinking, and falling into dust, because I knew Mitchell wouldn't have said something like that to me unless he had heard it from somewhere. And he wouldn't have heard it from anyone but Jo, or Aunt Anna, or Uncle David, whispered in dread over dinner or on the porch, an explanation of why my sister and I were always there, why our parents always had to leave us. They would use the same tone I heard low from the neighbors back home when I rode my bike by, or when Mom and I went to the grocery store and she gripped my hand and smiled at everyone she saw, they smiling too much and telling her how good she looked. We would go home and she would collapse on the couch, breathing heavy and falling asleep as Rose and I put the food away. Later she'd come into my room and thank me, her hands undoing my barrette and smoothing out my hair, tucking it behind my ears and telling me she'd feel better soon. She'd kiss my nose and ask me to get her some water, and together we'd sit out on the back porch with Rose and wait for Dad to come home, she humming some old Nat King Cole song and rocking back and forth while she trailed her hands up and down my back.

Jo and I walked into the crib where the kittens were, and all five of them were awkwardly falling and walking about on kitten paws, large ears perked, their tiny lungs mewling and talking. Jo reached in to pick two of them up, and unlike the last time, the mama cat didn't lunge for her wrist, or hiss threateningly. Jo handed me a small calico, and I suddenly felt very sorry for it.

The kittens squirmed in our arms for a while before wanting down again, to run around and wrestle with their littermates.

"Aren't they just the sweetest things?" Jo asked me. "They are just the cutest, tiniest little things ever, of all time. The cutest."

I saw some of the other cats on the opposite end of the barn. Mangy and thin, eyeing the grain bins constantly, ears pricked for any sign of mouse flesh. "What will happen to them?" I asked Jo, leaning down to pet an all-black kitten, brave enough to stray away from Mama and its siblings, and trying to climb the slatted boards of the crib where they slept.

"Oh, I'm not sure," Jo said. "We'll keep them around, I'm sure, because Daddy always says there can't be too many cats in the barns for all the mice. Usually, a few of them die when they start wandering outside." She put a finger in her mouth, and slid the nail along the ridge of her teeth, cleaning it. "A hawk will pick them up, sometimes, or they'll get lost or something. But we keep them all." She squatted down and began to coo again at the kittens and the mama cat. "And aren't they just the cutest things? Aren't they just the tiniest little itsy bitsy things?"

I began to feel light-headed; the damp air and heat in the barn coated my tongue. I leaned against the wall when the clopping of hooves made Jo stand up and squeal, "Oh, Junie, here one comes! Let's go, come on!" and she ran to the end of the barn, scooped up a cat, and climbed to the loft.

We headed up the ladder, Jo struggling with the cat under her arm, me trying not to look down. I always had a fear of heights, and not the actual heights themselves, just the methods of getting there. Ladders, elevators, big staircases that looked down—none of them sat too well with me. But I just climbed, knowing that when I got to the top, I'd feel a whole lot better.

The hay behind the ladder prickled at our arms and elbows, and the constant dust, the chaff of the dried husks and hulls of the grain made the air look thick and underwater, with sheaves of light from the slatted roof shooting down, like a pond.

Jo made it to the top quickly, and set the cat down in order to smooth back her hair, electrified in the heat. Her forehead was damp, and she had small streamlined red streaks shredding up her arms, either from the hay, or from the kittens down below.

I pulled myself up into the loft, the bales wobbling and tipping, birds swooping up above, and the cat flopped over and Jo rubbed its thin belly. She skootched over to the ledge, and while the horse we had first seen was already at the end of the barn, its long pink tongue stretched into the water trough, another approached, heading towards the door.

Jo stroked the cat's velvet ears and said to it more than me, "You ready?"

I nodded and we leaned far over, her hand like a clamp over the cat, and we waited for the horse to get closer.

Jo always dropped the cats; I knew it didn't hurt them, the drop not all that far down, and they're lean and lithe and used to leaping. Their claws sank easily into the horse's hide before they sprang to the ground and ran towards a stable, or a hole in the boards. Jo was always good with the timing, when to release, knew when the horse would be directly under us, how to hold the cat, and we'd done it hundreds of times. I'd watch, and she'd laugh and clap a hand over her mouth when the horse would buck and neigh, whinny, and scream with the sudden pain before it lunged out of the barn and galloped off into the field.

When the glossy ginger hide came closer and closer, Jo picked up the cat and clutched it to her chest, rubbing under its chin. I could hear it purr and saw its eyes slowly close, slowly fall asleep, and when she reached out over the edge, I grabbed her arm and whispered. "Wait, let me do it."

She said, "You sure?" the two of us having gone through this before, me taking the cat and tilting out over the loft, and then at the last minute I'd thrust it back at her, unable to let go of the squirming fur, and pull back from the edge, scared. I didn't know what it was that would make me decide to do it, and then right as the horse was passing by, I'd chicken out and give the cat to Jo. Jo never made fun of me, or tried to make me do it. I suppose the fact that the cats never ran from her or bit her or clawed at her on the ascent to the loft should have made me feel better about the whole thing—they never held any grudges and weren't scared, and so I shouldn't be, either. The cat she held rolled in her arms, one of those barn cats starved for affection, and its mouth was open and showed sharp pointy incisors and the small sandpaper tongue. When I leaned toward her and took the cat its small motor still rumbled and quaked, and with the horse clopping closer to us I knew I wouldn't have time to thrust the cat back. Either I dropped it, or it didn't get dropped at all.

I looked out at the approaching horse and tried to think like Jo must have thought when she dropped the cats. How fast is the horse walking? How fast will the cat drop? How wide is the horse's back? I lay on my stomach, my arms out in front of me like I could fly, the cat dangling like a small baby, and I felt Jo next to me, quivering with her small shallow breaths. The horse stopped briefly and threw its head back to bite on its withers, and small insects floated from it like a linty cloud. It resumed walking, and the cat's hindquarters started to pummel my hands, small staccato mewls coming from its throat, and Jo whispered, "No, not yet, not yet, not . . . quite . . . yet!" The cat squirmed in earnest now, and clawed at me as I held it tighter, and I watched the horse come closer and closer before I finally felt the sickening lurch in my stomach, the rangy tang of the horse's hide float up to me, and then, amazingly, I let go.

For a brief moment, I felt a small thrill in the back of my throat, at the edges of my mouth as I saw the fur fly down and heard the cat hissing. But then I realized I had leaned out a little too far. When the cat careened down from the loft, claws on all four paws extended, it raked across the side of the horse's belly and didn't land on the horse's back. The drag along the hide slowed the cat's descent, but it still landed thickly on the wooden floor, stunned but not hurt, ears back, crouching low. The horse felt those tiny needles pull down its flesh, immediately erupting in small stinging lines of blood. Jo and I watched in horror as the horse reared back and brought its front hooves down full force on the ground, narrowly missing the cat who unfortunately darted to the back. The back hooves, the ones Aunt Anna always warned me to steer clear of, the back hooves that once landed on Uncle David's toes and caused all the nails to blacken and fall off, the back hooves roped with muscle, thick and tall and strong, kicked with all their might and hit full force in the middle of the cat's belly and chest. The horse's eyes rolled as it made contact with the cat, and as the cat hurled to the ground, the horse trotted out of the barn, shook its mane and neighed, and headed off toward the stand of trees.

Jo and I stared frozen from the edge of the loft at the crumpled cat lying in the middle of the floor. It looked like a small sack flung on the ground, and when Jo's tiny gasp finally squeezed out, I pushed away from the ledge and started to shake. She shoved past me to the ladder and scrambled down, and I followed her as best I could. My hands slipped off the sides of the ladder, my feet missed rungs, small gasps and tears crowding the back of my throat.

When I caught up to her, Jo held the cat in her lap. It was limp, its eyes rolling back into its head, small lines of blood rolling from its nose and its mouth like strings of licorice. Jo stroked its back lightly, talking to it.

"Is . . . is it OK?" I asked, my voice small and scared for her to look at me.

She sniffed and rocked back and forth and said, "I don't know. It's not doing anything. Junie, what do we do? Junie, the poor kitty, what do we do?"

I knelt down next to her, my knees scraping the wooden floor, and put my hand on the cat's chest and rib cage. It felt like cardboard, all folded and broken and bent, soft beneath me where a few minutes earlier it had been firm and ridged, rumbling with purrs. It shuddered beneath my palm, and the small pads of its claws extended and curled, and then went limp. I knew it was dead.

Jo rocked back and forth, stroking under its chin and rubbing its triangle ears, talking to it and asking me, "Junie, what do we do? What should we do?" I wasn't sure if she was scared for the cat, or scared for herself. We had been told thousands of times not to play in the loft, and to always leave the horses alone because they could be so volatile. The times we slept up there Aunt Anna and Uncle David thought we were in a tent set up in the pasture, and when we played up there, we always kept a watch toward the house to make sure no one saw us, especially my sister Rose who surely would have told had she ever seen us misbehaving.

"Jo, Jo," I said, taking her hands as the cat rolled off her lap softly. "Jo, we have to get rid of it. No one will notice if one of the barn cats is missing. We've gotta take it somewhere."

Jo stared up at me with her giant eyes rimmed with red, her eyelashes stuck in clumps. Her lip quivered and she nodded at me slowly at first and then more firmly.

"You're right," she whispered. "We can't let anyone know. And it wasn't your fault, Junie, it wasn't. But you're right. Where can we take it?"

We knelt in the hay fragments and the dirt, the heat rolling over us like an ocean, and with the dead cat between us, Jo and I thought of all the hiding places we knew. I had a headache and felt dizzy again when Jo stood up and said, "I'm going to go get a sack, and I know where we can take it. Johnson's Lake." She walked into the stables, searching, while I sat with the crumpled cat, making sure no one was coming.

Johnson's Lake was where we ended up on almost all of our daily journeys. It was a short walk through the woods, past the willow tree on the edge of the yard, down the hill to the creek, and into the small inlet where the water lived before heading into the lake. A small bridge on the road crossed over the inlet, and under the bridge, where the water was shallow and warm, reflecting green light like a thousand broken bottles, Jo and I swam and splashed, and looked for the small snail shells that burrowed into the muck. Mom and Aunt Anna went with us one time, dragging along rubber rafts to float on, their sunglasses perched on their heads, and they brought baskets filled with grapes and peanut-butter-and-jelly sandwiches and small squares of brownies. Mom had lain on the raft, her dark hair a puddle around her head, and she squealed every time I splashed her with water. I hung from the foot of the raft and kicked softly, propelling us into the lake, the water deeper, and deeper, and darker, and cooler, until just Mom and I floated out in the middle, far from Anna and Jo. The small gold chain around her neck twinkled in the sunlight like a cord of electricity, and she trailed her painted fingernails in the water, leaving ridges of ripples. When we were out far enough, I stopped kicking, and let my body float up to the underside of the raft, my head down by her feet, just above the water, my feet just barely making it to the middle of the raft. I could feel the curves of her body sinking down into the water, resting above me, and we floated like that for a long time, me bobbing up against her, she sleeping and twinkling and trailing.

"I found one," Jo said, breathless, and she knelt down in front of me and the cat. We stared at each other, and then I leaned forward and scooped up the limp body, the fur on its face matted with blood, the small delicate head dangling, and I shoved it into the sack. I heaved it on my arm, and we ran out of the back of the barn and headed toward the lake.

As we walked, the sack banged against my thighs, and I was trying to find the best way to carry it. I wanted to drag it, but the knocks and bumps on the ground made me feel bad. When it was on my shoulder it had scratched and rubbed me raw. I finally held it in both fists and clutched it to my chest like I was praying, and the sack bumped against my belly but didn't rub against anything.

We reached the edge of the lake, and the ground below us was thick and spongy. I dropped the sack down with a heave and saw it softly tumble to a side. I sat down and let the dampness sink through my shorts, then started to unlace my sneakers.

Jo and I had been silent during the walk, and when we got to the lake she immediately sunk her hands into the mud and pulled out a fistful, looking for the snail shells we liked to find.

She turned triumphantly to me after a few dips and pulls through the mud, a shell sleek in her hand. She worked her fingers under the snail still lodged in it, digging at the brown, wrinkled body. She popped it out and flung it into the water, then cleaned out the shell in the water and brought it over to me. It was pearly and roped with ridges, small and delicate with its curved opening and tiny pointed middle. "For you, Junie. To add to the collection when we get home." She put it in my palm and smiled at me. Jo stood over me for a few minutes while I rocked a little, then plodded to the water.

"Well," Jo said, "we'd better get in. I mean, we have to get in to do this right, you know." And she pulled off her shoes and hefted up the sack, dragged it to the edge of the water, and waited for me.

I walked around and gathered rocks and stones, wishing we had grabbed something heavier on the walk over. I took the sack from her and opened it up, trying not to stare at or hit the now-stiffening body. I filled it, hoped it would sink, and walked to the edge of the lake with Jo.

The cool water felt good lapping at my toes. We waded in and then had to start kicking as we drifted farther away from the bridge, deeper into the lake. The muck at first swallowed our feet, and walking was difficult with the sucking ground. The deeper we went, the more the seaweed began to tickle below us, small silky caresses on the bottoms of our feet, and soon we swam, me hauling the sack that already pulled against me, Jo paddling feebly. Jo was never as good a swimmer as I was, and when we got to the deeper part of the lake, I said through my teeth, "You stay here, and I'll go out and drop it. I'll be right back, OK?"

She nodded, knowing she would get too tired if she went out with me, and

I began to go further, out into the deep and cool, just like I had done with Mom that day so long ago. The sack pulled at me and I had to wrench my arm to carry it along. When the weeds no longer dangled towards my feet, I thought I might be out far enough, and I began to tread water.

The reflection of the trees on the edges of the lake seemed to meet at the trunks with the real trees, making giant two-peaked creatures, and the sun slid down far in the sky, melting like an orange Creamsicle. I knew once I let go of the sack, the cat would sink far down to the depths, and no one would ever know what I had done to it. But it bumped against my legs softly, and I could almost feel its tiny outline, and I suddenly thought of my mom, floating almost exactly where I was now. I couldn't let go of the sack, even though Jo called, "Come on, Junie, come on!" I couldn't let go of that sack even though the cat pulled downwards as hard as it may have ever pulled on anything, the stones reaching for the mucky landscape below where it would be swallowed up. I couldn't let go even though I was tired and panting, and my legs burnt with exertion and my head tipped back to look at the sky, my ears dipping below the surface sometimes to hear the dull hum of the water.

The sack pulled harder and slipped out of my grasp, and as I began to cry it made one gentle tug, snaked around my legs, and sank down, down, down to the coolness and dark. It was gone.

I started to swim back to Jo and to shore, my face wet with tears and with the lake water I kept sinking my head into. I paddled halfheartedly, and then flipped and floated awhile on my back, the sky above me orange and pink, and on the far edges bruised purple. I floated the same way my mother must have that day, and I suddenly and desperately wanted to remember pulling her back to shore on her raft. I wanted the end of that memory I could only seem to capture half of. I wanted to see her drift into shore and wade through the water, climb back on the beach laughing and damp and happy. I couldn't remember it.

I wanted to swim back and find the sack and the cat again; I wanted to bring it back to shore and hold it. Its small pointed face and matted fur, its rumbling belly and tipped slanted eyes.

I wanted to find it, but I had let go. I had let go, and once you let go, you can't grab hold again.

DiabloNene

PHILLIP R. REALMO

I might not know the exact reason, but it seems to me that everything I do when I'm drunk seems to feel slightly different. Some might even say better. For example, the girl at the end of the bar could normally be pug-fugly but in time, with a few beers in your system, all that could miraculously change. She is suddenly a distant cousin of Jennifer Lopez. The song that is bumpin' on the club speakers could be some B-96 bubblegum-pop piece of shit, but tonight, after consulting with Mr. Corona, my lawyer and my adviser, it is the best fuckin' song I've heard since the "Macarena." So needless to say, as the liters of alcohol enhanced my body's sensations, I found myself in the urinal of Dante's Hip-Hop Club taking the best piss of my life. Ever.

About an hour before, some asshole had pickpocketed my sense of balance from right underneath my nose. I think it was the bartender, but I'm not too sure. With no further proof than what my instincts told me, I inconspicuously ordered another drink and blended in with my surroundings like some sort of human chameleon. The bastard would never suspect me now! I kept one squinted eye on the bartender as the other one wandered around, surveying the room.

An hour passed and I tired of that foolish game. Sometimes I let my imagination run wild like white-trash children in Kmart. Dante's was going on like a motherfucker, yo! Tonight was the night to be! Especially since Sal, Papo, Dre, and myself had just finished our finals and the semester. Many nights had been sacrificed to the gods of disciplined studying and good grades, but tonight we sought to reap our reward. Dante's was jam-packed with enough sexually explicit distractions and illegal vices to sink our teeth into. Friend and foe alike were in attendance, but such is life. Far be it from me to let some old, high-school drama get in the way of my sinning. Just in case things got out of hand, I brought Jambu, my monkey knife.

What is a monkey knife, you ask? It is a souvenir from Peru brought to me by Ron, a good friend of mine who went there over the summer. It's about ten inches long and butt-ugly. On top of the knife is an old goat's horn about six inches in length, bone colored and slightly curved. Below the horn is a set of bright red stones positioned as the eyes. A small pointy nose is carved under the eyes with a menacing grin, filled with rotted human teeth positioned precisely underneath the nose. What makes Jambu a truly spooky artifact is that it is made entirely of dried snakeskin with old monkey hair glued onto the back. When you pull the horn, the upper half of the mouth pulls free to reveal a sharp, six-inch blade. Anybody could sneak a switchblade or one of them plastic box-cutters into a party, but it took true skill to sneak in Jambu. That's a story for another time, though.

The way I figured it, anybody could sneak a switchblade into a party and appear threatening. My goal was to flash Jambu, the monkey-knife, to show motherfuckers that I don't fuck around. That's my philosophy. Of course, I would never even dream of using it. It was only for display. I despise violence. In all actuality, I'm as meek as a lamb.

But anyway, there I was standing in front of the urinal, pissing next to Dre, listening to Papo, who sat on the sink behind us, ramble on about "the man" and all the adversity he had faced in the first grade. I leaned my forehead against the wall, looking for my lost balance.

Dre turned to me. "Dog, I'm taking the best fuckin' piss of my life!" He was swaying back and forth like one of those inflatable clowns you can't ever seem to knock down. I placed my right hand behind his back to steady him, while with my left hand, I was steadying my other friend. I stood on tiptoe to regain my composure.

"Me too, dude," I retorted. I let go of his back and continued with my duty. Slowly, I moved my head from side to side, searching for that elusive cracking noise that would relieve the stress in my neck. CRACK! Ahh, there it was. Papo continued as if he were never interrupted.

Papo cleared his throat. "So then he says in a deep-ass voice, 'That's my lunch tray, bitch! You gonna gimme my lunch tray!' Then he snaps his fingers and two of his boys show up. I'm outnumbered by these big, white, gay muh-fuckers, and I start to feel like Tim Robbins in *The Shawshank Redemption* 'n shit, right? So I say, 'Fine. I don't eat, don't nobody eat.' And BAM! I slammed my tray on his fuckin' head. But get this, that muh-fucker just stood there and took it like he's Schwarzenegger 'n shit. He bent down and looked me dead in my eye and said, 'I'm a kill you, bitch!'

"So I said, straight from the top of my head 'n shit, I said, 'Oh yeah! Well, I'm, uh, I'm rubber and you're… glue! Whatever you say bounces off me and sticks to you, bitch, 'cause you crazy glue!' BAM! I slammed that nigga one more time with my tray and he passed out. And I'm the patsy that got sus-pended! Fuckin' travesty 'n shit. I come back two weeks later and that fool's spread the rumor that he created Rubber vs. Glue, when he knows I invented that shit. White people's unoriginal than a muh-fucker, yo."

"First of all, muh-fucker," I said, shaking my finger at him, "I've known you since kindergarten, so how the hell are you gonna tell me you went to Catholic school when we both attended the same ghetto-ass school in Humboldt Park? Secondly, I remember when that third-grader stepped to you. But if memory serves me, and correct me if I'm wrong, bitch, but, uh, didn't you provoke him by pinching his sister's ass?" Papo was no longer looking in my eyes. Both Dre and I knew Papo was bullshitting for bullshit's sake, just trying to keep us entertained while we pissed. He made outrageous claims from time to time, but the landmark case of Rubber vs. Glue was preposter-ous! Pure tomfoolery!

Dre interjected while he motioned me to give him a cigarette. "And how the hell are you gonna claim ownership to the landmark case of Rubber vs. Glue, huh? You got a lot of nerve, muh-fucker." I swear that guy was a mind reader when he was drunk.

The door swung open and hit the wall, snapping our heads to the slam's direction. Sal had just strolled into the urinal. He was smiling cheesily and walking cautiously, trying in vain to play off the fact that he was rocked. We looked at him for a brief second as he made his way to a urinal, then our heads turned back to the conversation.

"All right, then," Papo said as he got off the sink. He turned around to check himself out in the mirror, lifting his nose to perform a booger-check, straightening his collar, and flexing his muscle. He turned back around to face us. "Fuck you, you drunk muh-fucker, and fuck you, you tall bastard. I didn't provoke nobody by pinchin' some girl's ass 'n shit. She provoked me. Second, it was summer school, so that's why you weren't there. Shit, you can't even remember when's the last time you got your ass some play let alone muh-fuckin' kindergarten 'n shit, nigga. And, finally, I did invent Rubber vs. Glue. You bitches are just too ignorant to realize. Check yo-self."

The "tall bastard" was me. The inane conversation left me a bit drunker than I already was and slightly more confused. I couldn't even remember what the hell we were talking about. Papo and Dre, tired of arguing, thumb-wrestled to see who was going to buy the next drink. Sal swayed side to side like tall grass in the wind. I checked my watch to see that it was about ten minutes shy of being midnight.

Papo stopped thumb-wrestling Dre. Dre lost. He was looking at Sal, who had this strange smile stamped on his mug. "Hey, papa! You straight, Sal?" Papo asked. Sal had turned around slowly while he zipped up his pants. "Careful with where you point that thing, bro. We don't want no accidental shootings 'n shit," Papo continued.

Sal shot his arm straight out in the air, cutting out all the stupid shit we were saying. He does that anytime he feels he has something important to say. He held his hand out in the air, his index finger pointing at me. No, not me. At the silver crucifix hanging around my neck.

"Guess who I just met at the bar, bro? Guess?" Sal asked me.

"I do not know, sir. Um, do I know him or her?" I replied. I also smacked his hand down. I don't really like people pointing their fingers at me or anything else for that matter.

"Is this rhetorical, muh-fucker?" Papo had muttered under his breath. Him and Dre were getting restless, longing to return to the bar and away from this piss-puddled bathroom.

"I just met Michael. The Archangel Michael. He who fought Beelzebub, the Lord of the Flies, many, many moons ago," Sal said nonchalantly. He smiled widely, believing his own story. I glanced at the faces of Dre and Papo, searching for a clue.

"Pull the left one, bitch, that one got bells," Papo snickered. "Archangel Michael? Dude, I knew you were a silly muh-fucker but not a crazy one. You sure it wasn't Mikey? That no-neck ex-marine who sells gym socks and pornos up by Maxwell Street?"

Sal wiped his nose, brushing off what Papo was saying. "I think I know an Archangel from a crackhead, muh-fucker."

"Muh-fucker, you wouldn't know your dick from a Burger King straw, bee-atch! Let alone a muh-fuckin' archangel 'n shit. Ricky let this silly man know," Papo said, pushing me forward.

"No, no, no. Wait. Let the man speak. I'm intrigued, sir. Please continue. You were sitting at the bar when, out of nowhere, the Archangel Michael, 'he who killed the dragon many moons ago,' sat next to you and struck up a conversation. Continue," I urged him on politely. It's not every day your boy is drunk enough to have chit-chats with heavenly beings. No, sir, unlike Papo's story, this was an entirely different and more delicate matter.

Sal backed away a few feet, preparing to tell his saga. "I was just chillin', y'know, mindin' my own business, cool like the other side of the pillow 'n shit. I was at the corner end of the bar, close to the exit. The bartender had just told me that I already had my last drink. I told him I couldn't remember, and to just give me another one to jog my memory. 'Nope,' he said. So I sat back and threw my hands up in disgust. I remember I said, 'God! Why hast thou forsaken me?' Then, out of left field 'n shit, this blond guy, he just appeared, like one minute I turned around and he wasn't there and next—POOF! Right there. Right next to me. Well, he taps me on the shoulder and says, 'It ain't God that's forsaken you, buddy-boy. You did it to yourself.'

"First, I thought 'What's this white muh-fucker doing on Division Street?' Then, I squint one eye and take a closer look. Not just at him, but all around me. The whole club was empty like my beer bottle, yo. Not a damned soul around. I must've turned ten times on my stool till I got all dizzy 'n shit. Still not a sign of life. This blond guy was just sittin' there. Dressed like the Fonz 'n shit. Leather jacket, tight-ass jeans, fuckin' snakeskin boots!! And this long-ass, blond, curly Afro-thing on his head. Fruitier than a muh-fucker, yo.

"'Buddy-boy?' I said to him. 'Who the hell are you to tell me it's my god-damn fault?' So this guy snaps his fingers and POOF!—just like that, two unmarked beer bottles appear in front of us 'n shit. He picks up his and taps it against him as if to say 'Salud!' Then he chugs about half of it, all the while he's trying to stare me down. He puts down the bottle and says, 'I'm Michael. Archangel Michael.' 'What? Miguel Angel?' I asked. 'No!' he said. 'Archangel Michael! The great warrior angel from Heaven.' I nodded in understanding. Whoever he was, he was sure full of himself. That muh-fuck-er could've told me he was a Vice Lord or Regis Philbin for that matter and I still wouldn't have cared. 'So, what are you? You Folks? G.D.? What?' He just ignored me and pointed at my beer that had just appeared.

"Man, I shit you not, I took one gulp of that beer and I was ready just to bust a nut in my pants, dog! It was the best goddamn beer in my entire life! Crisp and light, the taste, like, lingered on my tongue, holding onto it like it didn't want to let go. Then it slid down to my stomach and sent this warm-ass feeling all over my body, the way hot cocoa does 'n shit, right. I kept drinkin' and drinkin' and puttin' it away like it's nobody's business, afraid that it would run out 'n shit. I wasn't even gaggin' or anything. But you know what the best part was?"

Silence. He stopped in the middle of his story. I expected him to keep talking, but I guess the question wasn't rhetorical. I turned to see that Dre and Papo were also expecting Sal to keep talking.

"What? What was the best part, dog?" I finally asked.

"THE BEER BOTTLE NEVER FUCKIN' EMPTIED, MAN. I stared at it as I was drinkin' the fucker." Sal held his hand like he was gripping a bottle and put it way up to his lips, as if the invisible bottle was perpendicular to his mouth. "I drank and drank and still nothin'. Fuckin' Michael had to push my hand down to stop. That nigga looked at me and said, 'You got a lot of heart, buddy. Too bad I ain't here for fun, Sal. I'm here to talk business.' 'Business?' I asked. 'I'm afraid so. The Big Man sent me here. He sent me to warn you.'

"Well, since he was the Archangel Michael, I could only assume that the 'Big Man' was God, but the warning? 'What warning?' I asked him. I stared at the beer bottle, ready to swipe it once his attention was diverted. 'Well, God, my boss, y'know. He wants you to quit having so many relationships with so many different women.' 'You mean stop being friends or stop fucking?' I asked. 'Don't use such words of which you know not the origin. You know where 'fuck' originated from?' 'No,' I said. 'but I'm sure you'll tell me.' 'Fornication under consent. It's an acronym.' 'Really? No shit?' I asked. Like that shit nugget would ever come up in 'Final Jeopardy': 'It has come to God's attention that you have done many a young woman wrong. Leading them on with the promise of a mature relationship. Just as quickly as you finish having sex with them, you dump them, leaving them feeling insecure, troubled, and worthless.' 'Vindictive?' I asked. 'On occasion,' he said. 'Well, it's finally going to catch up to you. Change the error of your ways tonight, buddy-boy, or forever will your soul be damned. Mark my words.' We stared at each other for what seemed like a minute and then, just like that, he got up and walked away. I blinked and everyone was back to their normal selves. So then I had to come tell y'all what happened."

For a brief second, and I do mean brief, I was pretty fuckin' mesmerized with his story. I was picturing it and everything, wishing I could've been there to experience the glory. Trippy-ass shit like that never happens to me. Then, in my left ear, I heard a small, righteous voice whispering in my ear. It was my lawyer and advisor, Mr. Corona. He reminded me that Sal was Sal. Nice guy with a great sense of humor, but either way, he was still drunk as a skunk. And if I was really the intelligent man I claimed to be, I would not fall for such bullshit. He was off his rocker.

I followed Mr. Corona's advice and began laughing my ass off, but I was a bit late. Papo and Dre were already laughing and heckling him. "POOF! What an asshole! Ask Michael when his next album is coming out," and so on and so forth. Rookies. My mind quickly overflowed with primo insults and such, but my timing was off. Salty-ass Sal had already left the bathroom in anger. I was left there with numerous insults and no one to release them upon.

Papo and Dre kept talking their smack. I, on the other hand, turned to face the mirror, splashing water on my hair, checking my nostrils for any hidden debris. "*L'esprit de l'escalier*," I mumbled to myself.

"What's that?" Papo asked me.

I was running my fingers through my hair, searching for the elusive "wet, tussled look" that drives the women crazy. I couldn't accomplish it and settled for the "I'm-so-cool-I-don't-got-to-comb-my-shit-to-get-laid" look. I doubted it would work. "It's French," I said to them. "It means, 'spirit of the stairway.' It relates to those few precious seconds—" BAM! The bathroom door kicked open and slammed against the wall. I didn't see anybody kick it in the mirror's reflection, but I turned around to see that, in fact, somebody had—a very large somebody.

There, in the doorway, was one of the darkest, ugliest motherfuckers I have ever seen in my life's entirety, but he sure did dress smooth. Pimp. His outfit, I mean. From head to toe, this six-foot-eight-inch gigantic behemoth was dressed in pure white—ivory snakeskin boots with white leather pants, milky trench coat over his frosty turtleneck and ice white Fedora hat, even his goatee was albino. His snow-colored eyebrows lowered as he looked over at Papo, Dre, and myself. The only thing that contrasted with his outfit was his dark, chocolate brown skin. Truly amazing.

Standing beside him was a curvaceous, voluptuous, caramel-toned female in a white silky miniskirt, complete with the white pumps designed to make my nipples hard. She was the patron saint of wet dreams, and she knew it. Her jet black hair was long, smooth, and shiny. I searched for my reflection in it and was surprised when I caught myself walking over to her, sniffing the air like an animal in heat. I stopped myself. Their outfits combined made my eyes water with their luster.

Peripherally, I looked for any kind of reaction from Papo and Dre. They were frozen in their tracks, too. Suddenly, I felt alone. The room—hell, the entire club—fell silent in those brief seconds. The door swung closed and we jumped back to our senses. We all tried to play it off nonchalantly, like we'd seen these kind of people all the time in rap videos.

"*L'esprit de l'escalier*," the ivory-clad man said in a deep, cavernous voice. "It's French. It refers to those few, precious seconds after you part company with someone and you think of all the, uh, well, for lack of a better term, 'cooler shit' you could've said. All the things that could've made you sound more slick and witty than the person from whom you just departed, shit you could have said to save your own life. The Spirit of the Stairway. Am I right, Ricky?"

I looked at him warily, unsure of who he was and what to say. Spirit of the Stairway, my ass. I couldn't say shit! Either way, I think I had a good idea of who this guy was but there was no way in hell it could be.

"God?" I asked.

The lights turned off. I let out a frightened gasp in that moment of darkness and instantly reached out with my right hand, feeling for Papo or Dre's shoulder. The lights flickered on and off in a bright crimson. The walls looked like they were bleeding. The man in white took off his hat to reveal his shiny bald head. "No, not quite," he replied with a low, scary chuckle.

"Oh shit," I thought, "I'm going to hell."

"No. Not you. I'm looking for a . . . ," he trailed off as his hand calmly searched his pocket and pulled out a crinkled piece of paper, "a Mr. Salvador Robles. Good-looking guy, muscular build, bald head, snappy dresser, arrogant, cocky, pompous…you know who I mean," he said to us.

Screw this. There's no way shit like this happens to people like me in this type of neighborhood. This guy must be bullshitting. I put on my game face and stepped up close to him. "And who should we tell him is looking for him?" Did I sound hard core? I hoped for my sake that I did.

He shrugged his shoulders as if he couldn't believe my ignorance. He bent down till his mouth was near my ear. "*Pues, yo soy el Diablo, nene. ¿Quien tu crees?*" Translation: "Well, I'm the devil, boy. Who do you think?" Great. This muh-fucker speaks Spanish, too! Now we're really screwed! "Oh. One other thing. Don't step up to me like that," he growled at me as he cracked his knuckles. "That goes for all of you. You'll be barking like a bulldog, but you'll go out like a bitch."

Luckily, Papo stepped up next to me, his chest puffed out and his arms crossed. "Well, DiabloNene. What you want our boy for, huh? What he do now?"

DiabloNene. Catchy name. He looked at the girl next to him and snapped his fingers. The girl, who amidst all this chaos and confusion still managed to give me a hard-on, stepped up to me and Papo and winked at us. She opened the door and strolled out. Dre tried following her, but I grabbed him by the collar and pulled him back. As fine as that girl was, something about her wasn't kosher.

DiabloNene resumed looking at us. He reached his hand into his pocket, felt around, and pulled out a few Polaroids. He handed them to me. The first one had some girl who looked vaguely familiar. "Jessica Martinez. Age 21. Of Puerto-Rican and Colombian descent. Not a bad combo, if you ask me. About three years ago Jessica and a few of her friends attended Club Babylon on a Saturday night. At the club, she had one too many drinks, oblivious that she was being hunted by a certain ill-intentioned individual."

I turned over the next Polaroid and saw, in the foreground, Jessica Martinez hunched over at the bar, appearing more than a few sheets to the wind. In the background, I could see Sal approaching her. "Sal is well known for his promiscuity; Jessica is not. Believe it or don't, Jessica was actually a virgin before she met Sal. But you know Sal. Being the smooth, dapper individual that he is, he charmed and danced the Victoria's Secrets off poor, unsuspecting Jessica."

I turned the next picture over and, as quickly as I did, turned away in disgust. I handed it to Papo who did the same. I didn't get a good look at it, but I swear it looked like Sal, buck-ass naked wearing only cowboy boots and a construction hat, doing some obscure Kama-Sutra-type shit. Too much information. Papo handed the picture to Dre who stared at it with a smile.

Dre chuckled, "I was doing the same shit last week!"

"I know," DiabloNene said. Dre shut his mouth immediately, shuddering at the thought of being watched while he did the nasty.

"Nonetheless, Sal promised her a phone call, saying the usual, 'Yeah, we'll hook up next week; you get your girls, I'll grab my boys, and we'll go dancing or something. I'll call you, baby.' And the girl believed it. One month later, Jessica goes to the doctor and finds out she has gonorrhea."

We all let out a collective groan. We had no idea Sal had gonorrhea and the thought of all the girls that Sal slept with . . . Shit! The whole city would be contaminated within months!

"Nothing to be worried about, really," DiabloNene went on, "but she comes from one of those strict, religious families that go to church every Sunday. She couldn't show her face around her mother and father when underneath the curtains she was harvesting genital warts. So, in desperation, she turned to me. Sold her soul to see Sal die a gruesome, horrible death. I know, I know . . . Selling your soul because you have gonorrhea hardly seems like a rational thing to do, but hell, who am I to complain? 'A soul is a soul is a soul,' as we say in my neck of the woods." The next few pictures were of Jessica and DiabloNene shaking hands. Jessica with a voodoo doll of Sal, and some up-close-and-personal photos of the aforementioned genital warts. I began to feel queasy.

Dre lit a cigarette. He inhaled deeply. "So Sal is pretty much damned then, is that it?"

"Pretty much damned, y'know. I know he's in here somewhere. I can smell his imitation Drakkar all the way from the seventh circle. So if you gentlemen will excuse me, I will leave you to your business," DiabloNene said and reached for the door.

"WAIT!" I shouted. "Um, is there any way you can give me and my associates a moment to discuss a few things?" DiabloNene nodded and looked at his watch. I walked over to the furthest stall that was in there and stepped inside. Dre and Papo followed me in.

"What?" Dre said.

"What do you mean 'what?' We have to do something," I whispered to him.

"Who's 'we?' You got a turd in your pocket, muh-fucker? We ain't got to do a damn thing. Sal played himself," Dre whispered back.

"What the hell are you planning to do, anyway? That's El DiabloNene, man. You know who that is?" Papo asked me. "That's Satan. Beelzebub. The Lord of the Flies. Old Scratch. Muh-fuckin' evil incarnate 'n shit. 'WE' can't do a muh-fuckin' thing. We have no power, Ricky! None! He does! You see how fluently he spoke Spanish? Muh-fucker's too dark-skinned to be pullin' some shit like that!"

"Unless he's one of those dark-ass Dominicans or Cubans or some shit," added Dre. I stayed silent for a moment. How could the night have turned out to be like this?

"'Old Scratch?' When did you read *Faust,* nigga?" I asked Papo.

"I'm not as dumb as you two think, Ricky. Ghetto doesn't mean ignorant."

"It don't mean 'pussy,' either. Jesus! I knew you muh-fuckers were stupid, but I didn't know you were cowards," I replied. "I don't give a fuck if he's a Korean midget with blond dreadlocks, motherfucker. Sal is our boy. OUR BOY! Remember that time he jumped in when we got in a fight against those Kings? He jumped in when we were outnumbered, and he saved our lives!"

"I appreciate the flashback, bro, but Latin Kings and evil incarnate are hardly the same thing. What the fuck do you want us to do? You want us to box?" Papo asked me. His whispering was beginning to get loud. "You want us to step up to him? What the fuck is that gonna achieve but stall him for a few seconds?"

"So you're just gonna stand there and watch him get killed? Huh? What the fuck is wrong with you, Papo? You've gone chicken-shit on me?"

"Fuck you, Ricky. Fuck you and fuck Sal. What the fuck have either of you fuckers done for me that I got to be riskin' my life, my FUCKIN' SOUL, for you two worthless bastards, huh? What'd you do for me that I'm suddenly indebted to you?" Papo was getting closer to me as he got louder.

"Damn it! I just told you that Sal saved your life! Ain't that worth something, you moron!" I got closer to Papo, too. Never back away. My father told me that once.

Dre stepped in between us and gently tried to push us apart, but we were both stubborn and angry. The situation was too much to handle right now. We were puppets, victims of our new machismo. We weren't hearing Dre.

"Yeah, bitch! My life's worth somethin'. It's worth more than gonorrhea, a'ight? It's worth more than some dumb ass who's so anxious to have sex that he can't spare a few seconds of his life to put on a condom and now he has to pay for it with his goddamned soul. It's worth more than your stupid ass that wants to be a fuckin' hero. YOU CAN'T DO SHIT! Look before you leap, Ricky!" Papo yelled at me, punctuating the last sentence with a hard shove on my chest. I stumbled back and hit the wall of the stall.

"Oh, it's like that, huh?" I reached into the back seat of my pants and unsheathed Jambu, the monkey-knife. "You feeling froggy, Papo? Go ahead and jump!" Papo's eyes widened. My heartbeat raced as I waited for any sudden movement. We froze there, in that position, as the red light of the room pulsated with the suspended rage that was caged in my veins. I looked at the knife for a long second and felt ashamed. I dropped the knife onto the ground and stuck my hand out to Papo. His eyes watering, Papo grabbed it and shook it firmly. I whispered to them, "I don't know what to do."

Silence. The truth was that I had no plan, just the urgency to do something. I could not, in good conscience, just let this prick come up from Hell and take my friend's life. Dre put his hands in his pocket and sighed.

"We can pray," Dre mentioned.

"HA!" DiabloNene broke out into a loud fit of laughter. It made me shiver. I couldn't see him from where we were standing, but I could imagine him. We were seriously outgunned. Here we were trying our best to talk quietly so that Diablo couldn't hear us, when all along we were being played. I had a feeling that prayers would only make matters worse. Where the fuck was Michael when you needed him?

I looked at Dre and Papo. I held their gaze for what seemed like an eternity. I thought about what I could do, if in fact there was anything that could be done. My lawyer and advisor, Mr. Corona, had left for the day, about the same moment I shit my pants. I snapped out of it. Standing up straight, I unlocked the stall door. Dre grabbed my arm.

"Ricky, what are you going to do?" Dre asked me. "You're not going to use Jambu, are you?"

"No," I said to him. "It wouldn't work if I wanted it to. I'm just going to talk him out of it." I opened the stall door and stepped outside. To my surprise, Papo followed me.

DiabloNene was waiting for us, leaning against the wall with his arms crossed. I stepped to within a few feet of him. "I have a proposition for you, Diablo. You ready?"

He stared at me calmly, unflinching. "Go ahead," he said.

I continued, "I'm willing to wager my soul that I can make Sal go celibate for two whole years. Completely virgin. That means no kissing, no grabbing, no flirting, no nothing. Not even masturbating. If I lose—well, my soul is all yours, mine and Sal's. But if I win, Sal and I never see you again, not even in the afterlife."

I let the full weight of my words and wager truly permeate the air. Once again, there was that uncomfortable silence. DiabloNene lowered his eyes and seemed to ponder it. Slowly, he raised his eyes to meet mine and said, "No dice," and began to open the door.

"Wait!" Papo yelled out, "add my soul to that little bet."

"Mine, too," Dre added. I turned and smiled at them. This would certainly make him reconsider.

DiabloNene smiled and licked his lips. "OK. It's a deal. Three souls for the price of one." Immediately, he pulled out a neatly folded piece of paper and a ballpoint pen. He handed it to me as Dre and Papo crowded around me to read it. It was a contract describing in detail what just came out of my mouth. I read and double-checked every word in that contract. With the ballpoint pen, I signed at the dotted line and initialed on the three lines below that. Just like that. Dre and Papo did the same.

We handed the contract back to DiabloNene, who proceeded to fold and place it in his inside pocket. I sighed with relief. Papo and Dre patted me on the back and mentioned that we needed a stiff drink. We laughed nervously to conceal the fact that we wanted to cry. Fuck a drink! I'd never drink again, not if I needed to spend the next two years making sure Sal didn't get laid. Poor guy. It was cool, I'd do enough for the both of us.

"Well, gentlemen, see you around." DiabloNene put on his hat and winked at us as he opened the door. "Hey Diablo!" Dre yelled out. "Who was that fine-ass girl you were here with?"

DiableNene chuckled. "Why? You want me to hook you up? Sorry, Andres, but she's already spoken for. She's the—how do you say—physical embodiment of vengeance. See, if Sal were a junkie, she'd be an injection of the finest heroin."

I looked out of the door and screamed in horror. About fifty feet away, Sal was in a secluded room on the opposite side of the dance floor, handcuffed to a chair with his eyes closed, his head bobbing up and down to a James Brown song. In front of him, Diablo's companion was dancing seductively, giving him the lap dance to end all lap dances.

I ran out of the bathroom and onto the dance floor. I tried pushing my way through but kept getting pushed back. That drunk feeling that I thought I lost when Diablo came in—well—it returned with a vengeance. Papo and Dre were behind me, screaming out Sal's name, yelling for him to stop. Nothing. The music was too loud. James Brown was too loud. Suddenly, I felt a heavy finger tap me on the shoulder. I turned to see DiabloNene towering behind me. Papo and Dre pushed forward, ignoring him.

"If Sal were an alcoholic, she'd be the best bottle of tequila a soul could buy. But, Sal is a womanizer, and payback, as they say, is a bitch." I turned to see Papo getting knocked down to the floor. Dre was still making his way through but with little result. Then, in the secluded room where Sal was hand-cuffed to the chair, I saw the girl pull off all her clothes in one gentle tug, revealing the gorgeous body that would be his downfall. Sal turned his head in my direction and looked me dead in the eye. I shouted at the top of my lungs, "NO! STOP IT, SAL!" He didn't hear me, though. He just winked at me. The door to his room slammed shut. I turned to see DiabloNene smiling widely, his face changing, transforming into something I had never seen before. I screamed in horror. I saw Papo getting lifted up by two bouncers who were ready to throw him out. I saw Dre falling to his knees, clutching the sil-ver crucifix around his neck. Then, without warning, all the lights in Dante's went out. POOF! Darkness surrounded me as I felt a large cold hand grab me by my throat, squeezing my life, my rage, my fear, and my soul out of my brave, foolish body.

White Boy

SYIENNA B. INGRAM

“A muthafucka tryin' to explain the game to a lame is like a scientist tryin' to explain physics to a wino…it can't be done." White Boy tilted his head to the left so Samella could continue the pattern of finger waves started fifteen minutes earlier. Her shop faced the main highway, Route 53, going towards Joliet. Big brown letters spelling out SAMELLA'S SALON: WHERE THE NAPS GET SNAPPED BACK adorned the entire window, leaving only enough room to welcome walk-ins as well as to advertise the many styles in which women could get their hair done. Finger waves, freeze curls, press and curl, perm, twists, locks, braids, and wash and sets were the main courses on the menu. The smell of burning hair always lingered inside the shop, for it was Samella's territorial mark. The paint on the walls, once the color of red, was faded, masked by dirt that seemed to have been untouched for decades. It was the death mask of the life that the structure had known a long time ago. There was no artwork to decorate the walls, with the exception of photographs from various magazines depicting professionally done coifs that made every American woman's hopes and dreams of beauty seem reachable. Her shop wasn't much to look at, nothing to see at all, yet it was a testimonial to the principle of hard work.

It was Wednesday, the designated slow day of the week. Samella didn't schedule many clients on Wednesday, just a few. She wanted to get in and out so she could go home and be with her family. White Boy was her last customer, and she looked forward to him coming in every Wednesday for his hair appointment. He was a quick head to do and they always had good conversation.

"Bitches kill me how they always say that niggas be forcin' them to do shit. I don't put no gun up to a bitch head to make her do nothin'. If she want to ho, that is of her free will." White Boy was white and a pimp, yet he had a good heart. He was immersed in black life as deep as a malt-liquor billboard. He was accepted and loved. He remained where he had always been welcomed. Nobody gave a damn if he was white…he was human and that was the only thing that mattered. He had been pimpin' for as long as Samella had known him, thirty years. They grew up together and even dated before he got locked up for something "he didn't do." Average height, with neck-length sandy blond hair and sea blue eyes, White Boy was a sight to see. Even though he was falling victim to the law of gravity, he was still handsome. Every girl he ran upon still fell under his Rasputin-like influence whenever he came around. Like flies to shit, these women flocked to him hoping he'd provide the substance for their growth.

"You a mess, White Boy. You need to leave that bullshit alone, find yourself a woman, and call it a day."

Samella tilted White Boy's head to the front so she could wave up the back. White Boy's business was the main topic of the day.

"Samella, I don't be doin' shit to them girls . . . now this bitch want to sue me, sayin' I took all her money. The judge gon' have a field day with this one." White Boy gazed intently at his shoes. Though he masked his despair through talking shit, he was nervous. He had never been sued before, and this was a battle he wasn't ready to fight. Something in the night air didn't feel quite comfortable, and he was unsure as to why.

"White Boy, look, you have to go ahead and fight this or not. You got the power to pick and choose your own battles. Why is she accusing you of takin' her money, anyway? You her pimp, so you basically s'posed to give her money, right?" Samella turned White Boy's chair toward her so she could wave up the front.

"Girl, you know the game . . . that's what it's all about. You make money and then give it to me so I can help you handle yo' shit. What I'm doin' ain't no different than what the government does since its incarnation, you dig?" White Boy laughed and licked his tongue over the gold treasure embedded in his teeth.

"I know that's right," Samella responded as she turned White Boy's chair back around towards the window. "The world is filled with pimps and hos, and we'll just talk about those I know."

Both Samella and White Boy laughed, bringing ease to the atmosphere.

"Naw, but she suing me 'cause I didn't want to make that bitch my bitch, you dig? I was just fuckin' her. And you know how some muthafuckas be getting they emotions involved in shit after you done already let them know out the door that you just tryin to get yo raw off, you know what I'm sayin? Now she says she pregnant. She vengeful just like her mama."

"Who her mama, White Boy?" Samella said as she stood back and admired her work.

"Latonya Mitchell. The dark-skinned sista who use to go with Jermaine, crack-addict ass."

"White Boy, you mean to tell me you was fuckin' a kid? Boy, don't tell me no more."

"She ain't no kid, Samella, that bitch seventeen." White Boy wiped the dripping wave solution from around his neck.

Samella shook her head in disgust and passed White Boy a hand-held mirror so he could fully admire the artwork done by a master. "That don't mean shit. You messin' around with somebody whose mama went to school with us. That ain't cool. White Boy, you finna be fifty-five years old. Stop." Samella sat in another chair directly across from White Boy. He passed her a cigarette.

"Samella, I know I need to get out of the game . . . but I'm in too deep to get out now. I need a pair of good boots to help me sludge through the shit if I ever decide to."

Samella laughed and crossed her legs. She gave White Boy a full-body, up-and-down glance. She noticed that he was still as good-looking as the day she met him. "White Boy, change your life. You too old for this, in all honesty. You still got yo' looks, you still as charmin' and smart as the first day I met you." She passed him a book of matches. White Boy glanced down at the book and noticed that written on the back of it with a black marker were the words, "To thine own self be true."

"Like this matchbook say, Samella, to thy own self be true, and I don't know what else to do. Pimpin' is all I know. It is as second nature to a nigga like breathin'. You know what I'm sayin'? What Imo do? I'm damn near sixty, ain't never worked a legit job in my life. I want to change, but I'm scared." White Boy's words and honesty shocked Samella. Here was a man who had taken a life, abused women and drugs, and done God knows what else confessing that he was scared of living.

"Scared, are you, White Boy?"

Taken aback by the question posed to him, White Boy smirked and simply said, "Yeah . . . I'm scared. Righteousness is not something I know too well." White Boy turned red. His eyes allowed water to form but not to fall.

The ashes of his cigarette became a leaning tower ready to topple over at any moment. "God is the core, White Boy. You have to submit to HIS will in order to understand life and its beauty. You done blocked that experience for so long dealin' and involvin' yo' self in bullshit that it is time now to reevaluate yo' life and make peace with yo' past. Better do it fast so you can have some good karma."

"Make peace how, Samella? What you talkin' 'bout? You been smokin' weed?"

They both laughed as Samella continued on with her plea.

"I'm just sayin' that it's time to grow up and be a man. Step up to yo' responsibilities. If that li'l girl knocked up, take care of that baby. If the court decides that you pimpin' her wasn't right, pay her. Everything happens for a reason. God is a bad muthafucka!"

They both laughed, and Samella rose up out of her seat to use the bathroom. "I'm finna go take a shit. Imo be back in a good twenty minutes or so."

"Gon' get yo' shit on, girl. I ain't goin' nowhere," White Boy said, followed by a burst of laughter from the both of them. Samella went into the back.

White Boy had time to gather his thoughts now that he was alone. The wind battered up against the window, shaking the frame as if it were unconscious. White Boy's mind was at ease after the conversation with Samella. Maybe she was right, yet he thought and seriously contemplated changing his life around for a mere two minutes. The thought of settling down and living a "normal" life quickly disappeared as the salon door slammed shut. White Boy looked up into the eyes of his seventeen-year-old mistress. She was scrawny, wearin' an oversized brown trenchcoat. Her face was that of an adult, yet her eyes revealed that she was still a child. Her hair was pulled back in a ponytail, and her skin, the color of burnt sienna, was streaked by tears and snot. Before he could stand up, she pulled out a silver magnum and ended White Boy's life. A single bullet shot to the forehead sent him back into the chair that he had just risen from. Samella, startled, came out of the bathroom only to be met by a bullet to the chest. She fell immediately to the floor, clutching her wound.

"Fuck all y'all! Who's the bitch now?" The child mistress exited the shop as quickly as she had come in.

The bodies of Samella and White Boy remained as still as a picture. The expressionless face of White Boy turned purple, while the body of Samella made one last attempt to live but expired as soon as she reached White Boy's feet. The wind continued to blow as the sun eerily set. Its reddish yellow glow covered the bodies like a shroud while the radio softly told of the traffic buildup on the Eisenhower Expressway.

Brian's Dream

DAVID OLIVER

I was in the desert again. I saw the Iraqi soldier fall to the ground. I heard his blood splatter against the dry desert floor. I was in a dirty house. Goats baah-ed outside; an infant screamed in another room. I saw his face; it hung in a frame on a gray cinderblock wall with Arabic writing underneath it. The baby's scream intensified and a woman shouted in a foreign tongue. Glass shattered, and then there was silence. She stood in front of me, two eyes peering at me from beneath dark, thick eyebrows. She suffocated in her tight black veil. Her eyes slit through me like a fresh salmon at the fish market. I quietly sat down in an electric chair.

I plunged a knife through a closed Bible. As I thrust the blade again and again, shreds of Scripture jerked out and floated throughout the room. I set the ragged book on fire and felt God rise in the flames. I saw hell in a desert where hungry tanks roamed and gunfire resonated in the dry air. I heard the screams and cries of children; I heard broken glass and helicopters. The stench of burning oil and disease was a pleasing scent to the Satan who ruled these dunes of death. I saw the chair again and pointed my rifle at it, riddling bullets against its crude metal frame. It sparked and laughed; it refused to die.

The gritty sand crawled upon my skin. The harsh wind spread the tiny grains everywhere, into the corners of my eyes, into my ears, underneath my fingernails. They entered my closed mouth and tightly nuzzled themselves against the tops of my gums and against my wisdom teeth. It was a torture without pain. The woman walked toward me again over a dune. The sand and rocks pummeled her, but she walked unfazed. Her eyes were locked, as were mine through the scope. She had something in her arms. She walked closer and closer, leaving no footprints in the sand behind her. She stopped and held a dead baby in the air with one hand. She shook it at me. Its head flailed and bounced violently. She held it by its thigh and waved its pale torso like a white flag. I was not programmed to understand surrender; I fired at her until she was gone. The baby lay at my feet. I looked down but only from a clinical perspective. I attached no emotion to the lifeless child. For in hell, emotion is weakness, and I would never be called weak. Another soldier scooped the body up in a shovel and took it away. A tear formed. I fired my gun at it relentlessly until it was gone.

Death is comfortable here. You feel its presence and ignore it with respect. You pour water into your hands and drink your reflection as the sun laughs wildly in the sky. You know that guilt lies over there on the other side where the vultures play. You let it rot and die and never claim it as your own. Guilt is the enemy here. The fire consumes you. You either forget why you are here, or you pretend that you once knew. All you know is that it is better to kill than to die. Death takes no sides.

I saw the soldier rise and the blood flow back into his brain like a film run backwards. I waited for the bullet to go back into my gun. He became a boy kicking a ball in a dirty village where homely cows meandered and moaned, where violence and fear spread like disease, where there was no Mickey Mouse or Scooby Doo. I killed that small boy because they said he was wrong. I killed him over and over again. He strapped me to the electric chair, and the hot current sizzled through my veins. He pointed my gun at me. I saw myself through the scope. The sky began to rain blood. Dark, soulless puddles formed just below my bare feet. I struggled to keep my toes from touching the blood. It swallowed me. I fought and thrashed against it; I struggled for air. The sour taste of blood touched my parched lips. Its rank smell tingled against my nose like ammonia. I felt my face break through the thin brown skin that formed on the surface. My head became submerged; I no longer had the strength to lift it. I floated to another place.

I hear an ice-cream man's bell ting-a-ling a block away. I taste the scratchy sweet texture of Froot Loops on my tongue and can smell fresh-cut grass wafting in the soft summer air. The woman stands in my room. The baby is alive and gently cooing. She points the baby at me. My head snaps back, and I feel my funny bone crack against the hardwood floor as I collapse. My heart pounds. She puts the baby in front of her face and looks at me through its eyes. She screams at me. White threads of spit roll up into the corners of her mouth as she screams. Her anger burns. She puts the baby on top of me and sits down in the electric chair. I look at her through the baby's eyes and see myself in the chair. I reach for my gun, but it's gone.

Baby-Cakes

KELI STEWART

The old women sat on Mrs. Collette Simmons's porch one summer afternoon like young girls, listening to a story of a first kiss. The smell of freshly cut grass from down the block and smoked meat cooking on her stove pervaded their noses. In various positions, some even sitting on the steps in muu-muus and various flowery frocks, nine women listened as Collette Simmons in all of her orthopedic glory gave instructions on how they could be young again: "Ah's don't know why Ah did it. Well, yes Ah do. But Ah's don't know what came ovah myself. Seem lak' tuh me when Ah notice anythang, Ah wuz justa movin' down de walkway lak' a slow-motion loco-motive. Can you picture me justa movin' at my ol' age? But Ah could smell her comin'. Smell lak' de perfume dem dere's haughty women usta wear when Ah's a chile. We's hadta walk tuh de schoolhouse. We's all had our few books an' a burlap croka' sack. All's us had our bread and beans in de same sack. Me an' my siblings four. We's walk past de station. Seem like tuh me dere wuz always somebody comin' into our town or tryin' tuh git de hell away from it. Ha! Dem haughty women would line up outside de train station lookin' all purdy wit all dey purdy colors and such. Dem warm wraps wit de fur around de collar and dem brim hats cocked tuh de side lak dey wuz a movie actor. Dey wore lace an' satin-like dresses. Look lak tuh me dat what dey were wearin' wuz some undergarment, way it hung off dey skin. Me an' my sista useta wish we's wuz dem. Sometime dey's throw little chocolate mints at us. At our feet. Ah's useta save mine fo' a long time. Seem lak tuh me, 'dose thangs wuz too good tuh eat. Dey's wuz wrapped up in gold paper. We's walk past dem wit our heads down, though. Sometimes we didn't even see dem mints. Mama useta say don't stare at no white folks fuh too long. Dey li'ble tuh lynch yuh fuh jus' lookin', even chil'ren. Dey have an' dey will.

"But de lady dat walk past my house reminds me of de haughty ladies. Seem lak her dress jus' be made for her, an' dat's it! How her dress hug her body jus' perfect-like, jus' lak dem haughty ladies. Somebody else git in it an' de breast part be too small or too big an' de zipper won't zip. But it be just perfect on her. Way she walk, you would think dat she wuz de Queen of Egypt instead of what she be. First Ah thought she be one of dem street ladies, and if she wuz, oh! Ah wouldn't set my eyes on de laks of her. But when Ah's sees her it be durin' de day, lak she be goin' tuh de afternoon job. She justa walk past switchin' her behind, plump lak a pig ready tuh be took tuh de market.

"Ah's remember when Ah's wuz a hot thang. Ah had some long purdy black hair! Jus' lak a Indian, Ah did. Ah's wuz perfect. Dat be de way God made me! Ah's didn't have nothin' tuh push up tuh make lak dis an' hold down so's Ah's could git into dat. Many menfolks wanted tuh court me. My daddy had tuh turn down many mens dat wanted tuh marry me. Dey come, sometimes dey might have some flowers or some chocolate. Say, "Mr. Johnson, sir, Collette in de house right now?" "And what if she ain't?" my daddy say, lightin' his pipe, outright bein' mean tuh de young man. Tryin' tuh run him through de wringa' tryin' tuh git tuh me. Me an' my sista be in de livin' room justa gigglin' all low, 'cause Daddy try tuh ack a fool. Ha! Dem wuz some good times. Seem lak tuh me de times went an' gone away. Frank done died. Oh! Ah's wishes he wuz here wid me. So Ah's just go about doin' what Ah's be doin'. An' dat's sittin' on de porch watchin' folks. Dat's when Ah first seen de lady. Ah's call her Baby-Cakes 'cause she smell so good an' look good, too. Every day 'fore de little chil'rens git outta school at two-thirty P.M., Ah sees her walkin' down de street. De menfolks, dey just be lookin' and gawkin', just about droolin' lak wild wolves when she walk past. De womenfolk be envious fo' dey husbands, but Ah's be envious fo' me! Ah picture what it be like again, tuh have soft skin, and perky breasts and wear high-heels, ain't gotta use no devilish cane. Knees be so bad sometimes Ah's can't even walk.

"She just smell so good. Reminds me how Ah's useta be. A pretty gal, befo' babies an' such a thang. Ain't no nasty feelin's though. Oh! No, ain't no sucha thang as nasty feeling comin' from dis body of Christ. Oh! Lordy no!

She's just be so purdy. Ah's just wants her skin. Look lak chocolate. Reminds of 'dose mints. Dey roun' and smooth an roll ovah in my mouf. Ah's feels lak if Ah's taste her skin, maybe some of dat young stuff rub off on me an' Ah's be young a' gin.

"Ah's wuz just by de gate, balancin' my weight on de gate, 'cause if Ah don't Ah's fall flat on my face. Ah hadta let my cane go if Ah's wuz goin' tuh do what Ah did. An' it seems like when Ah did dat, my stockin's just slid right off, but Ah's figure if Ah's don't do it now, Ah ain't neva gon' do it, an' Ah stay old fo'eva. Ah's seen her out de corner of my eye. How Ah's stayed on de gate is 'cause Ah's pretend lak Ah's talkin' tuh de mailman up de way. An' she came up de way, just switchin' her behin'. She had on all polki-dots. White and red, wid de white gloves, shoes, an de purse tuh match. Hee! Hee! Hee! Ah's just stan' dere lak Ah's wuz waitin' fo' de mail. You know, hummin' lak 'La-la-la-la,' twiddlin' my thumbs. She wuz comin', an' soon's she got one inch past me, Ah snatches her up by de back of her dress. Look lak a flyin' bird pickin' up de fish outta water! Done tore her dress an' all. Baby-Cakes done fell out of her heels. But she ain't fall. No, Lordy! My one chance lak dat? Ah's wuzn't gon' let her go 'til Ah's did what Ah's did for nothin'. Ah lean forward when Ah's got her close enough 'cause Ah's still got my hand on her dress, an' Ah licks her. Lak she wuz one dem lollipops. She taste like Florida Water and sugar cane! In all de commotion my wig done fell off an' such a thang. An' right den an' dere, Ah's felt somethin' in my skin. Felt lak magic all though my body. Lak it wuz gettin' filled up wid de Holy Spirit! Hallelujah! 'Cause you see de one thang is dat she musta thought dat she got caught on de nail or de fence. Ha! De shock li'ble tuh git'cha quick dat, you won't know what happened. Seem like Ah's could fish wid my bare hands, Ah's so quick. She turn around. Seem like she didn't know dat dis ol' tongue wuz on her flesh. She let out a scream, cuz Ah's don't think she knew it wuz me. Hee! Hee! Hee! By den my hands wuz jus' folded up on de gate lak Ah's didn't know what happened. Ah says, wit my stockin's 'roun my ankles an' my wig on de groun', 'Now, watch yo'self, baby. De nail on dat gate been gettin' folks fuh years.' An' now Ah's young a'gin.

"Youth! Baby-Cakes made me young. See!" Collette Simmons bucked her old eyes wide, stuck her head out like a turtle and turned it so that each woman on the porch could see her youthful skin. She rubbed her gums together, making her lower jaw stick out, as lipstick lay waiting in the creases of her lip. Her blue eye shadow caked up in her wrinkled eyelids, as she lifted her arms up in the air and shook them, moving the flab that years and gravity had settled at the base of her arms. The old ladies maneuvered to see and exclaimed, "Oooohhhh!" at the youth Collette proclaimed, and they all swore that she *had* changed.

That very night of the incident, Mrs. Collette Simmons wringled her way into her vanity chair she hadn't used in thirty years. She pinned her hair up into a slight pompadour. She applied two brushes of lipstick on both lips with her shaking hands and pressed her lips together. She felt clumps of old lipstick on her lips. The blue eye shadow that she wore thirty years earlier sparkled in its iron container. She took the hardened mass and applied it with her fingertips and then dabbed her face with foundation powder. She sat on her bed and pulled a red sequined dress up over her knees quicker than she normally would. With her slip hanging off her shoulder she stood up in the dress, with fringelike tassels all over. She dusted the dust set into the mirror with a red-feathered fan she had gotten out of a shoe box high up in her closet, inched her way up, and squinted her bedazzled eyes. Mrs. Collette Simmons smiled at what she saw, and humming a song she had forgotten the words to, began to shake her shimmy, making the loose tassels on her dress move every which way.

Scripture

TAMARA MICHAEL

If it wasn't for the fact that he was a preacher, I wouldn't have sat and waited in a chair that was so uncomfortable. Maybe it was a way to get rid of the bereaved or the troubled who always tended to stay everywhere too long, especially in Pastor Will's office. He had the shade completely drawn, which was fine with me since it was so bright outside. The light was still bursting through the bottom and edges of the cheap shade, like some kind of explosion was happening in the yard. Books were everywhere. You would think he'd only need one book in his line of work, maybe a back-up, but not this many. He'd told me he put up a new painting of Jesus behind his desk, but he hadn't mentioned it was so darn big. Jesus was carrying the cross up to Calvary with mean-looking people caught in the painting with screaming mouths open. The crown of thorns was jammed on his head with red droplets of blood dotting his temple. He was almost naked except for a large cloth around his waist that kept the whole thing from being too immodest. Somebody must have taken the time to do Jesus' hair because it sure did look clean and curled for someone who'd been beaten with a cat-o'-nine-tails and forced to carry a wooden cross through that mob. It was something to look at, but I bet it cost too much.

There was a paper in the center of the pastor's desk. Although it was upside down, I could finally make out that it was a daily schedule of some sort, written in neat hand. Grace and Mitchell Anderson, 3:00. *There* were some newlyweds who weren't gonna last. I didn't blame Mitch for wanting to drink all the time; Grace always looked like she just bit into a rotten apple. It was only one o'clock; surely he didn't think I was going to sit here with him for two hours.

The pastor's door opened, and he marched in like a man with a bayonet up his spine. He had a pale face like many pastors but, unlike most, his skin had an unlimited pearliness to it that was almost feminine. I guess because of his fine skin it was strange to me that he had a broad forehead topping off a face that always had a five o'clock shadow from what looked to be a ferociously thick set of whiskers. It put you in mind of a thug or at least some kind of tough guy, and he couldn't have been further from either of those. His nose was pretty large but straight, no telltale bumps on it from old fistfights.

I was sure he still considered himself a young man. I didn't get up, but I did return his calm smile.

"May, early as usual. Thank you for coming. Coffee?"

"No, thank you, Pastor." Not from that second-hand coffee machine that someone had unloaded on him. Men never made good coffee anyway.

Pastor Will sat down behind his desk across from me. In a flash I wondered if he was trying to intimidate me, somehow. It wasn't working. He was a little uncomfortable; I knew this because he always slowly clenched and unclenched his hands when he was out of sorts. He had on brown pants and a brown shirt. Maybe he should've considered wearing his Sunday preacher robe during all of his pastoral duties; it might inspire more respect.

"May, I want to talk to you about last night, when we were at Ruby Lash's." He looked me straight in the eyes. I'd never noticed that his were more gray than blue, but I didn't go around staring at his eyes, either. I didn't have much choice but to look at them now unless I wanted to stare at half-naked Jesus on the wall or the brown carpet on the floor. I stiffened but didn't drop my own eyes as he went on with his little speech.

"You know that I think highly of you and of your devotion to God, and that I am your friend, not just your pastor. You've helped me in passing many a person into God's waiting arms, and I want you to know I appreciate it." The "but" was surely coming, wiping out all the needless compliments.

"But I want to ask you, and I want you to know that we can talk about it—you know that these conversations are private. Why did you stop at Ruby's last night? I had not called you."

The pastor was a frank man; there was no other way to handle country people. He was a passing good man, but I'd noticed that he didn't know anything about spirits except what the Bible told him, while it was in my blood to know. As a rule, people never give up easily, looking for some last-minute solution to a body that's already quit. It seems to me that animals and humans don't die all that differently, fighting it to the very end. Everyone fears that last breath—the crying family, Pastor Will and me standing over some old man or woman, or the occasional young person who's struck down with a malignant disease the doctor can't cut out—dreading that last wheeze. To me, it's one of man's finest moments, respecting the quiet, trying not to muddle it with talk, and the air in the death room sets to tingling as the mouth releases the spirit with one last exhale. One look in their unquiet eyes, with my firm hand on their brow, and they know that I am there as a friend, to smooth the way. I know the words to the language of this ceremony; it stays the same, and I like that.

Pastor Will performed his duties well, but he was mainly a comfort to the living left behind. He'd never even talked in tongues that I knew of. I thought it best not to mention those things at this very moment. *Why* was I at Ruby's house? What a question. More like, "May, how have you kept from taking a cleaver and slicing her open down the middle? What a woman of God you must be to resist such justice." People ask all the wrong things. Pastors are the worst; they know what they should be asking, but of course they can't. Those robes are heavy in more ways than one.

"I saw your car in Ruby's driveway. I was on my way home from the store. I thought maybe you needed some help, is all. Ruby *is* about to drink herself to death."

Pastor Will kept looking me straight in the eyes. He was getting angry, as the clenching and unclenching was getting faster. He didn't even want to come close to talking about any of Ruby's personal problems with me.

"May, you didn't even knock. When I came into the living room you were standing in the middle of it shaking her daughter. Hazel's just a little girl, and you absolutely terrified her. And you could see what effect it had on Ruby when she walked in."

I stiffened even more. If he made me any more tense he was going to cause me to crack some bones. I'd seen what effect I'd had on Ruby, all right. First of all, Hazel was a child who needed shaking. She was twelve going on forty. She hadn't been terrified, she'd told me to get out of the house, that she knew where her daddy's shotgun was. She looked straight at me and said, "My mom doesn't want you to set foot near me. You get out of here, you *bitch*."

Everyone knew the child said any darn thing that came into her head, and Ruby was too drunk to know it. I had knocked, but very, very softly. The screen on the door was torn and the white paint mostly chipped away. The knob looked like it would've come off in my hand if I had yanked very hard. A person couldn't knock on that door too hard, it'd fall right off its hinges.

I had thought that maybe Ruby was finally dying. Standing there on her little porch that smelled like rotting wood, the metal chairs and tables that would have been just right for her and Jack to sit in on a summer day and drink beer, now looking like rusted metal corpses. She'd planted too many viney bushes and plants too close to the house. Everyone knows that honeysuckle and trumpet vine take over everything if you let them. Those trumpet flowers that were too big and too orange were hanging off spindly, untrimmed branches from gutters along the roof of the porch, so I'd had to duck my head. It seemed like she had to be dying, that the house wasn't gonna stay standing one minute more, the flowers and vines trying to make all that rot somehow pleasant. I could smell it, and I could see it as I'd seen it a hundred times before, there's something about the way death marks a house before it even enters it. But I couldn't hardly tell someone like Pastor Will all of that. He'd run and go look it up in the Bible, and if he didn't find it then it wouldn't be true. "No, May, there isn't anything in here about trumpet vines and death…"

I knew that if the pastor had come to the door he wouldn't have let me in. I just walked on in before Hazel could even answer my knock, but there's no denying that I *had* knocked, that's for sure. That little green-eyed creation had squarely faced me and hadn't flinched. Now I had to explain myself to the pastor, and of course *she* didn't have to explain anything. I'm sure she flashed those sparkly eyes at the Pastor with a sweet smile which hid how sharp her little teeth were. I'm sure he saw a darling, creamy-cheeked girl with a mangy, brown, secondhand dress that didn't cover the scabs on her knees that her mother never thought to get after her for picking. Pastor Will, who was always seeking out poverty so that it could break his heart, would not fail to notice that Hazel's black, scuffed shoes were second- or third-hand-me-downs, were at least a size too big for a little girl who was not a lick bigger than she should be for twelve years old. With her hair bobbed off at her chin, which I knew the barber did for free out of pity even though he never cut a woman's hair as a rule, she could still look pitifully young. That youth downright disappeared if she was hissing at you like a rabid cat. But Pastor Will wouldn't have seen that side of her.

I just stood there after she'd called me a bitch. I didn't expect much from a child of Ruby's, but that did get me for a minute. She'd stomped her foot hard.

"I said get out of here, you old church buzzard!"

What she'd needed was a split lip that'd fill her mouth with blood and shut her up. But I was the adult, I was the Christian, and I acted like one.

"Now, Hazel, I know your mama's not doing too good. You're gonna need some help. Just look at you. I could be a real friend. Maybe we could see about getting you a decent dress."

She looked like she could spit bullets until I mentioned her dress. Prideful thing, just like Ruby. Ruby was always too much of everything, too much cleavage, red lipstick, nail polish, high heels, and shimmery stockings. She was one of those women who never walked fast because she'd lose the chance to roll her hips. Hazel didn't have two pennies to rub together, but I knew it'd be just a matter of time before she acted like her mama and drew men's money to her like pigs to a trough.

She wiped her eyes savagely, set her mouth in cast iron, and through gritted teeth hissed, "You're an ugly bag in an ole flour sack. Even if she is dying, you don't hold a candle to my mama. You got the face of a dead person."

I don't even remember grabbing her shoulders, but I do remember thinking once I realized that I was shaking the life out of her, that she was lucky it wasn't her throat I was squeezing instead.

Pastor Will didn't hear any of what she'd said to me, he just walked in and saw her dissolve into a little sobbing heap on a dirty rug on the floor, after he caught me shaking her. The lamps didn't even have shades on them. Bare bulbs always make everything in a room worse. What was I gonna tell him when he'd missed everything important, like usual?

"Well, Pastor, I thought you would need my help, that maybe I'd missed your call because I'd been in town at the store. It isn't a secret that she ain't long for this world, now, is it? And it isn't no secret that Hazel says anything that comes to mind, and I won't even tell you what she said to me, and my trying to come and help her mama and all. Under the circumstances, I think it was generous of me to even stop to attend to my duties with you."

Pastor Will let out a breath that it seemed he'd been holding and looked down at his soft hands clenching and unclenching. He was not admitting defeat, but rallying his thoughts and calming his words. He looked up, stern as God himself. The painted Jesus with his cross was rising up above Pastor Will's head, and I understood why he'd put it behind his desk.

"May, I think you need to talk about those 'circumstances.' It was a long time ago, and I don't think you've let go. Your face when you were shaking that child . . . May, I thought you were going to take a bite out of her. I know that you were set to marry Jack years ago, but you can't hold that against Ruby and certainly not her child; it was his choice."

That was a blow; I didn't talk about that with anyone, but I was tougher than a couple of words. Anyhow, I knew that he would rather die on the cross himself than tell anyone what went on in his office, so if he wanted to talk, fine, then we'd talk. He definitely thought highly of himself, putting my life on the table like that.

"First of all, a woman getting pregnant with a man's child—if Hazel even *is* Jack's—doesn't give a man much choice, now does it, Pastor? Yes, Jack and I were set to be married, and yes, Ruby trapped him, but I wouldn't take it out on that child, and landsakes, it was years ago. I don't need to talk about it. I've got a husband and child of my own. I just thought you needed me, is all. That's all I've got to say about it, Pastor."

Earl was not much of a husband, but he was a provider and a fair father. Iris was a good daughter. She did what she was told when she was told to do it. If I told her to go get a jar of canned tomatoes she didn't come back with pickles like most girls her age had a tendency to do. In any case, she was the only child. She looked just like me, which I guess was OK as Earl had lost all his hair and had such thick eyelids that you could barely see his brown eyes. She wore her black hair in one long braid down the back, just like I did. Her skin was better than mine on account of youth, but it wasn't so good that it wouldn't turn into what mine has, susceptible to lines around the mouth and eyes, no natural luster of the cheeks. We both had deep blue eyes, not the light kind which I've noticed are susceptible to cataracts.

Speaking of eyes, the pastor's were flashing a little, like a campfire that I was containing. You couldn't let loose with some instincts when you were a man of God like you could if you were your own person.

"May, I am not against you. I'm on your side, I want to offer you spiritual comfort. I want to unburden your heart. I don't think you see clearly, where Ruby and Hazel are concerned. I think you do things that you normally wouldn't. May, she is in pain. She never recovered from his death."

He looked down at his hands. He would have made a terrible father; good thing he didn't have any kids. Too soft inside and out. His voice sounded coated with reluctance, disappointment, but I knew he had to be mad to say what he was saying.

"If you can't offer Ruby and Hazel true spiritual comfort and love, then I think you should stay away."

He was losing himself. He couldn't begin to think that he knew what had actually happened in my life, what I'd suffered.

"May, I thought she was going to have a heart attack last night when she walked in and saw you. I know you've exchanged words before, and she doesn't want you in her house. Surely you *knew* that. I had just gotten her calmed down, and then she saw you…It was horrible after you left. Hazel was terrified, she thought her mother was going to die."

That little creature wasn't afraid. Hazel had probably purposely goaded me into grabbing her so that the pastor could see. Her little mouth was as evil and hard as a hundred-year-old rusty nail; if she could've covered her words with poison and pierced my heart with them, she would have. That's for sure.

The only reason I'd ever started helping with him and all of his dead was to be there when Ruby passed. That and the fact that he clearly had no idea how to handle the newly departed. I wanted Ruby's eyes to die with the sight of me burned on them. I wanted to be the last to whisper in her ear, to refuse to pass her into the arms of God. I've waited a long time to see that last, terrified, choked breath rattle through those pretty lips of hers. I stood up, gathering my glasses and my big purse. The vein in my neck was throbbing against the buttons of my high-necked dress. I've always thought that vein would be the death of me one day, but not today. His tight expression didn't change, unsurprised that I was leaving. I could have almost laughed in his face right then and there about all of the things he thought he knew about death and people, about me, Ruby and Jack. He didn't know nothing.

"We didn't have words all those years ago, Pastor. You know, she was pregnant again. He was dead and gone, and she managed to steal one last piece of him. You didn't know that, did you? I did, she told me, right out here after church one day, like I was her friend." Pastor Will *hadn't* known that. He'd been too afraid to push Ruby to talk too much, so ecstatic was everyone that she was coming to church for the first time in her life, eaten up with grief over Jack's death. I leaned over the desk into the pastor's face.

"I told her that I'd seen him die, which I did. He burned up. Right in front of me, the sheriff and those deputies. I know you heard about it, but I was there. God put me there. He was trapped in that car, and he was screeching like the people in hell you talk about all the time. They told Ruby he'd died right away, but I told her the truth, that he'd roasted like an animal on a spit. You ever watch a person burn to death, Pastor? It's real ugly. Flesh coming off in flaming chunks, but the person don't die quick at all. They suffer like you don't even wanna know. I told her all about it. No one wanted to save him but *me*."

Pastor Will looked like some bile had come up in his throat. I made myself talk real slow, like you do to someone who's very sick.

"She lost that baby not long after. Too much drinkin' I guess. You know, if I'd been carrying Jack's child, it wouldn't have mattered what the devil himself said to me, I wouldn't have touched a bottle. I wouldn't have lost that baby."

My neck was sweltering, but the sweat on it felt cold and clammy. My breath was short. The pastor was trying to cover his shock. So he didn't know as much as he'd thought, after all.

"They held me back, just like you're trying to do. I don't think you're strong enough to hold me this time. Pleasant day to you, Pastor."

My back was straight, but my legs were rubber as I left the pastor. I didn't need him anymore anyway.

I had a dream that night. Jack's yellow Cadillac was burning in the holler off of Yankee's Curve, where he'd died. I stopped and pulled over, just like I had done on that day. I had Iris with me this time and instead of leaving her in the car crying I pulled her into my arms and ran towards the fire. The car was crumpled and burning; the tank hadn't exploded, just like that day, and Jack was in there somewhere, screaming like a creature in a steel-jaw trap. The dogwood blooms were gigantic, waving in the heat of the fire but the branches too green to burn. I ran to the car, straight into the flames with Iris; the sheriff was hiding his face from the fire and didn't stop me this time. The heat hit me but I didn't burn, I saw Jack trapped behind the crumpled wheel, screaming, his skin melting off, reaching for me. I touched his hand and instantly he stopped screaming, he stopped burning, his handsome face whole again, his white teeth shining. Iris burst into flames in my arms, her little face blistering, screeching worse than anything I'd ever heard. But Jack and I didn't burn.

I walked by Ruby and Hazel's house the very next day. She'd talked Jack into buying a little home in town, even though it was plain as day to everyone that he belonged on a farm in the country. Hazel was in the yard communing with the setting sun, her eyes closed, another wild and bra-less day for this girl. Her bare ankles had leaves, grass, and twigs grabbing at them in Ruby's overgrown yard. If yards could talk, this one would be screaming reds, purples and greens with all those runaway poppies, daisies, and azalea bushes.

That tight pink material that'd been worn and washed a thousand times but was still what somebody called a dress was clinging to two bumps that were threatening to become breasts on that girl. A triangle of dark hair was clearly showing, no underwear to hide it and dark as a devil's coal bucket. The hair on her privates looked as thick as a grown woman's; she was Ruby's child all right. Hazel opened her eyes and smiled at me real slow, like a woman with a ten-carat diamond ring on her finger. I wished the pastor could see that smile, she didn't look one bit scared of me; Ruby's thick, unnatural blood was slowly pumping through this one's heart. I hadn't really gotten a good look at her last night, as things moved so quickly. She had Jack's little heart-shaped face, with the chin delicate as bone china. She also had his lips, drawn on with a tiny, rosy paintbrush; his lips were still clear in my mind from last night's dream. Her eyes were green like her daddy's. How had I never noticed how much she looked like him? Probably because she still had Ruby's animal-thick, black eyebrows, and Ruby's hair, auburn and shiny, looking like heated molasses syrup, shimmery with shots of auburn and blond streaking through it.

The screen door banged open, and Hazel and I both looked. Ruby was in a red housecoat, leaning against the open doorway, her face sallow, her eyes squinting at the unaccustomed light. She had huge purple shadows under her eyes, looking like she had been through a beating. Her auburn hair was wild and tangled, uncombed and unwashed. There was still a pretty woman under that iron casing of sadness, but that was leaving her fast. I could almost feel her weak heart fluttering, her diseased liver failing her body. Her empty left hand was cupped around an imaginary bottle, as if it was so accustomed to holding a drink it didn't know what else to do with itself.

Her voice was broken from cigarettes and grief, sounding like someone had run a vegetable peeler up and down her throat. There was no real authority in her shriek, just hysteria, which has its own power.

"Hazel, you get away from that woman! Get in here right now!" Hazel looked me right in the eye and licked her pink tongue over her little white teeth, not moving a muscle.

"I said *move*, girl! You get away from her right now!"

She turned her back on me slowly and walked to her mother, stepping over the broken gutter that'd fallen on the porch. Ruby clasped her against her breast, backing up in the doorway, afraid to turn from me, like I would swoop down and snatch Hazel from her. The screen banged after them but I knew what was happening without having to see it.

I went home to my father's farm. Earl ran it almost as efficiently as Daddy had, although the old barn needed repainting. The house was unchanged from my parent's time: two bedrooms, spare furnishings, and parlor antiques that were rarely seen by anybody. Iris had a new best friend and stayed the night with her as much as possible, and Earl was always working. I went to my oak desk in the parlor and pulled out my mother's Bible with our family tree in front. The parlor was almost dark; it needed dusting; the day's particles hung in the air, barely catching the last rays of light. I carefully pulled out the yellowed clipping, smoothing it out.

> *The Rockville Sun Times*
> January 1, 1941
> Birth Announcements
> Jack and Ruby Hawkins announce the birth of their little girl, Hazel Hawkins. Hazel weighs eight pounds, five ounces. Mother and daughter are doing fine.

I took out Earl's knife that I kept in my top desk drawer. I looked out the window; the sun had set, the last light losing the battle to hang onto the planted field. I took the knife and very carefully cut a tiny square around Ruby's name, careful not to damage the slightly brittle paper. I wet the tip of my index finger and put it on the square, which stuck to my saliva and lifted out Ruby's name. In my neat writing, I printed out my own name in an almost exact duplicate of the paper's print, the square slightly larger than the one with Ruby's name on it. I took the edge of a pen and dipped it in my pot of glue, tracing the back edge with a thin line, placing it with steady hands on an empty square of the paper. It fit perfectly. The paper with my name was whiter than the original, but I had no doubt it would eventually blend.

I felt good. Better than I had in years.

Choices

B E R N A D E T T E   J O N E S

O ur second year of high school was a year of coming out, evolving you might say. We went from baggy jeans and big shirts, standing around the outside of the school like alien observers in search of a personality to overtake, to the wearing of short skirts and stockings, wobbling in high-heeled shoes, wearing too much makeup and flirting with any boys who showed the least bit of interest.

We looked forward to our lunch period; everybody who was anybody hung out at Gus's Greasy Grill. We were packed in that little cracker-box joint, big enough to hold only twenty-five people comfortably, a hundred at a time. We were shoulder to shoulder, fronts pressed to backs, reaching over heads, pressing down on shoulders, snatching at food bags when our numbers were called. It was the best part of the day. Looking back, we were just young, silly little children, trying to make our mark on days that will long be remembered.

Elmer, Janice, and I were standing on the outside of the restaurant. Acting silly, as we did every day. Elmer and Janice were throwing kisses. He'd throw her one, and she'd snatch it out of the air, squeeze it in her fist, bring it to her face, and smooch it all over her lips. Then she'd throw him one, and he'd jump high in the air, his feet two feet off the ground, left arm outstretched and groping the air to catch it. He rubbed it all over his body, like he was giving himself an oral massage.

Glen rolled up, jumped out of his raggedy blue Ford like the police ready to make a bust, grabbed Janice's wrist, and twisted it behind her back. The pain brought her to her toes. He slapped her in the face and upside her head, talking about how *he's* the only man she can throw kisses to.

Where I grew up, when a friend is in trouble, you don't just stand around and watch. You jump your ass right into the middle of the action. If you get your ass whipped, so be it. But you don't ever want to be labeled a sellout. You'll be alienated; the most important gossip traveling through the neighborhood will float right past you, and you won't ever get an invitation to the Friday-night basement parties.

I jumped Glen from behind and wrapped my arms around his neck, my legs clinging to his bulky thighs. I tried to put some pressure on it and cave in his windpipe, but I ain't never seen a motherfucker with a neck as hard as his. It felt like I was putting pressure on a steel pipe. He bucked his body like a wild horse and flung me to the ground.

Janice stood there crying as I lay on the cold-ass ground. He stood over me with his foot suspended in midair ready to stomp me in the face with his dusty-ass boots.

She didn't say shit.

"Bitch, I should stomp yo' ass." When I thought about it later, he was right. I needed my ass stomped for standing up for her, 'cause the next thing I know I saw him with his arm around her shoulder walking to his car, and I'm still lying on the goddamn ground.

I saw her the next day standing at the corner smiling like she'd just won the Miss America contest. I stepped up to her face—more like *charged* like a Russian Bull—'cause my blood was still running cold from the day before. I felt abandoned and victimized at her expense. I was once told the worst thing you could do to a friend was get involved with her and her man. Well, hell, at that time, I wasn't worth shit when it came to protocol. All I knew was my girl—so I thought—was in trouble, and I needed to help.

"You know you ain't got to take that type of shit from no low-down, disgusting, son-of-a-bitch like Glen," I tried to comfort her, but she just kept looking sideways at me like I talked some shit she couldn't identify with. Then it dawned on me why I was so angry, and I let her have it.

"How you gon' walk away with that motherfucker and I'm lying on the ground, trying to defend your ass, and he ready to ram his foot up my ass?"

"Fran, he wasn't gonna hurt you."

"How the fuck you know he wasn't gonna hurt me? Shit! He kicks your ass like he's got a license."

She hung her head. Now her feelings were hurt.

"He said it in the car." She talked to the ground. I was feeling bad 'cause her voice trembled.

"He didn't mean to hurt me, just had that jealous thing goin on, you know how a man can act when he loves his woman."

Now I had never, at that age, confessed to know about the love thing, but if that's what it was about, you could keep that shit. Glen was like a prize-fighter with his own human punching bag. Sometimes I felt I needed to be by her side just to yell, "LOOK OUT BELOW!" or "RUN TO THE LEFT!" or "HE'S COMIN' UP ON YOUR RIGHT!"

"Love? This ain't got shit to do with love. It's all about control, baby! He got your ass wound so tight around his fingers, you choking." I put my hand on her shoulder, wanting her to know how much I cared about what was happening to her. She jerked away.

"You got a man?" Her eyes locked on me; her head jerked at the end of her question, and she continued, "Until you get one, don't try to tell me about mine."

Oh, now she got this misconception of what a man is. But since she gonna throw that shit in my face about, *I already got a man,* I should give her a few facts about a real man.

"I can't tell you nothing about that piece of shit you got, 'cause I can't relate to no motherfucker slapping me upside my head talking about it's all in the name of love. But you can mark this shit in your book, when you see me with a man, you best mother-fucking believe he won't be knocking my fucking brains out."

"When you find a motherfucker who's desperate enough to claim your perfect ass as his own, let me know and I'll make the judgment call. He might not kick your ass, but you can best believe, he's gonna be one unhappy motherfucker trying to live up to your expectations."

As usual, we stayed mad for a couple of days, laughed the bullshit off, and went on as best friends. I learned over the years to let her handle her situation with Glen, but whenever she felt the need to talk, I was there.

Our first Homecoming, and all we talked about was turning out the dance. We practiced day and night on our moves. Janice was a big girl, but she had some moves that would impress John Travolta, from his days of *Saturday Night Fever*. She moved her hips like they had their own swinging pendulum attached. Her thighs were big and round and full of dimples, but she had no problems raising them off the floor. It was swing those hips, dip that body, throw them legs to the front, and spin. She spun around so many times and so fast you looked for her to wobble from dizziness, but believe me she didn't miss a beat.

We left school and took the bus to Madison and Pulaski—had everything planned; we were going to buy the same outfit, because Janice didn't mind showing off her body; she rather enjoyed the attention. On our way home walking to the bus stop, we were having girl talk like young girls do, about the fine boys at school and who we're gonna take from who at the dance. Janice stepped off the curb; I pulled her back 'cause I saw this dumb-ass driver peeling rubber and stopping on a dime at the curb in front of us. Glen jumped out of his car, walking with that gang-banging mentality that we're supposed to be scared of. He got the street corner blocked, cutting off the pedestrian walkway. "What the fuck you doing up here?" He got his nasty fingers all up in her face. Squeezing her jaws, her lips stuck out in a pucker from the pressure. His dirty and chapped hands full of black oil had probably been working on his beat-up trap on wheels, all day.

"Me and Fran came to do some shopping for Homecoming this weekend."

He looked at me with his bottom lip folded under his top teeth: eyes still got that early-morning crust in the corners, and sometime during the day he'd eaten something green because it was stuck between his front teeth. I know I shouldn't have done it, but what the hell, I did it anyway: I turned up my nose and rolled my eyes and called him a nasty fucker under my breath.

"You don't go nowhere wit no motherfucker unless you ask me first," he said.

Janice put her head down like a child being scolded by her parents. She looked pitiful, and it was pissing me off.

"Who the fuck are you, she got to ask your permission before she can make a move?"

"Stay the fuck out of this, Fran, this ain't got shit to do with you." He was flinching and flexing his arm, ready to throw me a punch.

"Glen, don't!" Janice grabbed at his arm, pretending to protect me. At that point, I was ready to take his ass on, fed up with his bullshit, and sick and tired of seeing her stretched out under his heels.

Before she could finish talking, he turned around, wrapped his hand around a fistful of her hair, and dragged her off to the car. She tried to pull back, but he started banging her on the side of her face with his fist. She tried ducking her head except she couldn't go far 'cause he still had a fistful of her hair. I stood there yelling, straining my voice, calling him every disgusting name that came to mind. The traffic came to a halt; a horn blared, cars sat bumper to bumper, the drivers had their heads stretched out of windows cursing. Pedestrians gathered, pushed and shoved with their bags clutched to their chests. Some laughed and pointed, seeing the situation as amusing; others shook their heads in disgust.

"Pity they have no home training," came from someone in the crowd.

"You no-good, low-life, rusty-mouth, corroded-dick, smelling-like-a-sewer shit, nappy-headed piece of filth. You beat on girls 'cause you know any man would drop-kick your punk ass and wouldn't give two shits about you. If I was your mama, I would've killed you myself when I saw what I gave birth to."

"Fuck you, prissy bitch!" he yelled over the hood of the car before he jumped in and pulled off. I lost my breath screaming at him. Took one long, deep breath and screamed, "Don't hurt her!"

PeeWee lived next door to me; he was the coolest teenager on the block. His parents let him stay out long after the sky turned from dusk to dark, and that was something all the kids on the block envied. Our curfew was when it started to get dark. You had to be in front of your house, not down the street or across the street in front of your house. My mom would say, "I want to see you when I look out the window." And if I knew what was good for me, I'd better be there, because I think she enjoyed embarrassing me in front of my friends.

PeeWee had his sixteenth birthday party in his basement. It was a *waist* party. His older brother, Greg, stood at the door with a tape measure, slid it around your waist, and however many inches you measured, that's how much money you had to pay to get in. I walked through the door wearing black leather hotpants, a white belly top with ruffles around the collar and sleeves, and an elastic band snug around my stomach. A pair of black patent-leather boots slid up my legs and stopped at the knee. Whore boots, they called them. I worked my body just like the sexy women I'd seen on television, switching my ass from side to side so I didn't just look sexy, I felt sexy. All I really wanted was some attention and to get into the party free. He charged me thirty-two cents to get in, unimpressed by the fantasy of a young girl. Janice had on a black miniskirt with a long white blouse, the tails hanging longer than the skirt, and a pair of black flat slip-ons. She had to pay forty-eight cents to get in.

The party was jumpin' when we got there. The room was dark, and the strobe lights blinked in rapid succession, forcing your eyes to flutter until they adjusted to the light. Bodies crossed your path in robotic motions, the faces unknown until you were nose to nose with them. PeeWee stood in the middle of the floor; it was time for the birthday dance. All the girls lined up and took turns dancing with him. Michael Jackson's "Bad" blared from the speakers; the bass thumped through your body. I had my arms resting on PeeWee's shoulders, one leg between his, his hands clutched my waist, and we were humping and dipping to the beat. I did a quick spin and gave way to the next girl.

Janice was dancing with him when I first heard the commotion. With the music, conversation, and laughter all blending together, I never looked up until someone nudged me with such force I almost lost my balance. Through the noise and the darkness I heard someone say, "It's Glen—tell Janice Glen is here!" Everything happened so fast; before I could get to her I heard her scream, the lights came on, and I saw him sling her against the concrete wall. The music stopped, and all eyes were on the two of them.

"You got your big ass wrapped around that motherfucker."

"We were just dancing!" she screamed back at him. He flexed his arm and pulled it back with his fist in a knot. She ducked from reflex. He grabbed the back of her neck; his fingers dug dimples in the skin of her neck and forced her out of the party. Outside I could hear her screams and the sound of his open palm against her naked face, the impact so powerful my body jerked with each strike.

I didn't see or talk to Janice for more than a week. She wasn't in school, didn't come outside, and wouldn't take my phone calls. When I did finally see her she had four small bruises on her neck, the black-and-blue spots clearing, but not completely gone. The side of her face had fading welts near her temples.

"Why do you put up with his abuse?"

"I don't want to talk about it."

"You can't talk about it, but you don't mind getting your ass kicked in front of everybody."

"He didn't kick my ass in front of everybody. We talked about me dancing at the party, and he said it just made him mad to see me dance so close to PeeWee."

"Janice, we all heard him slapping the shit out of you when he dragged you outside."

"Well, if your mind you own business maybe you wouldn't get everything all fucked up. You heard wrong—OK." She turned to walk away, then paused and turned back. "You sound like my mother. If you're gonna be my friend you have to accept me the way I am, and you have to accept the fact that I'm with Glen, and gonna stay with Glen. If you can't do that—then maybe you should find another friend." She walked away.

I grabbed her hand and squeezed it, got energy from it, visions: She came home late from work. He sat in his car waiting for her, looking for what, only he knew. She got out of her car without looking and walked towards the building.

He came up behind her, shoved her, demanded to know where she'd been. "Working," she thought, "Something you should be doing!" But knowing Janice, she didn't just think it, she spoke it, and that angered him. He pushed her with great force; she stumbled and fell to the ground. Finally, fed up with his abuse, she jumped up, charging her weight at him, grabbed him, out of control she flung him to the ground. Startled and surprised by her actions, he scuffled to get up, but she charged him again, swinging and landing punches while they tumbled on the grass and concrete. He managed to free himself from her and ran away in the direction opposite the building. She flipped herself over, used the flat of her hands for support, pressed them into a patch of dirt to balance, and pushed herself up.

Before she could stand upright, her back buckled, the bones crushed; the pain caused her to give up her struggle to stand. Another pain pierced her shoulder and the side of her face; she felt skin rip. She reached out at the object that struck her, and the pain cracked the bone in her elbow. She turned over in an attempt to hold her arm where it ached; her wrist took a mighty blow, and she was leveled to the ground. Through scrunched-up eyes she saw Glen standing over her; the tire-iron descended from over his right shoulder, coming down with enormous force—Wham!—across the bridge of her nose. The toe of his work boots slammed into her cheek, he raised his foot in a high-march style and brought it down on her face, then did a one-step hobble to keep his balance and brought his foot down again, and again, and again, on her face.

She pushed her head deep into the pillow as if she wanted to bury herself under the mattress. The swelling of her eyes less but still unable to close, her bottom lip quivered, the blood-stained flesh shimmered. She stared at my shoulders, her eyes set deep in a penetrating daze. Unsure of what she wanted, I lowered my body and gave her a light squeeze.

"Oh, Jan," the voice startled me, "I never wanted to hurt you. You have to believe me when I tell you how sorry I am." Glen walked to the head of the bed across from me, stroked her brow, and kissed her forehead. The tears poured from her eyes, and he took a delicate finger and wiped them.

"Do you want me to call security?" She shook her head no. He smiled up at me, grabbed her hand and brought it to his lips. I felt nauseated, could feel the bile rising to my throat; my vision blurred, refusing to accept what was before me.

"I talked to your doctor, he said you could come home in a couple of days. I've got the house all cleaned up for you, and I have a surprise, something you've talked about for a while." He leaned down and kissed the spot on her face that wasn't bruised. "Can you guess what it is?" The tears rolled down her face, her head shaking from side to side. She tried to speak, but emotions choked back the words. I wasn't sure what it all meant, but I was praying she wouldn't go back home with him. He lowered his body and pressed firmly against her chest. She raised her bruised arm, lowered it to his waist, then pushed him away. She waved her hand, excusing us from the room; she rolled her body on its side and stared through the silver railings.

I walked through the revolving doors out into the fresh air and sunshine. I breathed deep to clear my head and rid myself of the memories of her lying there, the cuts and bruises, the swelling and the blood, the sparkle that glinted through the slits of her eyes, then dulled when he walked to the bed. It was all up to her now. I'll visit her tomorrow and our friendship will last a lifetime. But for now, I'm going home to finish what I started before this nightmare began.

A Little on the Side

J. LYNN KALLIO

Pablo Morales was approaching forty and had worked in shipping departments for nearly fifteen of the twenty years he'd lived in America. There was no easy way to describe his physique—he wasn't a thin man, and he wasn't heavyset, either. Not an ounce of extra flesh showed on his five-foot-five frame—all the bones were tight and compact. His chest, forearms, and even his thighs were hard, knotted with muscle, giving him a likeness to a little bull. His skin was a brown-sugar color, his hair black with gray at the temples, his eyes deep brown and narrowed in a perpetual state of disgust.

But Pablo's trademark feature was the thick mustache that rested like a fat, hairy caterpillar on his top lip. Even though he kept it trimmed, it still crawled down either side of his mouth and gave him a constant frown, as thought he were the walking portrait of a stern conquistador.

All in all, most people at Star Brite now avoided Pablo if they could. On first impression, they guessed his attitude ran on the surly side—and they were right. Pablo Morales was bitter. He hated most whites, for various reasons, but he was especially disillusioned with the plight of his own people. Life in Matheson, Illinois, sometimes wasn't much better than it had been in

Monterey, Mexico. He watched the others sweat away behind their machines, the men blotting their faces with rough paper towels, the women with long braids wound around their heads like thick crowns of penance.

These people had entire families to feed and clothe on minimum wage. What made Pablo really burn with anger was how dumb the Mexicans were. They let the white ones rip them off constantly. The white asshole from Human Resources would set the Mexican's wage at five dollars an hour, maybe six if the Mexican already had experience in another sweatshop someplace. And all he had to do was staple cardboard boxes together all day, or maybe lift up 100-pound skids of paper over and over with his bare arms. At the end of a seventy-two-hour week, this new Penstrokes employee would probably take home two-hundred bucks after taxes—barely half the cost of rent.

It made Pablo sick. Usually after a lot of tequila, he declared that it was just a goddamned curse to be born Mexican. He himself had a wife and mother-in-law at home, three girls not yet grown, plus a wayward stepdaughter that had two babies of her own, each spawned from different loser fathers. Not to mention he sent money every month back to Monterey to assist his own aging mother.

That was why he sold drugs on the side, for a little extra profit. Sometimes he peddled cocaine, but mostly it was just marijuana. He rarely, if ever, sold to another Mexican. It was all the young white boys out on the presses that wanted his small Baggies of pot. Even his supplier was white. The only time white people even found a reason to acknowledge Pablo was when they wanted to get high. He thought about the deal he was to make that night as he sat down for his lunch break: pale blond kid on Press 54. Always paid in big bills. Drove a new, dark-green Cougar. Pablo wondered what it was like to spend all your cash on toys, no responsibilities.

By early afternoon, Pablo's feet began to ache from standing, so he never bothered to walk the several dozen yards to the cafeteria. Instead, he retrieved his mini cooler from beneath the rack of time cards and took his lunch right there in the warehouse. Since he wasn't Administration, he was not allowed to use the shipping office that sat smugly along the west wall with its soundproof insulation and soft carpeting. He and the other shipping guys ate at a battered metal desk that somebody had rescued from the Dumpster. The desk, with its dented drawers, sat on the runway strip between the six dock doors and the stacks and stacks of skids waiting to be wrapped. Eating out here was usually a real bitch—you either caught a freezing draft from the open dock doors in the winter, or smothered to death from the heat in the summer. But for the past week, they'd been lucky—it was cooler as summer wound down. In fact, that morning had even been kind of chilly, prompting him to grab his black wind-breaker on the way out.

Since it was Saturday afternoon, a predictably slow day, Pablo was by himself until second shift rolled in. He could take his time about eating the big lunch his wife had prepared for him. He opened up the blue cooler and began to withdraw containers of food—at least ten chicken flautas rolled up tight in their corn tortillas, a portion of seasoned rice, and Marta's specialty, black baked beans. His drink was a can of mango juice, and dessert would be one or two Camels from the pack in his breast pocket.

When the new operator from the front office approached him, Pablo thought at first that she was a Bindery girl, with black hair falling down her back and a modest outfit of jogging pants and a white Bulls T-shirt. But as she got closer, he knew immediately that she wasn't Mexican—the angles of her face were too sharp, not rounded and broad, and her color was more of an olive instead of the darker, toasted brown of Mexican skin.

As she came to him, he struggled out of his black windbreaker and tossed it onto the desk beside his carefully laid-out food. Then he picked up a plastic fork and heaped a generous amount of rice into his mouth. The girl stopped a little uncertainly at the left side of the desk. Her eyes darted around and noticed the pigeons that perched in the rafters thirty feet above.

"Hi," she said at last, when it became clear that he was not going to acknowledge her. "Do you know where the time cards are? They're finally trusting me with the payroll, but I've never been out here before, and I can't add up the totals until I get the time cards."

With his mouth conveniently stuffed full, all Pablo could do was nod toward the black metal rack that was bolted to the wall beside him. To reach the time cards, she had to squeeze into the space behind his ratty chair, which rankled him. He hated it when people got too close. But since she was an Office Person, he was less inclined to react when she invaded his space. Better just to ignore all of them and get on with his life.

He heard her rustling around with the manila time cards, then came a thud and a cry. He guessed she'd smacked her elbow on the time clock that rested just below the rack. When she squeezed past him again, he caught a whiff of flowers—her perfume or shampoo or something. She stopped at his left side and began to shuffle through the time cards.

"Hey, not many people worked back here last night," she observed. It seemed like she spoke right into his ear. "Are you guys short-handed?"

Now Pablo was fully irritated. He slumped forward a little, getting ready to shovel another forkful of rice into his mouth. Couldn't she see he was in the middle of eating?

"We are always short-handed," he hissed.

She nodded. "Hey, it's pretty quiet back here compared to the rest of the place. I bet you don't even have to wear earplugs."

"I don't." This much was true—only a tenth of sound from the giant rumbling presses managed to vibrate back to the shipping corner. One small thing Pablo could be thankful for: he wouldn't go deaf before his time.

As if the girl didn't notice his terse replies, she leaned over his shoulder to scrutinize the meal laid out before him.

"Are you eating authentic Mexican food?"

Pablo snorted. "It ain't Taco Bell, if that's what you mean."

"I never ate real Mexican until I started working here. You know Marisa, the folding supervisor? She gave me some corn tamales once. God, those were good."

These last few words were spoken wistfully, and Pablo sighed. Obviously the only way he was going to get rid of this girl was by feeding her. He pushed away from the desk a few inches and gestured toward the *flautas*.

"Go ahead, take one."

Now he was looking at her, at the hard, dark glasses hiding half of her soft face. The bridge of her nose was long and skinny, and her jaw sloped down sharply into a small, pointy chin. She wasn't full Italian as he had guessed earlier—she was mixed with something, maybe East European. Maybe Gypsy.

At his invitation to the *flautas*, her whole body perked up. She showed no signs of embarrassment, gave none of those "Oh, I can't, I'm on a diet!" excuses he heard so many white girls exclaim in restaurants. She slapped the time cards down, dove at the *flauta* container, and swooped one up. She took a huge bite, not caring that he was male, or watching her. After a few seconds, her eyes lit up like gray flames behind the thick glasses.

"This is even better than the tamales! Did you cook them?"

Pablo snorted again, the closest thing he could get to a laugh. "What, are you crazy? My wife wouldn't let me near her kitchen."

She gulped down the rest of the *flauta*, and then, much to his dismay, hoisted herself up onto the desktop.

"Do you mind?" she asked, her thin hand hovering above the food. He had barely given her a nod of his head before she attacked another flauta. He had a sudden instinct to rein in the containers of beans and rice, in case her mouth turned into a giant vacuum cleaner and sucked everything down.

"Your wife's a good cook. Like my mom," she said grinning. Her sneakered feet began to swing, her heels banging into the metal desk drawers.

"Your mother Italian?" Pablo asked, and then he could've kicked himself. He didn't want to start an entire conversation, for Christ's sake. It was, after all, his break time.

"My mother's only half-Italian, but she cooks like she's straight off the boat from Naples. I get tired of red sauce, though." She took another huge bite of *flauta* and peered at the name stitched in gold thread on the breast of his green uniform shirt.

"Pablo. Have you worked here long, Pablo?"

"Yes. Too goddamn long." He stopped, feeling a little sheepish about using the Lord's name in vain in front of her. "Uh…what do they call you?"

"Grace. Well, formally it's Graciela. Pretty ugly, huh?"

"No, it's a nice name." Pablo leaned back in the chair and crossed his arms. "I wanted to call my last daughter Graciela, but my wife she wouldn't let go of Victoria."

Having devoured her second *flauta*, Grace licked the tips of her fingers, then smiled. Pablo was momentarily taken back by the brightness of her teeth. So often he received contempt from the Office People if he happened to bump into them. It was like they were afraid his Mexican dirt might stain their nice suits and dresses if he got too close. But this was absent from Grace's demeanor. Her smile seemed genuine. It was a bit unnerving, and at the same time, infectious.

He felt the sensation of a grin tickle the corner of his mustache. Then, he followed her bespectacled eyes as they traveled downward, from his awkwardly animated face, to the casual arrangement of food on the desk top, and finally to the windbreaker tossed beside it all. When her gaze lingered a little too long on the windbreaker. A spike of alarm shot up Pablo's spine and made him spring erect in the squeaky chair.

The quarter-ounce Baggie he was to sell that evening had dislodged slightly from its hiding place and was hanging half out of the jacket's side pocket. He made a sloppy lunge for the jacket and shoved the Baggie back inside the folds of dark material, but it was too late. When he glanced back at Grace, her cheerful expression had melted away.

Pablo waited a moment as the light went out of Grace's eyes. His hands stayed frozen on the windbreaker, and for once in his life, he cared what somebody thought about him. Very slowly, and with a great sigh, he dropped the coat onto the desk and sank into the chair. He noticed a ragged hangnail on his left thumb and began to pick absently at it.

"You know," he said, "I hear people say all the time that you can be anything if only you try hard. A doctor, maybe, or a professor. But it's not true. I know it's not true—some people can't be anything better because of who they are and what they're born to."

Grace slid off the desk. She scooped the forgotten stack of time cards into her hands and kept her eyes lowered. "I better get back to my office."

There was a tiny moment of silence. Then, before she had the chance to walk away, he cleared his throat.

"So . . . you gonna tell the boss?"

She shook her downcast head ever so slightly. "It's none of my business."

Her slim body had shifted away from him, all her limbs poised on the brink of flight. Everything about her suddenly drawn-in posture accentuated fear. For some reason, that thought was almost more than Pablo could bear.

He spoke again, feeling a deep weariness inside his bones. "I ain't no saint. I done my share of stupid things. But I work my ass off, too. Ain't nobody can tell me I don't work my hardest. When first I come to this country, I take English classes—what good are you if you don't know English? Then later I take the class for the—what is it?—the GED. I work here for nine years and should be supervisor because I got seniority and I know what I'm doing. But somebody else, a young punk, comes in with lighter skin and a diploma from some university, and they give it to him instead. So sometimes I got no choice. You do what you gotta do. So I do *that*."

He gestured toward the pocket that contained the Baggie. Grace's eyes flitted quickly in that direction, then returned to a spot on the concrete floor.

"I don't smoke that shit, I sell it. And you think I like selling dope to kids? I got a son the age of those boys out on the press. I know they can get stupid and have an accident with a car, maybe kill somebody, maybe kill themselves. But I don't think about it because I got little girls at home who get hungry too, little girls who want a present from Papi on their birthday and pretty dresses to wear to church. My wife, she don't even have a wedding ring, and we together for twenty-six years already. But that's OK, we sacrifice some things, but we got food on the table and a roof over us that don't leak when it rains. So I do what I do."

This was probably the longest string of sentences that had been uttered from his throat in years. When he finished, he was amazed and troubled by the blur of unexpected tears in his eyes. He went on picking at the overgrown skin on his thumb.

Grace continued to look at the floor for a long time. She felt sad, deeply sad, as if a weight were being steadily pressed against her neck and shoulders. She knew what it was like to scrape by. All her life, it seemed, she'd watched Ma clutching her forehead at the kitchen table, surrounded by late statements and overdue bills and cigarette smoke. And whenever Grace or Joey would wander into the kitchen, hungry for something, Ma would lose her patience and scream, "Nothing's magically appeared in the fridge since the last goddamn time you looked!"

Standing there by the battered desk, in the shipping department of Star Brite Printing, she silently vowed that she would climb out of the life that was predestined for her. She vowed it, again. Then she raised her head and met Pablo's brown gaze.

"It's not up to me to judge anybody," she said. Her voice wavered a little, and she stopped a second to steady it. "Seeing that stuff…well, it just reminded me of my little brother. He's been in some trouble lately."

Pablo let out a grumble. "With drugs? That's no good. First time I caught my kid smoking this shit, I smacked him upside the head."

"Yeah, my dad pretty much had the same reaction."

Actually, Poppy had attempted to strangle Joey, who sat hunched forward on the couch, his listless hand aiming the remote at the TV but not pressing any buttons. The olive green iris in each of his eyes was practically eclipsed by the dilation of his pupils. She'd noticed it—had asked him what was wrong—and after Joey had mumbled "Fuck off" under his sour breath, all hell broke loose. Poppy had heaved his squat body from the recliner and thrown himself at Joey, arms straining, fingers hooked into claws. They both toppled backwards, Poppy's face blistering and furious, Joey's mouth open in a scream of rage.

"Who do you think you're talkin' to, you son of a bitch?" Poppy bellowed. And Grace had pulled mightily on their father's biceps, shouting over and over, "Poppy, let him go! Stop it, Poppy!" That had been last Sunday, the day of rest.

"But it was my fault," she said out loud, as if from a dream.

"Huh?" Pablo looked sharply at her. "Why you say that?"

"Because I was the one who noticed Joey's eyes, and I mentioned it. If I didn't say anything, it might have . . . ."

"Look, honey, it ain't your fault. Did *you* light the joint and stick it in your brother's mouth?"

"No, but . . . ."

"He's got his own mind. Ain't nothing you can do to change that."

Grace sighed and looked to the right, into the black, empty tunnel of Dock Door #6. They said nothing for a while, until Pablo reached for his unopened can of mango juice.

"So, you gonna help me finish these or what?" he demanded, gesturing toward the remaining *flautas*.

The Long Road Home

SHELLI JOHNSON

I been Junior Williams' best friend long as we been alive, which only been about ten years. We both live in Quincy, Alabama, which ain't noplace near anything else. You ask my mama, and she'd tell ya I'm a pretty good boy. Junior ain't like that, though. My mama said Junior's plain mean. She said he came out a his mama kicking and screaming, and he been that way ever since. He likes to pick the wings off files. I seen him do it. He lets them buzz 'round the ground in circles cause they can't fly no more, and then he laughs 'fore he squashes them with his shoe. He likes to wait behind the trees on the path home from school so he can hide from the girls when they come walking home, and just when they ain't looking his way, he jumps out scream- ing and waving his arms all over the place. Then, when they start running willy-nilly trying to get away from him, Junior grabs one of them by the waist and swings her around and kisses her right on the mouth. Well, that just makes them girls mad but instead of hitting Junior, which is what I woulda done, them girls all start crying and carrying on, and you never heard such a thing in your life. But Junior don't care, he just laughs the whole time and pulls their hair and pokes them 'til they all go running home. My mama says Junior's mean, but I know he ain't stupid. Sometimes, he likes to wait in the bushes behind the school for one of the coloreds to come by, then he lets fly some rotted apples he brought with him just to see if he could hit one of them in the head. Then, when he does, he stands up out a those bushes and laughs in their faces and says, "What you gonna do, nigga?" Like I said, mean as an old goat that Junior Williams is.

Summer was when one a them coloreds had enough of a white boy throwing rotted apples at his head, and he come after Junior. I weren't there to see it since I was already home, my mama yelling at me 'cause a somebody who looked like me was throwing mud balls at the clean sheets on the clothesline. Weren't me, but there ain't no telling my mama that when she gets a thing in her head. So I had to find out by listening to Mama and Daddy talking when they thought I was in the bed. Mama heard it from Mrs. Carver, she lives down the road, and she heard it from the nurse at the hospital, and she heard it from the principal where me and Junior go to school. I ain't been able to talk to Junior since it happened, but this is what I heard my mama saying:

The Williams boy said there was a colored at the school that come up behind him and took him to the bushes behind the playground. Junior says that colored pulled down his pants and covered his mouth so he couldn't scream. Boy said he tried to get away, a course, but that colored wouldn't let up none and ended up raping that poor child and then, then, that colored smiled right in Junior's face and told him if he told anybody, that he'd hurt him again. Can you imagine? Well, I know we all reap what we sow, and Lord knows Junior been mean as the day is long, but Lord, I don't think Junior deserved this.

'Twas August a 1910 when the white boy says my husband Booker done something to him. It was hot as Satan hisself that summer. But the day I went talking to that boy's daddy, that day it was raining soft, but it ain't cooled the day down none. Alls it made was the heat stick to your skin and sweat pour down your back. I went to that white man's house cause I knows Booker ain't never done nothing to nobody, so I takes my children and goes to the boy's house, goes to talk to his father—

"Massah Williams, suh?"

"What you want?"

"Massah Williams, suh, I's Ida Thomas, suh. I's Booker's wife."

I watched him clench that jaw a his real tight and stare hard at each one of my babies. Then he says, "Don't want no niggas here."

"Please, Massah Williams, suh, my husband, Booker. Hain't done nothing wrong. Hain't hurt your child. They's gon kill him you don't stop this. Please suh, these his children, please don't let they daddy die."

"I ain't got no use for no niggas. Don't you come near my home again or you and them children the ones going to be dead."

He slammed the door in my face and my babies' faces and left us standing on his porch with the rain soaking us clean through. I held my hand up to knock, but after a while, I jus let it fall back down to my side.

"Mama, le's go," my eight-year-old boy said. "He don't wan talk to us. Mama, le's jus go."

"No. I jus cain't set by and let them men kill your daddy. They's gon kill him for what they says he done. But he ain't hurt that white boy. You near the same age, and Daddy never laid a hand to your head."

My daughter was the one finally made me walk away. She five years old that year, and she done broke my heart. "Mama," she said. "I wan to go, I's all wet wid rain, don't wan stand here no mo, Mama."

I watched them walk away, the black and her two children. They was clean for niggas, and I wondered what she had said to Pa that got him so mad, so I snuck out the house and ran down the road.

"What'd you say to my daddy?"

Nigga din't seemed surprised to see me. She just went on talking—

"You named Miss Mary, right?"

"Uh-huh."

"I wants your daddy to help my husband and they daddy." The black moved aside so I could see them two kids standing and dripping water behind her. "They's gon kill him for what they say he done, but in my heart I knows hain't done like they say. Hain't hurt your brother none, Miss Mary. You a smart girl, cain't you talk to your daddy? Cain't you tell him stop this before they done killed the father a my children?"

That black grabbed hold both my arms then, shook me back and forth. She had tears coming down her face, and before I could tell her to let me go, she fell to her knees and was looking up at me, begging.

"They gon lynch him come sundown. Please Miss Mary, boy ain't got much time left tell the truth."

I was in that clearing waiting for them to lynch that nigga that done hurt my son. That nigga, he was standing barefoot with them clothes a his all covered with piss from his own self and spit from the men 'round him. The sun was sinking in the west, and that nigga he was but sweating good. We had him all trussed up while we was waiting for the judge to tell us to go ahead and kill him. Judge said, "This here nigger been accused of dragging Junior Williams to the bushes behind the elementary school and sodomizing him."

That crowd caved in on that nigga, and somebody yelled, "Kill that nigga!" One of them did him a blow across the head, knocked that nigga into the dirt. Next one kicked him in the back, made that nigga scream out. Judge din't put a stop to it so them men kept on. I just watched the thing happen, happy that nigga was finally getting his. Somebody was yelling, "Got me a nigga dick here. Got me a nigga dick here." Then they was taking that nigga's cock out a his pants. That nigga really started to scream then, and them boys 'round him was just whooping and laughing at them girl cries he was making. Somebody must a grabbed his balls then 'cause that nigga started making this low, "unnnh-unnnh-unnnh" sound. That's when the judge finally said, "Knock it off. Can't kill the nigger if he's already dead." The crowd backed off, and I could see that nigga just plain as day with his tongue all flopped out of his mouth and him drooling all over hisself.

Judge stepped up with the Bible in his hand. "We all know this here nigger done what he's been accused. God says, we got to punish the wrong. Ephesians chapter six, verse eleven, says put on the whole armor a God, that you can stand against the devil. We don't wrestle against flesh and blood, but against the rulers of darkness, against spiritual *hosts* of wickedness in heavenly places. This here nigger is the wicked one. Bible tells us we got to throw our darts and kill the evil among us. God made the law, and the law says we got to sentence this nigger, Booker Thomas, to die by lynching this very night."

My sister Mary brought a Bible to me and says. "Junior, you gots to swear on the Bible that you's telling the truth."

"I ain't doing no such thing," I told her, but she wouldn't hear none of it. Made me put my hand on that Bible and say that nigga done what I said he done 'cept he din't do it so I couldn't lie with the Lord looking down on me, so's I said, "I can't."

Well, Mary's pigheaded and she wasn't going to let me not do it, so finally I said, "All right. That nigga done nothing to me. He done nothing. Just looked at me funny, like he was better'n me, so I made up that story show him that he weren't better'n anybody."

Mary grabbed hold a my ear and done dragged me out the house. "You going to tell Pa before they kill that black, you understand? His kids ain't going to have no daddy just 'cause you a little liar."

I said I wasn't going to do it, but Mary was eight years older and a good lot bigger than me, and she whacked me across the head with her hand and yelled, "Now go!"

So I walked to the clearing, thinking the whole time I could just run the other way once Mary wasn't looking no more, 'cept that Mary must've had the same idea 'cause she decided to follow after me and she din't let up til I walked into the center of them men and told them I done lied 'bout the whole thing.

They din't kill my boy that day. White boy showed as they put the noose round a branch. Booker been my son thirty-two years. He the first a this family not been a slave. But what they had done to him that night jus' showed me ain't a white man alive worth nothing. Them white men cussed and spit on my son 'fore they walked out a that clearing. Not a one of them men beat that white child. Ain't done nothing but drag that boy home by his arm. And my son? They left my son so the rope 'round his wrists flayed his skin and 'round his ankles made them swell so that was a week 'fore he could put on a pair a shoes. We was all hoping his eyesight come back, but it been a few months now and he still cain't see nothing. Doctor says it was the hit he took to the back of the head, said hain't never likely to see again. Ida, she came talk to me the other day 'cause she don't understand why the law din't do nothing 'bout what happened to Booker. I said, "Chile, law don't care 'bout the blacks. Ain't a law made that care 'bout the blacks." She young though. She don't understand how it is.

Ida been my wife ten years. First time in my life, I wake in the morning and cain't see her. I hear her though, she be crying. She think I'm sleeping, but I hear her next to me. She breathe hard when she sad. I touch the sheets where she been, and they wet from her crying. I ain't been with my wife since them men. Every time we together like that, I thinks a them white men pulling on me down there and spitting on me down there.
"Got me a nigga dick here! Got me a nigga dick here!"
I think a that, and I think a my wife. I cain't do nothing. Ida, she think it her fault. Ain't. But she think it. Sometimes I hears her praying to the Lord, she asking for me to be healed. They's times, when I don't hear nobody, I curse the Lord for leaving me remember what them men done. Ida, she don't knows that I curse the Lord. She say, "Lord gon see us through. Lord gon deliver us, Booker, you gon see." I tells her I ain't never gon see agin. She say, "You gon see I'm right. That's what you gon see."
I said I ain't never gon understand. Ida she say I don't have to understand nothing. Alls I got to do is believe, she says. She tell me that white boy gon get his someday, she say I ain't got to fret over nothing. I tells her I wasn't doing nothing but walking past when that white boy hit me on the side a the head with a rotted apple. I thought first it be my brains leaking out, but it was

just apple juice and apple meat sliding across my head. I looked at that boy, and I says, "Why, boy? Why you do this to me?" That's all I said. I din't touch that boy. I just asked him why. And that boy gets this funny look on his face like he done tasted something that tastes bad and says to me, "Go on, nigga, go on home, or I'm gon hit you agin." So's I went on home and wiped that apple off the side a my head, and I din't think nothing more of it 'cept to wonder when it was we was gon be able to walk down the road and not be afraid. I din't think nothing more of it 'til them white men come to my house and drag me outside and down the road telling me I'm gon die for what I done to that boy.

With Friends Like These . . .

STEPHAN J. JACKSON

The first time I went to my buddy Ryan Beger's house was the first and last time that I have vomited from something other than alcohol poisoning or having my body host to some kind of virus with malice written in its DNA. Don't get me wrong, I love Ryan. He used to play guitar in my band until his alcohol problem got in the way of his showing up for practice—the nerve of us for booting him—and he was the kind of guy who answered every question like he thought you were an idiot, a slitting of the eyes and a mouth half open in disbelief that you didn't know that a car even had something called a timing chain within its operating structure or some other similar fact. He drove a rusty blue Camaro that smelled like cigarettes and baby powder, and he couldn't hold a job for more than a month, but goddammit, I loved him for his witty derogatory observations of people and his inability to move past the subject of guitars or the aforementioned Camaro.

I was going to his house to have a couple of beers with him. Yeah, I was only eighteen and he was only twenty, but what the hell else were you going to do on a lazy Wednesday evening in the dead of summer? He picked me up at about seven and as I saw the two cases of Miller High Life rumbling atop the subwoofers underneath his pneumatic hatch, I knew that he had a slightly different idea about the length and consumption value of our couple of beers.

When we arrived at his apartment building, the yard was strewn with tipped-over pink bicycles with training wheels and other various instruments of childhood tossed about. Ryan grabbed both cases of beer, tossing one under each arm like he was carrying tires in a pit crew, and we headed up the back stairs to his second-floor pad. What I failed to mention is how comfortable I was in the ride over, the air conditioner blasting inside his car, and just how much like an oven the world outside it felt. It was the kind of night where you walk outside and the sweat buds out from the pores and creates a rapidly shedding and replenishing second skin. During the walk from Ryan's car to the back door, a distance of about forty feet or so, the salt was already stinging my eyes, and I slopped it off my forehead in a wet scoot, spraying an arc of saline into the night. And being told nothing about Ryan's living quarters, I yearned to reach Ryan's back door, all the way across the continent, and feel the cool bite and slight tingle in the lungs that would greet me as delicious conditioned air flowed over me and turned my shirt to a frozen chain mail of iced sweat which would have to be cracked if I wanted to move my arms above my head. But like I said, being told nothing about Ryan's living quarters, I stepped instead into a stale inferno smelling faintly of feces and rotted plaster. *No A.C., goddamn,* I thought to myself as I saw the beer cans bulging dangerously out in their cardboard cases as the contents began to boil and steam inside.

The trek up the narrow, steep flight of stairs was making my legs wobble. I was coming upon heat stroke and fast. I needed a glass of water or some liquid. I just knew that if I were to poke my arm the flesh would not bounce back, and I would have a shallow, fingertip-sized depression as a badge of my first battle fought with dehydration. Congratulations. But I made it up the stairs with my consciousness intact, and I stepped into Ryan's apartment.

Now Ryan had earned himself the nickname of The Garbageman for no reason other than the usual quality of his female companions, but I had absolutely no idea how close to the mark we actually were when we crowned him with such a name. That faint smell of feces that I mentioned earlier was sacrilegiously strong inside his apartment. There is no analogy more fit for my discovery than the truth. Imagine walking into a boiling hot, nonventilated room with about six piles of dog shit cooking on the floor like ground beef on a burner. The smell hit me in the face and raced furiously down into my lungs and stomach like oxygen rushing in to fill a vacuum. I was almost doubled over with it, and I could feel the color of my face bleaching as I fought back the strengthening urge to roll my eyes into the back of my head and puke into his sink. But then that would be rude in front of his overweight mother who was sitting in the front room in nothing but a bra and a bedsheet, a cigarette hanging from her mouth and her flip-top box sitting on the bed, a heap of ashes inside the propped-open lid. Where most people put their couches, televisions, easy chairs, and potted plants, there was Mrs. Beger's bed next to half of a Nordic Track machine and a couple of scattered piles of dung, old and new.

"Hey, jackass, who's your friend?" the woman asked in her four-packs-a-day-for-the-last-thirty-years voice. I was introduced as Steve, and Mrs. Beger gave a nod and went silently back to staring at some spot on the wall—or perhaps it was at the flies, I don't know and don't care to. And then we went into Ryan's room, or more appropriately, Ryan's collection of piles of stuff, and who should be in there but a haggard-looking girl in her twenties wearing a pair of overalls and a half shirt which nicely ornamented her obviously pregnant abdomen, and a little toddler in purple feetie pajamas with a round vacant looking face smudged with dirt.

Each room seemed to be hotter and worse smelling than the last. And Ryan's collection of piles of stuff had a kid with a very obviously dirty diaper and a mangy little terrier, who of all things ran up and bit me right on the hand and then rushed out, presumably to relieve itself on the carpet once again. This room did have the luxury of an open window, and my eyes spied an oscillating fan. I had to fight back the urge to leap across the room, tap the thing on, and stand directly in front of it soaking up the blowing air like a junkie orgasming from the injection of a fix, but I thought it untactful, what with a staring contest going on between Ryan and the girl. It thankfully ended with her grabbing the dumbfounded child ruthlessly by the arm and dragging her out of the room without so much as glance my way to acknowledge my existence. As the two exited, the rank smell of the baby's diaper wafted gracefully up into my nose, and I once again had to contain my stomach from turning inside out. The girl slammed the door behind her, and two seconds later swung it open with equal violence and grabbed a pack of GPC cigarettes that was on the floor near where she had been seated. All right, she was smoking for two now; why leave out all the drama?

Ryan set down the beer atop a tremendous pile of clothes and gave a middle finger to the still-rattling doorjamb and indicated to me where his couch was hidden. As I cleared away a pile of magazines, an ashtray, and a hockey jersey, Ryan ripped open the cardboard beer case, tossed me a nice warm one, and cracked one open for himself. And you know what? It is truly wonderful how adaptable the human body is and how one can even get used to the smell of hot shit if the situation should present itself. It was now only vaguely causing retching feelings in my throat and causing my mouth to water in that way that we have all experienced that leads to expulsion of the nutrients within us.

The heat didn't even seem so bad in here. Sure, there was no breeze, but at least I could fan myself with one of his outdated magazines, and just in case you're wondering, the oscillating fan had no electrical cord in back, only a dark hole where a cord once was, and I guess it was used as more of a decorative item or conversation piece. I had a lot of questions to ask my friend, but tact held its leash around my tongue.

I sure as hell didn't feel like drinking that night, but I cracked my beer open out of respect for Ryan—he did buy it for me. Then I remembered my earlier coveting of a glass of water, and I asked Ryan if I could have one. He pointed me out to the kitchen and said there was cold water in a bottle in the refrigerator. I walked back out into the stifling room, gave a nod to Ryan's mother who was now reading a magazine, but thankfully covered up to her neck by her sheet. I went for the cabinet that housed the glasses, pulled out a tasteful little plastic number from some outdated era of McDonald's history when Mayor McCheese was still a pivotal character, and opened the refrigerator to grab the bottle of glorious Lockport tapwater. Now for the vomiting. Have you ever stuck your nose deep down in a compost heap and taken a healthy sniff? That's something akin to the state of affairs inside the Beger refrigerator. I don't know what was rotting in there or for how long, emanating that fibrous, almost sweet smell of the guts of old vegetables, but I do know that it was a miracle that I was able to keep myself from erupting as I ran back through the soiled front room and into the equally soiled bathroom (I made a guess as to which door and was thankfully correct) that smelled like shampoo and used tampons which only aggravated the situation. I heaved my guts into the crusty pink bowl of his toilet with the door flapping open behind me, the sweat running off of my face like someone was pouring a pitcher onto the back of my head. I held my hair back out of the three short bursts it took to empty myself, the tears blurring my vision, but I never once touched the bowl, for even in this state I had enough cognizance to think of the germ colonies that must be festering there in keeping with the theme of the rest of the house. When it was all finally over with, my knees were weak, my head was throbbing, and I felt oddly uncomfortable knowing that Mrs. Beger must have heard my little purging ritual and lifted not a finger and said not a word. I had had enough of that place and the faintly creepy people who were inhabiting it, so I wobbled my way back into Ryan's room, three empty Miller cans at his feet by this time, and told him to drive me home, blood-alcohol level be damned. I told him that I felt like shit, and he told me I looked like shit, and in typical Ryan fashion popped a can into his pocket for the road. I will never go back there again. Ever. And that's the end of my story. If anyone wants to know who the pregnant girl was; ask Ryan because he never fucking told me. He's shady like that.

* * *

The first and only time I ever went to Jeff Wilson's house was the most uncomfortable two hours I have ever spent in my entire life on account of a couple of animals. I met Jeff through this lowlife piece of shit named Sean who played guitar with my band for about two months. He brought Jeff to one of our Saturday-night practice sessions which usually ended up with us drinking ourselves retarded. Jeff was Sean's cousin, and as soon as I shook hands with him I immediately got the feeling that he was a nice guy. As the weeks went on and Jeff began showing up to more and more practices, I started talking to him more and found this to be the truth. Though he seemed kind of distracted and introverted most of the time, the kind of guy that you have to approach with conversation because he'd never approach you, once you did start talking to him you instantly liked him and felt like clapping him on the shoulder like you were old friends. I found that we had the same tastes in music and that he played guitar himself, and we made vague, noncommittal plans about working together musically.

Long after we booted Sean's ass from the band but not before he stole some of our bass player's equipment and sold it for dope money, Jeff would still come around to the practices and come out with us every once in a while. He was just a simple, old school guy. Right out of high school he got a construction job, and he talked about getting a home in two years. He was only twenty. And why the hell wouldn't I come over to his apartment and watch a movie with him? He lived about thirty minutes from my house in the dismal, oldish town of Lockport, and I fired up my minivan to go see him some long-ago Wednesday summer night.

It was the kind of night when it just felt great to be outside. Fall was rapidly approaching, and you could feel its tang in the air. I almost opted to take a jacket with me but wanted to cruise around in the breezy twilight with my windows down, breathing in the comfortable air. With Jeff's directions that I took over the phone, I was able to come upon his apartment building, which was in a bigger complex than I had imagined, and I had a little trouble discerning one building from another, but I finally found Unit 216 and rang Jeff's buzzer to be let in.

I walked up two flights of stairs until I hit Jeff's third-story landing, and he was waiting with the door open for me. And the first thing that struck me as odd was that he was wearing really short shorts. They were the kind you'd see kids wearing in high-school phys ed in the seventies, solid blue color shorts with a red lining around the leg cuffs and a vertical red stripe up the side of each leg. His pasty white, extremely hairy legs were displayed, unshapely, ugly things, and I had to physically move my head with my hands to keep my eyes off of them. But hey, this was his apartment and this was his own down time and who was I to say what he could and could not wear inside the comfort of his own dwelling? As I walked inside the apartment following Jeff he introduced me to "Mom and Doug," who I walked over and shook hands with. They were relaxing against each other on a cream-colored, very fluffy couch and watching some news program like "20/20" or "Dateline." His mom had a broad, pleasant smile that made her dark face crack into a thousand tiny lines. She was wearing black slacks and a cream-colored sweater that almost matched the sofa she was sitting on. Doug, who I'm guessing was Jeff's stepdad or just his mom's boyfriend, was a nicely dressed guy with a football player's build and a bit of a pot belly. He had round, gold glasses and wore a thick, brown goatee that somehow didn't seem to match his salt and pepper hair. They seemed like nice enough people, and I thought, "Hey, this guy's got a pretty nice family," but then I happened to stumble upon the rest of Jeff's household and my feelings about the whole situation changed pretty rapidly.

First off were the dogs that limped towards me like lepers with their hands out for a donation of my untainted skin. I guess these two monstrosities were Jeff's dogs and thus to be cared for by Jeff alone, because they never left the vicinity of his room. The first one to hobble over to sniff me had perhaps been a dachshund at one time but was now a walking tumor. Its head was roughly four times the size it should have been, and lumpy as a misshapen potato. Both of its eyes were glistening white cataracts. Because the weight of this creature's head was so great, its little spine had bowed up along its back and protruded about half an inch so that the whole animal was shaped like a rainbow. I guess it could maneuver its way over to me with its sense of smell, and the sensation of its bulging head brushing against my pantleg was about as pleasant as walking through an ankle-deep basin of fish guts. And then the dog's bloody buddy followed its tumorous brother's lead. This second dog was some kind of reddish brown, heather-colored Doberman that walked very slowly and shakily, perhaps because the front of its legs were nothing but open, bleeding sores. My uncle, who is a veterinarian, later told me that this was a nervous disorder that dogs could have, where they eat their own legs, and that it was pretty common among abused dogs, but I swore that first night I saw it that I had stumbled upon the world's craziest, self-cannibalistic dog, because after it gave me a few uninterested sniffs, it hobbled back over to its bed and went back to work chewing its legs and licking the slick, shining sores.

"Great atmosphere to watch a movie in," I thought, "amongst a couple of dying pets." Jeff, however, in his gym-shorted glory, paid the duo little attention as he pulled out his copy of *12 Monkeys* and popped it into his VCR. I found a spot on a couch off to the side of his room to sit in and tried to settle down to enjoy the movie, but anytime there was a pause in the sound I heard a slurp, slurp, slurp, slurp. I looked over in front of Jeff's bed where the Doberman had nested and saw it eating its own skin. The sound was like someone sucking soup out of a bowl in quick little spasms as the animal's long pink tongue spread over the semi-gelatinous goo that was its front legs. They looked like a pizza that had all the toppings ripped off except for a few scattered spots of pepperoni. They were that same pinkish, bloody-looking color with a few scattered scabs that would be re-eaten and the wounds greedily re-opened. Every time the screen was even a little quiet I heard that slurp, slurp, slurp, and I tried to block it out of my head and to unscrew the sickened grimace from my face and concentrate on the television screen. But then the little crippled guy bumped into my leg, and I almost kicked it out of reflex. It gave me a sniff, remembered me, and turned off in the opposite direction. I watched it bump into walls, into Jeff's metal Blackhawks garbage can, and into the other dog's ravaged legs occasionally. It was like watching the result of some toxic-waste spill. This little thing looked like a mutant, and not the good kind. It was the hunchback, the pitiable freak, and I was hoping it would just keel over and have an end to its misery, and it did look absolutely miserable.

The more I tried to watch the movie, the more I could only watch the dogs. I became mesmerized by them. It was like peeping out of my side window as I passed a car wreck on the highway. It was really nothing to gawk at, but I just couldn't help myself. I don't know anyone who could have. After a while I kind of grew accustomed to the sights and sounds of these dogs, but was half-introduced to another which finally put my discomfort over the edge. About halfway through the movie, I heard Mom say from behind the closed door, "Jeff, we're going to bed now. I'm going to let Andy out," and Jeff replied "OK, Mom." Immediately after I heard a door somewhere down the hall being opened, I heard a loud thud against Jeff's door which shook and reverberated on its frame. Outside the door I heard grunting, snorting, and a kind of weird whining that sounded like it was wheezing through whatever's nose was outside that door. I thought that not much could be worse than the dogs I was already sharing the room with so I asked Jeff if he wanted me to let the third one inside. What he said completely ruined my concentration on the movie and put me in fear of that thing out there splintering the wood of Jeff's door and rushing in, which the weakened-looking state of the door shaking on its frame only added to its likelihood.

"Oh no, don't let him in, he'd slime all over you. Half his face is gone."

That's what Jeff said, and that's what put the fear into me for the rest of the evening, though I didn't know exactly what he meant by it. I pictured the door flying off its hinges and some bleeding, slobbering thing with one eye and a missing bottom jaw coming to give me mucusy kisses and run its dry, homeless tongue on my hands. I kept cooking up fantastic ideas of what this half-faced dog might look like as it pounded at our entrance to gain our company. Suddenly I felt like picking up tumor-head and hugging him close like a teddy-bear for protection from seeing this half-headed monster should it erupt in upon us. As soon as the movie ended and I was almost losing control of my bowels from anticipating going out into the apartment and meeting that thing, Jeff said he was going to put it in the bathroom so it wouldn't bother us when we went out. As he left the room and I heard the thing outside whining again, I said goodbye to the two other dogs, careful not to look at their monstrosities and anticipated my drive home in my van away from this house of fucked-up pets.

Emotional Drain

MICHAEL A. WINNECKE

Salvador Mendez was always dirty. He never stunk, but his hair was always greasy, and the dirt under his long, hard fingernails was always a graying green that reminded me of what the sky must look like before a tornado. His clothes were always clean, and I think that was why he never smelled. He was quiet, only coming in to do his work, speaking when necessary, and promptly leaving upon the completion of his tasks. He spoke fantastic English for a man who had only been in the country for a year, and he told me once in one of his rare moments of conversation that he was studying Chinese from a book he had bought at the B. Dalton bookstore in town. I liked him a lot, mostly because he was easy to work with, and because he never would not do something asked of him. That made my job easier. He had only one stipulation: He would do no work that involved him working around running water. That meant no dishes, and no cleaning the bathroom. He wouldn't hose off the front walk or even run water into a pot and put it on the stove to boil it. We all thought it was weird, and laughed in private, making fun of Salvador and his fetish about faucets. But we never laughed to his face or even when he could hear us. And like I said, because he was so good at the other jobs that he was given and because he was so cheap to employ, we complied with his silly rule.

Over time, the two of us developed a friendship, or as close a friendship as you can have with a person who works under you. I did most of the talking, and he listened, responding when necessary, and as we grew more comfortable together, or at least as I thought we had, I got the courage to ask him one day why he wouldn't work around the sinks. He looked around uncomfortably and shook his head. I pushed a little harder.

"C'mon, what are you afraid of, drowning?" I chuckled lightly.

"When the water is running I can hear their whispers and pleadings. I hear their prayers." He paused. "I hear their suffering."

"Whose?" I asked him.

"The spirits, dead men and women and children who are screaming out in agonizing pain. I don't know who they are, or where they reside, but bad things are happening to them."

"You hear voices from the pipes?" I asked him, waiting for the punch line, waiting for the other Mexicans to jump out and we would all have a good laugh over the great gag that had been pulled. No such thing happened.

He looked down at the floor. I couldn't tell if he was ashamed or embarrassed or laughing. "Yes."

The word sort of hung in the air and then seemed to flitter away. I pushed my lower lip out, nodded my head and walked away. We never spoke of it again.

But I couldn't stop thinking about what he had told me. Dead voices coming from the sewers. Children pleading through the onslaught of water that poured from the mouth of a metal pipe. It made no sense. But it explained why he never seemed clean. And why he always came to work carrying his gallon of water that he bought at the White Hen every night before work. I became obsessed with the idea of what it meant if it was true. It scared the shit out of me to believe that kind of activity could exist on this plane. The afterlife, in my opinion, belongs somewhere different from where the current life is taking place. It also aggravated me that maybe he was playing a joke, and the Mexicans were having a good old chuckle behind my back. Eventually the idea put itself at the back of my head, and life went on as normal for all of us.

About six months after we had spoken about the water, Salvador lost his job at the factory where he worked during the day. Two weeks went by, and he couldn't find anything else. We gave him a few extra hours at the restaurant, but that didn't help much. Mark loaned him five hundred dollars so he could pay his rent, and I loaned him a hundred myself. Giving him that loan did something to me inside. It made me feel good, but at the same time, it made me feel like I had a power over Salvador. I exercised that power three days later when Jorge, the dishwasher, called in sick.

"Salvador, I need you to do the dishes tonight, buddy," I greeted him as he walked in the door. He looked at me with amusement in his eyes.

"Ha-ha," he mocked back, thinking we were playing a game.

"I'm serious. Jorge is sick, and you never do them. I'm sorry, but today is your turn." The joy flushed from his eyes. They became still, and wide.

"Please don't make me," he asked.

It was just like that. He stared me directly in the face and said please don't make me. I was in a bad mood already, and secretly I had been waiting for this exact moment. What would he do if cornered? Give up his little game and do the same work as the rest of us? (I say us, and yet I can't remember the last time I washed any dishes at that place.) Or would he stick to his guns and prove to me that what he said was true? And he was cornered, wasn't he? He had no money, and this was the only job he had. He would really have to be deep rooted in his conviction to walk away at this point. I stared back at him with a bored and irritated look plastered across my face. I folded my arms, rested my weight back slightly, and waited.

"Please," creaked from his throat, high pitched and barely audible. I just stood staring at him. His head dropped, and he walked away. I felt a surge rush through me. I had won.

I forgot all about Salvador washing dishes that night. The mood of the restaurant was very somber and quiet, and it wasn't until the clouds of my dark mood had moved on that I noticed just how quiet everyone was. I looked around at all of them. They were all doing their jobs, mechanically like they always did. Fryer baskets sizzled in the grease; the oven spun pizzas to a golden brown. I made jokes with the guys. They laughed, but it was forced. Finally, I pulled Reveriano aside, and asked him what was going on.

"Something is wrong with Salvador," he whispered.

"What? What's wrong?" I asked, a little too sharply. My heart was beating in my chest wildly. I didn't wait for him to answer. Quietly I sneaked toward the sinks in the back of the store. I was furious. Somehow Salvador had managed to make me look like a bad guy in all of the other Mexicans' eyes. I could hear the sound of the water as it collected in the giant sinks. Salvador couldn't hear me over the noise of the running water. I came up near him and felt my stomach drop, as a feeling of fear made all my hair stand on end. Salvador was sobbing, tears running along the crevice where his nose and face met. I stepped forward, and he must have heard me, because he looked up and in his drenched eyes I saw for the briefest second whatever it was he heard coming from those pipes. Those eyes reflected his agony, *their* agony, like a silver mirror, and I felt for that second what it was he had felt his whole life. His lips were parted and the tears ran along them before falling into his mouth. When he saw me he did his best to hide the display he was putting on.

I stepped to the sinks and turned off the water. We stood awkwardly next to each other, and then he stepped towards me. I was so frightened in that moment. Whatever I felt had scared me. I opened my arms, and he stepped into them. I hugged him, rocking slightly to try and comfort this pain he was feeling, this pain I had caused him. He cried openly and loudly for a long time. Every so often someone's head would pop around the corner and then disappear just as quick. Somewhere far away I could hear the phones ringing.

Vermination of the Grubbs

JAMES R. HEIN

The sun hit apogee. A jawbreaker of fire, white and pure. A dark blue dragonfly, glittering like a gemstone, buzzed past Barren and darted into the reeds at the roadside. School was out now. Summer vacation had begun and Barren walked along the highway, heading home. He sweat and listened to the smooth rise and fall of cars as they zipped by. Each car pushed the air and shoved his shoulder, and he squinted from it all. The push, the dust, that fucking heat. It was easier to look down as he walked. Just watch the gravel slowly pass under him. He wiped his brow, walked a little farther, and stopped to stare into a murky pond next to the highway. Clumps of crocodile-green reeds nodding and swaying slowly in the air like serpents stirring from sleep. But the pond itself was sleek and dark like polished iron.

As he stared into the pond, the low growl of his father's tow truck surprised him. He looked up and saw it shimmering in the distance like a mirage. A silver grille with headlights. It was an apple-red behemoth almost two cars high with monster truck tires and coil upon coil of heavy, grimy steel chain hanging off the rear winch and swinging side to side like an elephant's trunk. It neared Barren, slowed and pulled over on the opposite side of the road. The engine grumbled in idle. Painted in large, blocky white letters across the truck's side were the words, '24 HOUR TOWING.' Barren's father popped his head out the driver's window. A pair of sunglasses on a round, pale face, pockmarked like an old dart board. He grinned and waved for Barren to cross the highway. Then his arm hung out of the window, his hand dangling limp. As Barren crossed, he wondered what his dad wanted with him. They hardly spoke, if ever, due to a conflict of schedules. Just as he got home from school, his dad left for work. The two hurried past each other on the lawn without even a look, like two strangers running late. His father's eyes glared ahead; Barren's eyes looked down and tired. And on those rare weekends when the whole family was home for dinner, all three nibbled their meals in their own bedrooms behind locked doors, hunched over their plates and watching three different channels on the three different television sets. So for Barren to have his father drive him home was very strange.

Barren climbed in and slammed the door. His dad still grinned but his eyes were thoughtful under the sunglasses, his head a jumble of words. *My wife*, he thought. *My son. Those goddamn snakes. Barry, your mother's on the edge again. We've got to talk. You're down about something, too. It's obvious. But you can't wimp out on me now. I need your help, Barry. These snakes. I can't do this alone.* But Barren's father could never say these words out loud. He decided to pick up his son and wing the conversation on the ride home, hoping to find a less embarrassing way of expressing himself.

His dad turned the truck around. The two-way radio crackled with buzzing voices, raspy and nasal at once. Barren stared out the windshield and followed the slither of the double-yellow line as it flowed by. Sweat beaded on both their faces.

After a few seconds, his dad asked, "You OK?"

Barren shrugged and nodded.

"If something's wrong, you know you can say so. You can talk to me. Right?"

"Yeah. Sure, Dad."

"Because both me and your ma are concerned about you. You've been acting like an antisocial weirdo lately. Like a complete mope." He reached down to switch off his two-way radio and turn on the AC.

Barren shrugged and wiped his brow with his fist.

His father kept going. "You never say anything to anybody. Not even to say, 'Hi.' You lock yourself up in your room all day, never coming out except to eat and shit. And at night all you do is listen to your headphones in the dark. And it's so fuckin' loud, Ozzy the Bat-Eater is gonna make you deaf by the time we kick your ass off to college."

A pause.

"And," he added finally, "you seem down. Like you're depressed or some-thing."

Barren thought, *No, really?* He looked out the passenger window. Suburban strip plazas and homes had taken the place of the ponds and reeds. Barren saw a few homes float by, bright and squat. A strip of sidewalk flowed by like a conveyor belt.

After he made a turn, his father faced him. He had a look both angry and concerned, and his words were distinct and slow, as if chiseled from granite. "The guys down at the police station say that kids who take drugs act depressed all the time." His father watched him carefully, looking for any reaction.

Barren looked him in the eye. "Is that what you think? You think that I'm sad because I'm a pothead?!" Barren was aghast.

His father grinned with smug satisfaction and faced the road again. "You said it. I didn't." He chuckled, gloating that his trick worked.

Barren's anger squeezed his heart like a claw. What bugged him more than anything else was his dad being so smug about the whole thing. He had to say something. His face twisted into an angry scowl. "Yeah. Drugs. Must be drugs, right? Lord knows I have no reason to be depressed about anything! Can't be anyone else's fault but mine, right?" And then he added, in a barely audible undertone, "Everyone knows you two are so Shirley-Temple perfect."

Barren really didn't think about what he had said. It just pushed itself out like vomit. His anger degenerated into shame in one shaky breath, and he immediately wished he hadn't said anything at all. But the words were said, and his dad was not a man to take angry words from anyone, including his own son. He glowered and jammed on the brakes. Heavy chains swayed and slammed into the back of the truck. Barren's heart leaped, and his whole face felt numb and dry like rubber. His father pulled over to the side of the road, jammed the stick shift into park, then turned to him and screwed up his eyes. "We're not gonna start this shit again, are we?" His voice grew more and more mocking. "We're not gonna have us another little tantrum again, are we?"

"I am not having a tantrum!"

"You're not gonna start actin' like a fuckin' little spoiled brat?"

"I am not . . . ."

"Because if you do, I'm gonna smack the livin' shit outta you right here and now! I swear I'll jam your fuckin' head through the window! You're get-tin' way too fuckin' old to act like this! Grow the fuck up!"

They stared at each other. After a few seconds, Barren turned away. What was the point of telling his dad that he didn't smoke? What the point of telling him anything? *In fact*, he thought, *the whole reason why I don't smoke anything is just to spite you, you fucker. You're convinced I'm on every drug in the fuckin' book. You search through my drawers and under my bed almost every day. You ever find anything other than the* Penthouse *you stole? No! You didn't! Fucker! You were awful proud of yourself when you found those beer cans in my trash, though. To hell with you.*

Barren stared out the passenger window again. He saw a yellow lunchbox of a house. A lawn perfectly square and chalkboard green. A small black dog sat on the front stoop. It was on a leash which was tied to the front doorknob. Not a person was in sight. Panting, it stared deadpan at Barren and licked its nose with a tongue that glistened in the sun.

"Yeah. OK," his dad continued, softer now, "our family's got problems. Your ma's had it rough over the years. But it's nothing we can't handle. We have to work together to keep your ma afloat. Keep her out of the hospital; keep her from hearing voices again. You gotta help me, man. Me and you. We're a team. Y'know?"

Barren looked to his father again, fumbling for the right words, his voice cracking from the sting he felt in his throat. "But Dad, I mean, I know Mom's a schizo. I understand that. And I want to help. But I'm down. I mean, really. I mean, it's bad. I don't know why. But there are days when I feel like I'm going to explode. Days when it feels like nothing I do or say has a point. Days when it feels like no one understands me. I spend time with my friends, but instead of feeling happy, I feel used. Everyone either sees through me, or makes fun of me. No one ever talks to me . . . ," and he trailed off. Conversations with his parents always came out that way—confused. He always approached the problem from different angles, but it never came out sounding right. The answer kept lurking like a *kraken* among the impenetrable black tendrils of his tired mind.

But while Barren spoke, his father looked like he was on the verge of laughing, as if waiting for a punch line. And when Barren stopped, his dad laughed hard. Loud laughter filled the truck's interior. Deafening like a cannon. "Oh sheeee-iiiiit!" he grinned. "Hee-hee! Listen to you! No one understands meeeee!" he mocked with scrunched-up eyes. "Yeah, yer life is so fuckin' hard! Jesus Christ! Cry me a river, ya little baby! Ha-ha-ha! You got it so easy, you don't know! You think you know the world, but you don't know dick! You and your whole gang of dope-smokin', long-haired, know-it-all friends! Compared to your ma, you don't have a fuckin' clue what pain is, pal! Only a spoiled-rotten brat would say something like 'No one understands me' after what your ma has been through." And his father kept giggling, holding his hand to his eyes, his shoulders hopping up and down.

Barren stewed in angry silence. *Fuck him. He don't want to listen to me!*

Fuck him! I ain't sayin' shit now! Not after all that! Go to hell, you fat fuck! Next time you pull this shit about 'Go ahead, tell me anything,' you can just fuckin' talk to the fuckin' chains! After you get me home, I hope your fuckin' heart explodes in your chest!

After his laughter died down, Barren's father snapped his fingers and his face lit up. "Aha! I know what you need," he said. "You can kill a few snakes! That should get you out of your depression, huh?" He gave Barren a sad look with a pouting lip, then chuckled at his own joke. Barren scowled out the window and saw the dog again. There was a hairless patch of crimson skin along its side that Barren hadn't noticed before. It twisted its head about and bared its teeth. Jagged, white rows gleamed like wet coral in the sun. With an angry snap, it bit itself, and the skin flushed an even deeper red.

As the weeks passed, Barren tried a variety of humane alternatives to killing the snakes.

On Monday morning of the first week, he found a rusty garden shovel in the garage. Holding it out before him like a cattle prod, he approached the stoop. Snakes slithered into the crack to escape him. But there was a straggler that couldn't get to the crack in time, and it coiled itself up at the base of the steps ready to bite. Barren carefully scooped up the coiled straggler. It bit the metal a few times accomplishing nothing. But once he had the serpent, it sat still awaiting its fate on the shovel's tongue.

Holding the shovel out, Barren ran up the driveway, across the street, down and up the culvert on the other side of the street, ran across a baseball field and up a steep hill to a cluster of boulders. He flipped the shovel and dropped his passenger into the rocks. It slithered out of sight. Then, huffing and gasping, Barren ran back down the hill, across the field, down and up the culvert, across the street and back down the driveway. By the time he returned, the snakes were out again. As Barren approached, wiping the sweat from his stinging eyes, there was a new rush to the crack and a new straggler and the whole cycle started over.

He ran this relay dozens of times, but the number of snakes never dropped. Were the bastards slithering back down the hill at night? Who knew? All the relay did was give him a heat rash in his crotch from the constant friction of his inner thighs.

Week Two. While his mom was at work, he crept into the kitchen and carefully rooted through the cabinets until he found a huge steel kettle. He hauled it outside to the driveway and filled it with lighter fluid and threw in a lit match. An orange mushroom twice as tall as Barren blasted from the pot and slapped his face with heat. He jumped back and waited for the flames to go down. Soon, the kettle was belching smoke like a factory's stack, and he dragged the kettle to the crack, using old towels on the handles to avoid burning his hands. He held a small, battery-powered fan next to the column of smoke and tried to blow some smoke into the crack. He hoped the smoke would shoo the snakes out.

Anyway, that's what he told the fire department. The truck pulled up, a big red slab of metal on tires. The more Barren tried to explain his plan to the grinning men in blue, the more and more stupid he felt for trying something so half-assed. Good thing for him that the scorching rubbed off the kettle; his mother never found out. And his dad never woke up.

Week Three. He rigged his boombox atop the stoop and turned it up full blast. If *Piece of Mind* from Iron Maiden wouldn't flush out these snakes, nothing would. Barren started the album at "Flight of Icarus," but before the song was half over, his dad poked his head out of his bedroom window. With his hair disheveled from sleeping, he screamed down, "I'm trying to sleep, you fucking idiot!"

Week Four. The afternoon was hot and the sun gleamed off the white paint of the house, making Barren squint. It was insanely humid. The driveway reeked of tar. The high-pitched whine of mosquitoes droned in Barren's ears. Overhead, a jet traced its two lines of white smoke in the blue as it whispered its roar over the homes. His mom would be home from the butcher shop soon, and his dad would be rising from bed to go to the garage. This was the best time of the day. Both his folks would see that he was doing something about the snakes without having to speak to him.

In the backyard, Barren found the heavy coils of green garden hose, taped here and there with Band-Aid lengths of black electrical tape. He hauled it around front, screwed one end onto the water spigot, hefted the other end in his hand and smiled. *Garter snakes aren't going to want to live in a pool, right?* he thought. *The rush of water filling the nest will flush them out, and then they'll have to go somewhere else. Once they're gone, I'll seal up the crack.*

He approached the cement staircase. Snakes scattered as usual. He wedged the hose into the crack, listening to the metallic scraping sounds as it probed deeper. "Time to pack your bags, guys," Barren said with a grin and swatted a mosquito.

Barren turned the spigot. It squeaked with every grip and twist. The hose flexed along its length, and tiny puddles formed under the tape patches. From the spigot, he could even hear the low gurgle of water emptying into the crack. He waited, expecting to see the crack puke up a slew of brackish water and scared-as-hell snakes. Black strips and blacker water in a single, gruesome, and glorious deluge. *This is going to be so cool*, he thought. *Like what comes out of the Devil's ass when he takes a shit! Fuckin' awesome!*

After a good five minutes, nothing happened. The water kept pouring. But nothing came out of the crack. No water. No snakes.

After ten minutes, Barren started getting nervous. Where the fuck was all that water going? He approached the crack and wrenched the hose free. Water squirted out full force, and the backlash hit Barren on the jeans and the Ozzy concert tee. *OK*, Barren thought, *the water's running. It's not my imagination. What the hell is going on?*

He shut the water off as the garage door started to roll up. A beige station wagon pulled in, covered with freckles of rust all along its doors. Barren looked through the windshield to see his mom. She waved with a single flap of the hand, her expression tired and tombstone grey.

Without saying a word to Barren, she got out of the car in her bloody butcher's smock. She left the door open, and the car's door buzzer droned like a bee. In one hand, she held her white purse with the gold clasp, in the other, a plastic ice scraper. She approached the door adjoining the garage and the house. Using the scraper like a probe, she poked and tapped the wall to the upper right of the door frame, then the left, then she scraped the top of the door frame with one loud, screeching sweep. She would never let a snake fall on her again.

Barren walked up next to her and touched her elbow. He said, "Hi, Mom."

She jumped and looked at Barren for a moment with fear in her eyes and her shoulders hunched.

Barren searched her face with worried eyes. *How will she be today?* he wondered. *Will she snap at me? Or will she squeeze the living hell out of me with a hug so ridiculously passionate that you'd think she was rehearsing for a soap?*

She stared at him for a second too long to be normal. The car's buzzer gargled a little from bad wiring, but then fell back into its constant beelike drone. Then her eyes softened and her shoulders relaxed. She grinned. "How's my darling, darling baby?" Then she embraced him and squeezed the living hell out of him like she hadn't seen him in years. Barren buried his face into her shoulder, his eyes closed, smelling cow's blood and baby shampoo in her hair. She peered over his shoulder like a scared child, scanning for snakes.

After a few moments, they parted and she asked, "Your dad up yet, hon?"

Barren shook his head.

"I'm surprised we don't hear him snoring through the walls like a friggin' locomotive."

Barren nodded, eyes down.

Placing the ice scraper and her purse on the car, she undid the top button on her smock. "You know what he asked me the other day?" she began. "He asked if he could borrow fifty bucks. So I asked him why." She picked up the scraper and the purse again. "He says he wants to get a gun." She slammed the car door shut, silencing the buzzer. "I ask him, 'What the hell do you want a gun for?' So he looks at me like he wants to cry me a river and says some crap about going on tow calls in rough neighborhoods late at night. The guys on the police force think he should have one. The biggest bunch of bullshit I ever heard. So you know what I told him? I said, 'With your luck, you'll drop it and shoot yourself between the eyes.' He looks at me with that 'Why me?' face, then walks away from me laughing."

"The snakes will be gone soon," said Barren. "I got another idea—"

"That man. When I married him, he was so cute. Charming. Played the drums. Two years of college. He sold insurance, you know that? Made a decent buck. It was wonderful. But it wasn't even a year after I marry him and you know what he does?"

Barren shrugged. He'd heard the story before, of course. Knew the story by heart, because she never stopped telling it.

"Bastard goes and gets drunk at a party, tells his boss to go fuck himself, and loses his job."

A pause. The two stood there, Barren looking down and arms folded, his mother scowling at the empty space before her and shaking her head. She stuffed the scraper into her purse, the handle stuck out the top.

"Your father is an alcoholic. You know that, Barren."

Of course, he knew. He nodded slightly. "I haven't seen him drink in a while, though."

"That's 'cause we can't afford any damn beer," she muttered. She pointed a long, broken nail at Barren. "You, my dear, are the only reason we're living together. You're the only reason I'm wasting my time with this man." And she kept poking her finger toward Barren as if she were tapping a brick wall. "You. You. You. As soon as you're eighteen, I'm outta here, kiddo."

She stood for a moment longer, watching Barren. Her finger dropped. Barren felt her eyes on him and his insides quivered. He heard the bed springs rumble and squeak above him as his dad shifted in bed. *She's just standing there*, Barren thought, *staring at me like some freaking goth chick in a horror movie. Jesus. What the fuck, Mom?! If I say 'Hi' to you, you go off about how your life is living hell, and you make me feel like total shit! If I don't say 'Hi', you accuse me of not loving you and being antisocial, and you make me feel like total shit! What am I supposed to do?!* His vision clouded from tears, but he angrily pushed them down. He was upset, but this B.S. with his mother happened all the time. He should be used to it by now.

He looked up at her, and he wasn't sure exactly what expression he gave, but her face immediately tensed in a combination of a grimace and a glare. Her eyes were boiling with suspicious accusation. She said softly, "Ooo, is that eerie."

Barren, confused and self-conscious, unfolded his arms and wandered over to the workbench. He stuffed one hand in his pocket and tinkered through grimy tools with the other. Without looking at her, and in a voice as nonchalant as he could possibly give, he asked, "What's so eerie?"

"That look you gave me. That's exactly the look your dad gives me when he wants something."

Barren turned to face her. "Well, *I* don't want nothing," he said and looked away.

Her eyes remained suspicious, but a wry smile appeared; it was a look that said, *Yeah. Right. I know better.* She sighed and shook her head, mumbling, "Must think I'm a dumbass!" She turned and opened the door to the house. She froze in the doorway, one foot in the garage, one foot in the hallway, her hand still on the knob. Some seconds passed. Barren only had time to wonder for a moment what was wrong before she dropped her purse and covered her mouth with both hands. She wailed a wet, gravelly howl.

Barren jumped, horrified. "What the fuck?!" he whispered as he ran to the door. Just as he did so, his mom bolted from the doorway and the two hit each other with football force and danced in a flail of limbs next to the car. Barren felt the wind leave him, and he saw stars. Though he had weight on his side, his mother possessed the adrenaline strength of desperation. She scrambled past him, screaming, and ran out of the garage and down the street.

Barren regained his balance and looked through the doorway. It was a short hallway that led into the TV room. He blinked, his eyes adjusting to the light. Puddles of water mottled the hallway floor. The carpet in the TV room was a few shades darker than its usual brown. It was completely soaked. And the snakes were everywhere, lazily slithering here and there across the moist thick carpet.

Eyes and mouth agape in amazement, Barren dashed down the hallway. The carpet squished like wet mud under his shoes and he could already smell the rotten egg stench of the water. A few snakes squirmed across the carpet and slithered under the sofa to escape him. He hung his head and said, "Guys? When I said 'pack your bags,' that didn't mean I wanted dinner guests, OK?" And then, softer, to himself, "Dad is gonna have my ass on a frying pan."

After a few moments, Barren noticed that most of the water was pooled up near the crawlspace door. He slowly approached the door. Placed his hand on the knob. Turned it slowly and peered into the darkness. He reached up and turned on the crawlspace light, a single light bulb hanging from a wire and so dingy it glowed like a big butterscotch. From the brush of his hand, it swung like a pendulum. In the shifting light, he saw dirty black water covering the floor. All the cardboard boxes and Christmas decorations were soaking in it. (Somewhere, there had to be a breach that led from the crack outside to the crawlspace.) Wrapped around the legs of a plastic outdoor Santa, a snake lazily slithered its way up to the white beard. Barren stared at the snake for a few moments until he heard a voice upstairs.

"What the hell was that?"

Barren looked up the staircase to see his dad. He had nothing on but his BVDs and a scowl. His hair was up in porcupine spikes from sleeping on it funny.

"That was Mom," Barren answered.

His dad came down. Just as his big, callused toes lit onto the carpet, there came a loud jelly-like squelch. He yanked his foot back, grimaced and shouted, "Aw! Fuckin' gross!" Then he saw the snakes, littered all about the basement. His eyes bugged.

"What the hell…"

"Sorry, Dad," Barren said in a soft voice, looking away.

"That scream was your mother?"

Barren nodded.

"Where is she?"

Barren gestured out the hall door that led to the garage. "Halfway to Motorhead, Ohio, by now probably. She took off."

His dad bolted back upstairs. Barren heard him stomp his way to the bedrooms. The stomping ceased. A moment of silence. Then his father's voice barged its way through the house and down the stairs to Barren.

"Get rid of the fuckin' snakes! I'm going after Mom!"

Barren slowly walked into the garage and leaned against the station wagon. With a number of stomps, thumps, door slams, and engine growls, Barren heard Ernie get dressed, walk out the door, hop into the tow truck, and peel out down the gravel road, kicking up a rooster-tail fan of stones from the rear tires. Rocky hail stormed the lawn. Barren listened to the growls of the tow truck until they faded completely, and all that was left was the distant purr of a lawnmower.

Barren went about the snakes' evacuation with slow steps. He grabbed a pair of latex gloves from under the kitchen sink, then searched the house for a box or chest, but couldn't really find one. Not one that was empty. All the boxes in the crawlspace were soaked and ready to tear apart like paper the moment you tried to lift them. Boxes from the garage were stuffed with junk, and Barren didn't have the energy to empty any of them out. Eventually, he remembered his large, plastic toy chest. Shaped like a squatting frog and about the size of a suitcase, it sat in a forgotten corner of his closet. The mouth was hinged, so you could open its mouth and dump toys down its throat. That would work.

A few minutes later, Barren held the frog upside down. The mouth swung open and it puked toys all over his bedroom floor. Toys that he hadn't played with in years; G.I. Joes, a naked Cat Woman doll, bent Empire Strikes Back trading cards, a Tonka truck that he never liked—he thought construction trucks were boring—and a baseball that had cartoony black-marker doodles of spitting pricks and huge boobs all over it. He hauled the empty frog out of the room and down the hallway, all the while filling his mind with thoughts of self-loathing. He was a fuck-up, pure and simple. *If I had killed the damn snakes like Dad said, none of this would have happened. But no. I had to be a fuckin' wimp and try to save the damn snakes. Fuck. May as well kiss the Judas Priest concert next weekend good-bye. Why the hell is it that I never know I'm doing something wrong until after I do it? What an idiot. No wonder I keep squeaking by with Ds. Just fuck it all.*

He set the frog in the middle of the TV room, scooped up all the wriggling bodies, and tossed them, writhing, into the chest. Some tried to slither out, but Barren made a habit of shutting the lid with each new snake. Once he was sure he had found most of them—you never can be sure, the little fuckers could be hiding anywhere—he heard the tow truck's low growl from up the street. Dad was home.

His father had been gone about an hour. Barren heard them enter through the front door and walk up the stairs with heavy, slow steps. Feeling tired, he sat on the couch. His hands were sweating in the latex gloves, and the stench of the wet carpet still jammed up his nostrils, even with the hallway door open. Upstairs, the water ran a few times; the pipes in the walls gurgled. Barren heard his mother moan something strange that sounded like, "a lie, a lie." But then he listened a little closer and heard the name distinctly. "Eliza! Eliza!" Then a faint tap from inside the frog as one of the snakes slapped the plastic with its tail. Then, his father's voice called down.

"Barren? Where's your ma's meds?"

Barren took a few seconds to answer. His thoughts were muddled and slow. "I don't know. In her purse maybe."

"Where's her purse?"

"I don't know. In the car?"

"Go find it and toss it up to me, would ya?"

Barren pushed himself up off the sofa and plodded out to the garage with his head hanging. Actually stood in the garage for a moment and wondered why he walked out there. Though it was in plain view on the garage floor, Barren didn't notice the white purse until he had searched for a few moments. He picked it up, walked to the bottom of the steps, looked up, and called to his father.

Ernie's head and shoulders appeared over the banister directly above Barren. He held out an open hand. Barren tossed the purse up, watching it spin in the air like a sandwich. Ernie snatched it from the air, and his shoulders and head ducked out of sight.

"Dad?" Barren called.

"The snakes gone?" his dad asked.

"Is Mom OK?"

A pause.

"We gotta rent a rug shampooer. The phone book's up here if you need it."

"Dad? Is Mom OK?"

Another pause. Ernie's head appeared again over the banister, the skin on his pockmarked cheeks sagging like melted clay from the gravity. Below him, he saw Barren looking up. Eyes glistening. His face full of concern. Ernie glared at the sight.

"You bawlin'?"

"No."

"Better not be. You're fuckin' sixteen."

"Dad! Is . . . Mom . . . OK?" Barren asked, holding his gloved hands before him, palms up to emphasize his question.

A pause.

"She's sick."

"Sick how?"

"Sick sick."

Barren shook his head. Felt his lip quiver. A lump formed in his throat, which he swallowed. But it wouldn't go down. It grew into a spiked ball and threatened to tear his throat open. His voice cracked. "Sick I've-got-the-flu sick? Sick my-ankle-is-broke sick? Sick the-zucchini's-telling-me-to-kill-you sick?"

"Don't get smart with me!"

"I'm not getting smart! I'm just asking!"

"She'll be fine! She just needs to rest for awhile."

"Who's Eliza?"

A pause. Barren's dad looked like he was slapped across the face. And almost immediately Barren felt the tension in the silence as heavy as an iron chain.

Ernie bent down over the banister and whispered down in a hushed, slow voice, "Where did you hear that name?"

Barren started whispering too, though he wasn't sure why they were whispering. "Well . . . from her. She just said it."

"So? She shouts all sorts of names."

"Well . . . yeah. But all the names she spits off I know. She'll say yours or mine. Whenever she says Celia's name, I know she means my sister. And I know who God and Satan are. But she mentions this name Eliza a lot. And I don't know who it is. Dad? Who is it?"

From the bedrooms came an unearthly sound, a low growl that stretched to a high moan in an angry crescendo. It was his mother.

Ernie glanced in the direction of Dorothy's room. Looked down at Barren, then back to Dorothy. Then grit his teeth and threw Dorothy's purse to the floor. Nostrils flaring, he thundered down the stairs. And though Ernie was short, Barren shrunk at his approach. He had no idea what he had said or done, but he knew he was in deep shit. He backed into the hallway, backed into a corner near the door to the garage, but knew better than to run outside. That would only piss Dad off more. He looked down. Felt himself tremble. Ernie advanced like a man ready to kill. Ernie leaned in close, face red, teeth bared and menacing, until his nose was almost touching Barren's. He whispered with an irritated hiss. "You wanna know who Eliza is? All right, you little idiot, I'll tell you. It's only a little baby girl that me and your ma had a long time ago. It's only a girl who got hit and killed when she was two by some asshole bitch in a beater of a car!" Ernie's voice grew louder, forgetting, for a moment, his wife's sanity. His eyes teared, but he told himself that the summer air was really dry. And that he was *not* crying. "It's only a child that would have been your second sister, *if* she were living! It's only the most precious goddamn thing me and your ma ever had! And we lost her in the fuckin' blink of an eye!" He snapped his fingers before Barren's nose.

Barren just stared at the wet tile in the hallway. His father smeared the tears away. Barren glanced up, made eye contact with his dad who just scowled with a look of disgust. Barren looked down again. Started to finger the wall behind him with his gloved hands and could feel the groove in the wood through the latex.

"Fuckin' idiot! I oughta smack the living shit outta you!" Ernie hissed. "Don't you realize? Don't you fuckin' get it? There's a reason we don't talk about all this shit!" He poked Barren's chest hard with a callused finger. "There's a *reason*!"

"I'm sorry," Barren muttered.

"Yeah. You better be. She's borderline, OK? But your ma is schizo. We can't change that. And this is just the kind of shit that could send her over the edge! OK?" A pause. "YOU think you're so fuckin' smart. It's too bad they don't teach fuckin' common sense at your joke of a school! 'Cause you sure can't think for shit!"

Ernie leaned back after a few more seconds. He turned, marched across the squashing carpet, and noticed the frog, squatting on the wet carpet like a lawn gnome. He blinked. Lit a cigarette. Faced Barren again. Cigarette smoke exhaled from his mouth as he asked, "What the fuck is that?"

"The snakes are inside," Barren mumbled, not looking up.

His dad looked at the frog again, smirked and shook his head. "Pure genius. A fuckin' frog," he said under his breath. He approached Barren again. Took another drag and said, "Listen. Don't you dare fuckin' bring this up in front of anyone. *Anyone!* You got me?"

"Will she be OK?"

Ernie tilted his head and said, in a tone full of sarcasm, "Well, little cry baby, that all depends! What does it depend on, you ask? Well," and here, Ernie pointed to the squatting frog, "Depends on whether you get rid of the fucking, goddamn snakes! Something like this is all it takes! If past experience is any clue, once she starts hearing voices, that's it! Now quit being so goddamn stupid and move your ass!"

Ernie stamped back up the stairs, leaving a trail of smoke and a hint of B.O. behind him.

The thought crossed Barren's mind—if having snakes around was so dangerous for her, why didn't Dad help? But there was no point in applying logic to anything that happened under that roof. What did it matter? Fuck it.

Barren searched the garage for a dolly. Couldn't find one. Knew there was one in the tow truck, but didn't feel like getting it. Too tired. He settled for an old red wagon. He hefted the squatting frog full of snakes onto the wagon. Felt them shifting around inside. Strapped the frog down with bungee cords. Hauled the wagon up the driveway, across the road, the culvert, the baseball field and up the hill to the pile of boulders.

The sun was nearly down now. The sky full of cherry red and sherbet orange. The whole sky was crazy. Color everywhere. Like a piñata in your face and frozen in mid bust. A cloud of sparrows, black fluttering dots in the fading light, rose up in a wave from the rocks as Barren approached. They floated toward the house and landed on the roof and huddled on the shingles. Kids played a few doors down, their shouts and hoots echoing around the block. Barren sniffled. Wiped his nose with the back of his hand. Snorted up some mucus and spit in the grass. He still felt the pain of his dad's finger in his chest.

He set the frog down. Opened it up and tilted it forward, dumping out the tangled mass of snakes. They pulled themselves apart and slithered into the rocks. Barren looked over his shoulder to make sure no one was near. Then he squatted down, lowered his head and spoke quietly into the boulders.

"I don't want any secrets between us, so just to let you guys know, if I do find any more snakes by the house, they're dead. I'll kill 'em outright with the goddamn cleaver if I have to. But I promise to bring their bodies here. I'll set them by the rocks, and you guys can decide what to do with them. Eat them. Bury them. Ignore them. Whatever. They're your relatives, you decide. But I sure as hell don't want to hear any complaining! This is the way it's got to be. I'd change it if I could. Those of you that are up here should just be happy that you weren't left behind, otherwise you'd be living in hiding from me and my cleaver for the rest of your life."

He paused and looked up. The boulders rested black and silent like a heap of sleeping trolls. Slivers and specks of red light bled through the cracks between them. Barren turned and looked out over the homes below, colored pink by the red light of the sun. Black silhouettes of kids still lingered on the lawns, like small clusters of restless ghosts. With a final wipe of the nose, he turned and went back down the hill. He dragged the toy box behind him, and the hollow, plastic scraping sounds echoed throughout the lot.

And through the remaining days of that summer, Barren's idle thoughts, especially at night in bed while staring at his ceiling, the slanted patch of light from lamppost outside, focused on one thing—the sister he never knew he had. *I have a sister*, he thought. *I have another sister. I have a second sister.* As the amazement and the impact settled within him and tempered the walls of his silence, he imagined he could see right through the ceiling and see her. He could see her on the roof of the house. A young, happy, teenaged woman draped in a nightgown of golden leaves and silk and a head of hair that flowed out behind her like a blond banner. She never made a sound but mouthed laughter with perfection like a silent movie. She danced, her silhouette framed perfectly within the round canvas of the full moon. She did cartwheels, hugged the chimney and flew all about the house with giddy and enchanted abandon like a drunken spirit in the summer night.

Garden Vegetables

AUDREY QWEEN ROY-WICKS

The dawn of a new day was arriving, and you could hear the first breath of morning wiggle its way through the trees by the shaking leaves. Just about everybody in the small southern community had slept with their doors and windows open all night. Sally lifted her nose and enjoyed the fresh air as it flowed through her bedroom window. She was deeply rooted like the trees in the Mississippi red-clay dirt. The scent of an outsider a mile away would tickle her nose.

She heard the familiar cry of Esther's back screen door and smiled. Their houses were a yard apart, and she'd grown accustomed to that rusty creak after so many years. She kept waiting for the day when one of her grown sons would get a mind to fix it. They both reminded Sally of the silly yellow cat who ran around in circles, chasing flies all day. She imagined Esther sitting on the back steps with her jelly jar of peach brandy, nipping quietly until the sun came up. She'd do that some mornings every now and then. And Sally never interrupted.

The rattle of overworked fans humming steadily along the crooked path of old houses captured Sally's attention. They sounded like a trainload of bumblebees. It was a wonder anybody was able to sleep.

She stretched her arms above her head, enjoying the new breeze that slid over her exposed, thick, tan brown legs. It lifted that awful, aching Mississippi heat stuck inside every pore of her skin, as it brushed against the thin white curtains tied in knots above her head. They swayed like her front porch swing, steadily back and forth. Sally sat up, tugging at the sweaty gown stuck to her plump, rounded body like a second skin. She found her faded pink slippers and pushed up from the bed. It was her morning ritual to speak to God before he got too busy.

She stood at the back door, looking through the screen into her garden. It covered most of the backyard with its neat rows of everything you could grow under the sun: sweet peas, okra, collard greens, corn, green beans, and plump squash. All Sally ever needed from the market was a carton of eggs and fresh milk. When you stood in her back door, you were facing east. That's where she'd watch the sun lift up from behind the trees and bless her garden. The town's worst gossip, Henry Simmons, lived on the left side of the house, going north. Her good friend Esther lived to the south. On the back fence were several tall rows of healthy cornstalks. Toiling and tending the garden carefully every day had become her daily chore. Didn't leave much time for idle gossip and foolishness, and it gave her food to eat.

"Lord, what a miracle to see another day," she whispered, folding her hands under her chin. Sally closed her eyes and drifted into prayerful thought. She didn't hear the snap of crackling twigs, or notice little Esther easing into her patch of potatoes, but the prayerful spell was broken when the sagging, overstuffed pockets of Esther's holey gray sweater spilled onto the ground. Sally's eyes shifted over to the large peach tree that separated the yards where she saw a fat rabbit hop the fence.

Usually, nobody stirred much until Alma's rooster a few houses down started crowing. But a snake with two feet crawled around in the dusty blue morning.

Seeing someone, Sally placed her hand on the door, real easylike, and hesitated. Only Esther would be outside in that flowery yellow smock and holey gray sweater at four-thirty in the morning. Esther knew that Sally came to her back door every morning about this time to pray. *What's she doing in my garden?*

Then Sally saw Esther's back stiffen like she felt her watching. Before she could turn her head, Sally jumped back out of the doorway. She stood next to the stove, feeling so confused. This was a trusted friend. When she peeked outside again, Esther was hunched over, snatching cherry tomatoes off the vine.

Sally really didn't intend to say a word or mean to move one muscle. But when she stepped back on that loose board in the kitchen floor, it cracked like crinkling thunder. You should have seen Esther jumping up like a gun had been fired. Her dark, sagging face lifted like she'd seen a ghost, and large onions rolled everywhere from her smock.

"Esther, that you out there?" Sally cackled, hoping to make light of it, like she had just happened to the door and looked out for the first time.

But Esther's shame froze her right mind, and she couldn't find any clever words to explain her actions. Her mouth opened, then closed, then dropped again. Never in her last mind had she figured on being caught. She'd only been in Sally's garden twice.

"You want I should get you something to carry your food in?" Sally called out in a kindhearted voice. No need of ruining a lifetime friendship over a few garden vegetables.

But Esther took the wrong turn of emotions, and she angered instead of humbling herself. "What the hell you sneaking around scaring folks for?"

"'Cause folks in my garden shopping. But you welcome to what you got," Sally said. She pushed the screen door open and stepped out onto the porch. She forgot that she was still in her gown and slippers. She wondered what Esther was so riled up about.

"Sally, you done damn near gave me heart attack with that quiet, sneaky shit!"

Esther's sarcastic tone of voice empathized her cursing words with such nastiness.

That's when Alma's rooster screamed his ritual morning cry, and Esther's words floated over the ca-doodling rooster's crows and landed on Sally's last nerve. Suddenly, the rising sun shed bright rays of light over the garden like someone had flicked a lamp switch on. Sally just glared at Esther with both hands on her hips. That sure didn't sound like something one good friend ought to tell another when she'd been caught in the wrong. Sally never used cuss words, and she didn't exactly appreciate Esther throwing them at her right now.

"What you say, Esther?" Sally demanded, rushing down the steps and a few feet into the garden.

"I said I ain't got nothing you can't spare. Ain't a drop of harm done to your precious garden, either!" Esther's voice was high and raspy with defensive anger. It ignited a flame, and Sally's own emotions flip-flopped.

"Why, you bony little heifer! Don't you dare go getting a nasty mouth with me! If you'd told me you was needing, I'd have packed up this garden—and placed it on your doorstep myself!" Sally whispered fiercely, trying hard to hold her own voice down. No sense telling everybody their business. But

Esther only turned up her lips and waved her free hand like it was nothing. Before Sally knew it, she took off running towards the middle-south end of the garden where Esther was standing.

It was so funny to see Esther trying to hold her pockets and run down to the peach tree where the fence was so low at the same time. How Sally caught up with Esther when she was so close to her own yard is a mystery, but she did. She leaned forward and snatched a handful of the thin, gray sweater before Esther lifted a foot. And Sally held on for dear life, until her legs caught up with her hands.

You should have seen how Esther squirmed and twisted, trying to get out of Sally's strong grip. But she managed to wiggle herself out of that old sweater.

"Aw naw, you don't!!" cried Sally as she caught a handful of the back of Esther's smock.

Esther held onto her loot with both arms up to her chest and kept struggling. Sally managed to plant both her hands on Esther's shoulders and twirled her around. Now Esther felt like an innocent lamb unable to lift her eyes. Her hair had come undone, and she looked like an embarrassed kid who'd pooted at the supper table.

"What you running for? I done seen your dirt!" Sally cried.

Esther just stood there and couldn't speak. It made Sally so mad she shook that little woman hard enough to rattle the dead. And she didn't stop until Esther's matted gray wig fell off her bald head. With each shake, she thought how they'd been sitting on the same bench, at the same church, living a stone's throw away from each other most of their lives. Esther'd been in her house, and she'd been in hers. It was Esther who brung flowers for her husband's grave, and it was Sally who cried at the kitchen table when Esther's husband was stretched out dead in the bedroom. They done been through the fire and the storm, side by side, too long for this.

And the scent of coming rain flowed between them, as Sally's Christian conscience whispered in her ear.

That's enough. She's still your friend, it said.

Sally silently asked God to forgive her hasty ways. Her heavy shoulders dropped, and she let go of Esther. When Esther raised her chin from the ground, there was no shame in her eyes, only pain. Sally's anger slid to the ground beneath her feet, with the last whining crow of Alma's rooster. And the sunlight was bright over their shoulders. But there weren't any more words to say. Esther picked up her wig and slapped it on her head lopsided. Her ashy morning face burned from embarrassment. But it didn't stop her from gathering them spilled vegetables around her feet. She couldn't deny them, and she couldn't afford to leave them, either. An onion fell from the pocket of her husband's old sweater, and Esther bent over and picked it up, too. Then she heard the cry of her own rusty screen door, and her eyes rushed over the fence and up the stairs to her own back door. She saw her two sons standing on the porch in their undershorts and bare chests, looking right at her with her arms full of Sally's garden. Shit, what she gone do now? She done tried to teach them all they lives about what's right and wrong. What they thinking about her now? Esther felt faint from being caught twice.

She put her hand on the peach tree and stepped over the fence into her unkempt yard. All the time she was thinking back to a time when Sally and her were both young girls walking home through the cornfields from school. Esther remembered the day when she was scared of her own shadow. She'd always been a tiny, fragile thing, a prey for bullies and other girls to pick on until Sally became her friend. Sally was a tomboy back then, and loved to fish by the river down the path behind their houses. Esther reckoned Sally felt sorry for her, but time proved her wrong. Sally treated her more like the sister she didn't have, more than a friend. Life and marriage intervened and took some years away, but when Esther's mother died, she returned to Columbus and her friendship with Sally. She was much older, bitter, and filled with so many disappointments: her good man dead too young, and young boys to raise alone. She didn't realize they would never leave home, even after they were grown.

Esther's boys waited at the top of the steps for her. They reached for the vegetables in her arms, and she emptied her pockets to them too. All the time they were asking too many questions: "What happened, Mama?" "What you and Miss Sally fussing about?"

Esther's thoughts were crowded with questions too. Will her best friend ever speak to her again? Why did she cuss so much?

Esther's boys went back inside the house, leaving her alone on the back porch to think. And like everything wasn't bad enough, she looked up into that ugly, grinning face of Henry Simmons. He lived on the other side of Sally, and he was the worst nit-picking, backstabbing, loose-mouth gossip in all Columbus. She couldn't stand his big, wide, toothless, grinning face, with that long old head like a horse's. She just bet his clucking tongue was itching to tell his own version of the garden fight.

Sally wiped off the table, and looked up to see Henry leaning over his back porch rail. He smiled and straightened up. That old fool took his good time lighting that long, thick brown cigar. Sally put her hands on her cheeks, realizing that he'd seen it all. Good Lord! These folks already too hard on Esther, treating her like some outcast, because she loves her liquor and will speak her mind. She ain't ever fit in with them, and they'd love to bury her face in this forever and a day. It would shame her friend in the eyes of her sons.

You can't let this happen, that voice of conscience said, loud and clear.

Henry Simmons knew the women were watching him. He gloated in his momentary power. Sally glared at him from her kitchen window, while Esther's spirits were already shaky like the wood in her back porch. Henry Simmons strutted over to that broken-down gray chair on the end of his own porch. And he sat down ever so easy, and crossed his legs. This would be his offering to the daily conversations down at Willie's Barbershop later on when he went into town. Sally pushed though the screen door to see Esther standing over on her porch. And it broke her heart. The spitfire of her morning anger was gone, and the quiet voice of her conscience told her what to say. Without another second wasted, Sally's smile returned, and she lifted her voice to Henry Simmons first.

"What you think you saw is Esther's and my business, and not yours. A deacon such as you call yourself ought to watch what he says about good people around that barbershop today, or he might hear some uglier things about himself," Sally said with a smirk. And Henry Simmons stood up with raised eyebrows, like he was the one with the upper hand, not her.

Sally continued, "I seems to remember seeing Pastor Jenkins's daughter ease in your front door the other evening. She don't come out for so long that I done fixed my entire supper. And it ain't the first time I saw it, either. Now, I wonder what he'd do to you, if he knew his precious seventeen-year-old daughter was coming to visit you? And when she leaves her hair is undone, and her dress buttoned wrong."

And then Sally turned with a brighter smile and said to her friend, "Esther, you welcome to shop my garden anytimes you want. 'Cause us is good friends."

Esther blinked away the tears choking up her voice and said, "I wants to thank a good friend for her kindness."

"You and the boys come over for supper. I'd love to have some good company," Sally said loud enough for Henry Simmons to hear.

"Why, sho we'll come. And I'm gon' bring some green beans cooked the way you likes them," Esther chirped. Her smile was bigger than her face, and you could see all her missing, bottom teeth.

Both women waved, then went inside their houses, leaving Henry Simmons on the porch with his mouth open. And he wasn't grinning anymore. Sally's deep alto voice carried her favorite song out across the garden: "The Old Rugged Cross." Esther dried her tears and blessed the vegetables dumped into her sink that needed to be washed and peeled. Her sons were ready to eat.

Eliza Pinetree

CHRISTINE M. BELLETTINI

For the ghosts of Newfoundland.

Pine trees disappear in the summer. All the maples and oaks, the alders and the elms, spray the blue sky with hands of green that laugh and clap in the wind and leave no room on stage for the spindly, dark needles of the pines. Hidden are the pine trees in the autumn when the deciduous are wearing their death flags in riots of reds, yellows, and oranges. No, it's not until winter, when the forks of tree branches scratch at the night sky, holding silver moons in empty boughs, that we can see the fullness of the pine. Not until the fertile loam is covered in sheets of empty white can we feel the promise of green peeking out from blankets of snow. Her cascading dress of deep green comforts, as the wind spins through cracks in our homes, chilling our arms and hearts. Only with the oncoming starkness of winter can we know what, until then, has been ignored. Pine trees are how I always remember Eliza.

My papa had three daughters: me, Chloe, and Eliza. I was the youngest; fifteen years separated me from Eliza, sixteen years from Chloe. We lived on a farm in Bay Bulls with our two brothers, who by the time I was five had taken wives and moved out to the far edge of the property to grow their families. Chloe had taken my mother's place as the woman of the house. After she had pulled in buckets of warm milk from the goats, fished eggs out from under the bellies of angry hens, slapped the rugs clean of dirt, and set out breakfast for the four of us before the break of the day, she would lay long bolts of fabric onto the oblong kitchen table and cut out shapes of future clothing. Our mother was an expert seamstress, and her death had left a hole in the fabric of our community. But Chloe, as she always did, patched that tear with what she had learned from Mother, and soon she was taking in work from the town.

My sister Eliza never learned how to sew. When she wasn't helping Chloe about the farm, it was her job to bring the finished shirts, skirts, and dresses wrapped in brown paper and tied with cotton twine to Barbary's Cove in town. I would stay behind with Chloe and pick up scraps of material that had fallen to the floor and fill my tiny apron pocket with the treasures. Chloe would hum "Jug of Punch" while she cut, a straight pin clenched in her teeth. As I got older she would look over at me and say, "Maggie, make yourself useful, girl. Take those legs of yours and sweep the porch, or fill the terrene with warm water, or feed the chickens . . ." After the sun had pulled its head behind the trees, Papa would come back from the docks, his ropy hands carrying our dinner in a net. Then Eliza would return from town—Marny now back in his barn—without the brown packages but with the same cool distance she carried everywhere.

I thought my sister Eliza strange. She was always separate from us, and separate, I guessed, meant something bad. She and Chloe were only eleven months apart but they were as different as ducks from crows. While Chloe wore the sunrise on her cheeks, her blonde hair thick and curly, Eliza wore the dusk. Her hair was a dark red and straight as a whip, her face a mask of freckles blending into a heavy and mottled complexion. She never talked much and when she did, it was usually in whispers. I don't remember her ever having a conversation of note with Papa. He seemed not to want to see her. With me, especially when I was a child, it was even worse. Eliza would do anything to avoid me, turning her head away as I stared at her across the dinner table.

Once I remember pulling on her braided hair, full and hard with all my might. But she didn't scream or snap away, just sat there until her eyes filled up with tears, one tear dripping onto the table and splashing my arm. Then I dropped her braid and looked at her with a kind of fear, a kind of awe, and I knew that nothing could ever penetrate my sister's silence.

Chloe finally married Patrick McConnell from Conception Bay when she was twenty-five. When Patrick moved in with us, he and Chloe took my parents' room for their own, and my father moved into a tiny dormer with a curtain across the doorway. I shared the bed in Eliza's room, the side that was worn down with Chloe's weight.

I hated to share this bed with my sister, her body stiff and almost corpselike during the night. I remember the first month of sleeping with her, watching her nighttime ritual, the way she would push the ragged brush into that broomlike hair, its angry red strands standing up in static. She would often turn to me and ask if I wanted my hair brushed too.

I would ignore her. Once I even stuck my tongue out, which by the way she blinked slow and wide, I could tell pained her. Then she would climb into bed, stiff as a board, and fall asleep. Often, I would watch her sleep, her eyes twitching under her lids. Once I placed my finger under her nose to see if she was really breathing. The warm air was moist, and she coughed and wiped my hand away as if I was a fly fluttering about to disturb her dreams.

One night as she was brushing, preparing for sleep, she caught me staring at her from the oval mirror that hung on the wall across from our bed, the mirror that belonged to my great-grandmother. Eliza's face disturbed me, its furrowed brow, ruddy complexion, the flaming hair. Looking at her made me feel angry in a way I couldn't understand. But I had no desire to tell her this and I denied that I was staring. I wanted to run away from her, sleep on the cold planks of the parlor floor, but instead I told her that I wanted my hair brushed too. Eliza smiled, her almond teeth glowing in the dim light. She got up and made room for me in front of the mirror.

Whereas before I had seen my face small and her face full in the mirror, we were now reversed. The faces that stared back at me shared a lot, too much in fact, and I decided that was what disturbed me every night. How much I would have rather shared in my sister Chloe's looks. Eliza pushed the brush into my dark brown hair, which although not red, was straight and as full as hers. I couldn't remember the last time someone pulled a comb through my hair or brushed through it. I began to wiggle around, wishing I had never agreed to let her. She put her hand on my shoulder. "Maggie," she said quietly, "just a little more and I'll be done." I shut my eyes. Her movements were so meticulous and soft, the bristles of the brush gently scratching my scalp, that I let her continue until I felt her hand shake my shoulder. "Wake up, child. This is no place to sleep." And I stumbled into bed that night and dreamt about my mother holding me up above her body, her face shadowed by the great sun setting behind her.

In the years following, Mrs. Moriarty, the only other seamstress on the peninsula, had stopped taking in orders because her rheumatism had returned, and so Chloe's work increased. Eliza was barely home, making more frequent trips to Collier's and St. Mary's in Patrick's old truck that squealed when she left and rumbled when she returned. I stopped school, as was customary, after I finished the eighth grade, and my eldest sister said I could now concentrate on helping the family with the work to be done around the house. It was the last thing I wanted to do. Patrick and my father would leave before sunup to set out to sea, jostling each other with anticipation as they hoisted up their boots and slipped on their yellow oilskins. I had always wanted to go with them, but when I saw that only my schoolmates, with names like Henry, Aloysius, and Joseph were leaving to join their fathers out at sea, I knew that I would never be trusted with a net.

So that summer after eighth grade, I would sneak away after my chores were done, and sometimes before, and with the help of a stick of rotten oak, drop a line of cotton twine to the bottom of the muddy pond, a piece of pork fat sticking out of a curved straight pin. I never caught any fish, but lying there against a rock, my skirt tucked up in between my legs like breeches, I caught all the shapes in the clouds and their stories. Winding through the old cemetery on my way home, I memorized all the names on the toppling gravestones (and made up a few on the ones worn soft by rain and snow), imagining that my mother was not buried under the tombstone for Agnes Mary Morrissey but in fact lived in town, wore boots and breeches, and fished at sea on a boat called *Surrender*. I thought all these things and more, until it was much later than I could have ever intended, and I was forced to drop my fishing stick in the barley and run towards the house where Chloe would eye me from the billow of bread dough she was kneading, clicking her tongue at my stumbling into the kitchen, her voice a litany of, "Did you remember to…?"

When my father and Patrick would return from fishing, their boots filled with salty water, their hands painted with a mixture of blood and scales, they would be laughing, cheeks aglow with adventures I could only dream about. I was jealous. I would climb up on my father's chair, put my head on his shoulder and beg a story out of him. Patrick would lean over and toss my hair like I was a boy.

Chloe, her eyes thick with exhaustion, would clap her hands "Maggie, you're much too old for such things. Get your lazy bones over here to help me in the kitchen." And I would reply, "I would rather fish with Papa and Patrick than stay here and help in the kitchen." My sister would suck in her breath as if I had dropped some dirt on her carpets and my father would laugh.

"The sea is no place for a fine woman like my Maggie." He would look me in the eye as if he were telling me a secret. "You see, dear girl, the sea is a lady like yourself. But she's a jealous sort, and if she were to see your beauty, by God, she would sink the very boat you rode on. Think about all the men who would be lost at sea."

"But…," I would protest, but then we were all distracted by Eliza's return, the truck settling into the gravel just in time for her to join us for dinner. Papa's face would settle into a solemn mask, the same face he wore when the man from the bank in his pinstriped suit would have him sign the ledger in his painfully slow cursive.

In fact, it was one of these very nights when one of my epic pleas to join my father and Patrick got my first (and last) trip into St. James with Eliza. My mouth was full around the words, "You never let me go anywhere…" It was disobedient, and I fully expected to be sent upstairs with a shout and an angry look from Chloe. But it never happened. She stood in the doorway wiping her hands on a towel with a faraway look, her eyes widening upon Eliza who had come inside shaking her coat free from rain. Papa looked up at Chloe and back at Eliza and picked at the tobacco in the bowl of his pipe with his pinky.

That was when Eliza spoke directly toward Papa's head. "Let her come with me."

He didn't look up, just sat back into his rocker, his head pressed deeper against the wood, and it was Chloe who said, "Tomorrow you can go with your sister into town." And to Papa she said, "I can manage without her distraction for one day."

She didn't say it meanly; in fact, it was the kindest thing I had ever heard. Papa didn't disagree. He didn't say anything, eating his dinner in silence, retiring to bed early. The matter had been decided.

That night, I was so filled with anticipation I could hardly sleep until finally the dawn crested pink and soft into our window. That day, sitting in the truck with Eliza, the paper-wrapped clothing crinkling with each of my movements, I watched our farmhouse get smaller and smaller in the distance. My sister began to hum, "If I go to market, I go to market with my love, with you." Her spirits buoyed as we got farther and farther from home. I crinkled my brow with suspicion. This wasn't my sister; this wasn't the sullen woman who melted into the baseboards at home. And once in town, my suspicions were confirmed. This Eliza was bubbly, exchanging tales with the ladies at the Barbary Cove, a dress store in the shape of a ship, the door under a half-naked wooden carving of a woman whose skirt was the blue wave of the sea. Eliza's hand was on my shoulder as we walked down the cobbled streets of the dockside.

She stopped into a tiny store which had "Five and Dime" in large red letters painted onto the window. In the store, Eliza put her hands on my shoulders and pointed me in the direction of the long glass case filled with candy. I ran over. I slid my hand along the glass past the red and black licorice held together with a paper ribbon, past the round white sugar balls piled high in a silver bowl, until I came to a cluster of green-and-blue peppermint sticks the color of the sea. I tapped the glass twice; Eliza reached into her coin purse and put down a single penny. The shopkeeper stared at us long and hard. She had been staring since we walked in. Eliza stood behind me and said, "My sister. Mrs. Williams, meet my sister, Maggie." Mrs. Williams nodded at me and handed me the stick, her eyes glued to my face. Once out of the store, I bugged out my eyes like Mrs. Williams, pressing my fingers into the sockets to enhance the effect, and stared at Eliza. She laughed so hard that she had to bend over to catch her breath. She lowered her voice in imitation of Mrs. Williams and peered into my hair. "What do I see here, one cootie, two cooties?" It was my turn to laugh. I shared that peppermint stick with my sister, splitting it into two, our lips pursed around the candy, our fingertips turning green.

Eliza looked over at me and took the candy stick from between her teeth. "Maggie, do you want to see the best part?" I could hardly contain myself; could there be something better than this day had already revealed? I nodded without any hesitation. She grabbed my hand and pulled me along the cobbled street towards the opening between buildings where the blue sea uncloaked itself and grew along a forever horizon.

It was where the men put out to sea. I had never been so close to the docks before. The waves sprayed my face with a fine mist so that when I licked my lips, they tasted like Papa's beard. I closed my eyes, the briny scent of fish and sea all about me. Eliza's hand squeezed mine tightly. At that moment, I was sure she knew exactly what I felt. Beneath me, gray nets in need of repair were spread out on the wet wooden dock. There were gaping tears like great welts in the nets, places where I imagined some fighting fish had won his freedom. At one end of the crisscrossing ocean of net, these wounds were being woven back together by an old man who sat on a three-legged stool and smoked a thick cigar. Eliza and I watched him. He looked up and when he saw my sister, he grinned at her, tipping his hat and dropping the net beneath him. My sister beamed, and he began to talk to her using words I couldn't understand. There was a singsong to his speech, like the priests at Mass, and I almost dropped my stick of peppermint to hear my sister answer him in the same language. She pointed at me and the man smiled, revealing two missing bottom teeth. He grabbed my arms to hug me but I pulled away. Eliza said, "Don't be afraid, Maggie, this is my friend Señor Sanchez. His son Manuel is a fisherman like Papa." She almost swallowed the last words of her introduction, so small was her voice. But before I could see her expression, Señor Sanchez clasped me to his chest in a tight embrace. He placed two kisses on my cheeks rapid fire, first one, then the other. Once he let go, I folded my arms across my chest and was surprised to see my sister kiss the old man goodbye. I had never seen her so open and friendly with anyone in the family, let alone with this stranger.

On the way home, she lost her smile and sat quietly in the driver's seat while I watched the farmhouse grow on the horizon. Eliza turned to me and said, "Maggie, did you have a good day with me?" I nodded my head. My sister had changed forever in my eyes; she was different, someone I hadn't met before today. She continued, "I need to ask you not to tell Chloe about all the things we saw today, but especially about Señor Sanchez. I just don't think she'll understand, OK?" And I, not wanting for the day to end, agreed.

Although I wanted to go back out with Eliza the next day, Chloe had different plans. "Your work is here with me. Your sister doesn't need you tagging along," she insisted, and Eliza left without me.

I never forgot that day in town, and sometimes Eliza would bring me back a stick of the blue and green which I could make last for a week. But then she started coming home later and later from her trips. One night she didn't come home until long after we had finished dinner. Another night it wasn't until Papa and Patrick had gone to sleep. Finally one night, Chloe waited up for her. That same night, after my father had knelt to pray beside the little bed that was once mine and the house settled from a day of activity, the smell of cooked fish collecting on the ceiling, I heard my sisters in the kitchen.

It was Chloe whose voice trilled up to wake me out of sleep. I peered out of my blankets and through the crystal light of the half moon saw that my sister Eliza had not come to bed. I waited. Silence. Then like a wisp of smoke I heard my sister Eliza speak but I couldn't make out anything she had to say, just the yawning of a soft whisper. It was unbearable for me, surely something I must hear. I slipped on my socks and pulled my dressing gown out from around my knees. The floor creaked mightily, so I waited until I could hear the contralto of Chloe's response, then I pushed the door of my bedroom open. The light in the kitchen was on and it lit up the staircase. I crept down the steps one at a time, waiting for dialogue to muffle my descent.

Chloe was speaking: ". . . You should have known better . . . we're depending on you for—" Then Eliza's voice, ". . . How could I have done any different . . . this place is full of ghosts, can't you see?"

And Chloe's voice: ". . . All I know is that you are selfish; when Mama agreed to raise her as one of her own, it broke her heart…you will never learn…she's just like you…how can you leave her?" And at my final step it was Eliza that I heard: ". . . Been broken many more times than you will ever know. Every time she looked at me her head tilted with a question, every time I woke up to stare at her face while she slept reminded me that Mama took away the only thing that would ever matter long before I knew it existed."

My heart stopped. I was on the landing at the bottom of the steps. There was silence, thick and dark as the oncoming autumn. The house breathed in and out deeply with my sisters, with my father, with Patrick, and with the memory of my mother. No one spoke, and I looked down to see the light from that same moon that allowed me to see that my sister didn't sleep beside me, touch my socked foot. Then Chloe's response continued, hollow. It still echoes in my head even today. ". . . She knows only us, she belongs with us . . . ," and something beyond me had moved me to the edge of the bright kitchen light, yellow and starkly different from the silver shadow of the moon's illumination.

As I peered into the room, Eliza was weeping, her head down and pressed against Chloe's aproned shoulder. Chloe held her sister, rocking her as she would never rock children, as she had once held me, her niece. Time stopped. Every bit of who I was sucked out of my bones and dropped into my stomach. The chill of the winter had begun, leaving with it no trace of past seasons. I stumbled. Who were these people who had comforted me? The image of the gray-haired woman who I clasped to my heart as my mother, who had died and left me here, and all this time, the one I wanted was Eliza, the one who I slept beside at night, the one who I fought out of my heart. The truth rent me in two like a sparrow who, caught in a great breeze over the strange sea, wishes once more for the flat of the land, the hollow of a tree. Why didn't she let me know before it was too late? My heart broken, I stumbled back upstairs to crawl under the covers on her side of the bed, but my feet and my eyes drove me into the white light of the kitchen, into the shame of my new mother's face, and for the first time I saw in her brows and skin and teeth my own features. The pain of that knowledge left a slow bleed in my mind that filled my throat with silence, unspeakable silence.

Eliza had pressed her head up away from Chloe's shoulder, her cheeks streaked with tears, and I'm not sure to this day whether she saw me or not. But she looked up and her brows clenched as if the sight of me was not real, as if I were a haunting castabout to warn her of some terrible memory, or of some terrible future. Some days I'm sure, some days I'm not. But all I know for sure is that Eliza is gone.

She left the next day for good. The man named Manuel Sanchez was the reason. She was to be his bride, and although he would never return to Spain, he was taking her away to Labrador where the fishing was better. And I remember that when she climbed into his truck, wearing the skirt that Chloe had sewn for a customer, I held my Papa's hand wondering who I was. And as she waved back at us from the window, I understood for the first time what it meant to be alone. As she drove off for good, becoming smaller and smaller on the road that led out from us, I imagined that all the trees bowed down to touch the truck, dropping their leaves on the road, preparing me for the emptiness of winter, with only the pines whispering, "Remember me."

Killa fo' Life

JOSEPH HERMANEK

Caesar wasn't playing when he grabbed my arm, pressing it against the smooth top of the drafting desk. He came to school for one reason that day, to initiate me. To cut a symbol on my arm, to mark me his brother for life. I was ready to bleed for *mi familia,* ready to prove my loyalty to my fellow Latinos with my pain. Shit, when he ran his blade down my arm, slowly cutting a thin, neat line, I didn't move a motherfucking inch. I withstood the pressure. Watching, ignoring the fire that flared, gritting my teeth, forcing myself to swallow whatever the hell I had to; I was through caring, through dreaming. The gun was in hand, and I was ready to pull the trigger.

The black GDs over in the corner knew that, the whettoes in the middle knew it, and so did my boys. I was broke. The ghetto life, drugs, and death—that's all I had, and that's all a dumb motherfucker like me could ever hope to have.

What I felt I could see in Caesar's eyes, they were empty, hard, unforgiving. He was almost done cutting *Killa* into my flesh, and you could see he liked it, every minute of it. His passion for pain was what earned him his street name, *loco*. It wasn't no rumor that he enjoyed fucking up puppies' eyes with knives. Shit, every motherfucking Latino in the neighborhood knew it. Caesar liked watching blood run, liked it when it was all over him. People feared him, 'cause they knew he was a killer, knew he had the guts to pull the trigger and not look back. He didn't waste time bullshitting when it came down to business—he was a hardcore motherfucker, a fucking desperado.

"You like my work?"

I nodded; the word *Killa,* engraved in my flesh, bleeding like a motherfucker, was somethin' I'd never forget.

"It ain't finished yet. Gonna need more time."

I looked over at the six or seven GDs crowded into the corner, playing around with some dirty ho they had encircled, laughing. "Cool, whenever you ready, I'm ready."

"Teacher's coming."

"Get me something to clean his arm off with." Someone handed Caesar a bottle. Unscrewing it, he emptied the shit on my arm. My flesh burned like it was on fire; I bit down hard on my lip, wanting to punch the bitch who emptied it on me. Whatever the shit was, it sure as hell didn't feel like water.

"What the fuck, this is window cleaner, dawg," someone said.

The bell rang; they wiped the blood off of my arm with paper towels, and Caesar grabbed my shoulder. "My boy don't care. Hell no, he like pain. Ain't that right?"

I nodded; no hesitation. I pulled the sleeve of my shirt over the cuts and looked up towards the doorway, to see the teacher staring at me.

"What are you guys doing back there?"

He stopped us at the doorway after letting the blacks and whites out. "Hey, I asked you a question."

"Nothing," Caesar smirked, "nothing at all."

"I don't want any trouble in this room, you hear me? None of this gang stuff, do you understand?"

"Whatever you say, bro."

Grinning, we walked out, Caesar mumbling something to Eric and Rico. They both laughed as they turned back to look at the teacher. "I'll catch you guys after school. I'm gonna talk to Miguel awhile."

They nodded, leaving me standing with Caesar. "Come on," he looked towards the bathroom door, "we got some shit to discuss."

I nodded, following him into the bathroom. Dirty towels were littered everywhere, strewn on top of the stalls and on the worn blue tiles of the floor. The smell of piss was heavier than the smell of weed. Two white kids, smoking joints, jerked, turning scared eyes on us as we came in.

"Get the fuck out of here!" Caesar yelled, and they obeyed; shit, they ran, knowing better than to look him in the eye.

"See that, Miguel, fucking whettoes got no balls." I smiled, nodding my head. "We Latinos, we got pride, pride in our heritage, pride in our culture. The white boys play dead, while their 'hoods get taken, running scared when things get rough." Caesar rolled up his sleeve; a date had been engraved into his arm. "See this date? That's the date my brother got shot, defending our turf."

I focused my eyes on the numbers.

"Gunned down in a drive-by, by GDs. Ain't no better way to die than that, *ese*."

The door opened. I turned to see that the drafting teacher was watching us in the doorway, holding bloody paper towels in his hand. "What is this?"

Caesar smiled at me before turning to look at the teacher. "What's what?"

His face reddened. "Don't get smart with me—the blood on these towels. What did you do?"

"I don't know, man, maybe you should ask your wife, no?"

We laughed and the teacher grabbed Caesar's shirt. "I'm really getting sick of your mouth."

"You best watch where you put your hands, teach, don't you know I'm *loco*?"

I moved closer, unblinking.

The teacher pulled his hand off him, looking at me for some unknown fucking reason, questioningly. "Just get out of here."

Caesar walked past him, eyeing him down, smiling. "Wise move, gringo, wise move."

I followed behind him, glaring as the stupid *puta* grabbed my shoulder, stopping me near the door, "Not you, Miguel. I want to talk to you."

I knocked his hand away from my shoulder, balling my hands into fists. Whatever this fucking bitch was thinking I didn't know, but there was no way in hell he was gonna keep me from leaving. I looked at Caesar standing behind him and saw him shake his head at me.

"Meet me at my crib tonight, OK, bro, and we'll finish what we started."
"OK."

He left, the door slammed shut, and the teacher shook his head at me. "What are you doing with him, Miguel? I thought you were smarter than that."

"Who the fuck you think you are? You don't know me."

He sighed. "Miguel, all I'm saying is if you need help, I'm here."

I laughed, knocking my shoulder hard into his as I walked past him. Grabbing the doorknob, I stopped, to give him one final, hard look. "You want to help me, do me a favor, keep your ass out of my motherfucking business."

Everyone came to Caesar's crib when they needed shit—crack, weed, guns; he sold it all. The rusted, red wrought-iron fence, his two pit bulls, Blanco and Feo, fighting to break free from the wooden post in the back-yard—none of it was new to me; I'd been coming to his crib for around two months now. Whatever I needed—money, drugs, bitches, he gave me. He treated me like real family, unlike my ma and pa, whose broke-ass selves never gave me a motherfucking thing but poor excuses. Caesar wasn't like them: he didn't bullshit me with fake promises and false hopes. He kept it real: he always kept his word and never failed to tell it like it was. That's what this was to me; this initiation was becoming part of a real family, a family that offered me more than just bullshit.

I had no second thoughts as I walked up his porch. I was so hyped; I near-ly slipped on the third crumbled step of his porch, tripping if it had not been for the rusted white railing that rattled with age as I grabbed it. The front door opened at the noise, and Caesar's shaved head appeared in the doorway, smil-ing at me. He was holding a bottle of Corona.

"Hey bro, come on in."

I swaggered into his empty front room, the smell of weed thick in the air.

"Let's go. We gotta finish that arm."

I followed Caesar through his kitchen, stepping over a man who lay asleep on the floor, no doubt passed out drunk. Some stupid slut was laughing at me, sitting at his kitchen table, her eyes glazed. Damn, I couldn't believe it, I knew her—Alfredo's kid sister, tripped out on crack. She used to have a fine-look-ing body and a nice face; now I could barely recognize her, she was so god-damn pale and thin. Passing her, I didn't have shit to say. I just walked by, down into the basement where Caesar's boys were waiting, lounging in chairs, slouching on walls, smoking joints, and watching TV.

"Cool, he here," one said, and the rest got up, about fourteen Latinos, standing around us.

Caesar downed some Corona, placing the bottle down and pulling out a switchblade. He flicked it open with a flick of his wrist and said, "I hate leav-ing work unfinished."

He pulled up my sleeve, and there it was, *Killa*, the skin around it all red. It would be done soon. I'd be a Latin King. Drop out of school at sixteen. After I tell that teacher to suck my motherfucking dick—fucking *pendejo*, can't get his ass off my mind. Watching Caesar's blade slice through my flesh, I imagined the teacher's white face watching me. Fucking, dumb-looking mug. The kind you want to beat up just for looking at you. Shaking his head at me, telling me I'm wrong. Mr. Answers, always thinking he knows best. Trying to stare my ass down, but I just sit there, feeling the blood run down my arm. A whole motherfucking flood, dripping, spattering Caesar's yellow-tiled floor red.

"Killa For Life." Caesar read. I looked down, seeing the letters, freshly engraved in my skin, watching my blood continue to pour forth from the cuts. "It looks good, no?"

I nodded. "I like it."

"Hey," Caesar looked at Rico, "get him a towel."

"You the man now, *ese*," one laughed, pouring Corona on my head. The others laughed too, the first one running his hand roughly through my hair. Some of the alcohol dripped in my eye, the shit burned, and my vision blurred. Someone wiped my arm with a towel.

"Hey, Loco, why don't you show him your movies?"

I looked up at Rico, then looked to Caesar. He stood silent for a few moments, watching me. He smirked.

"Why not?"

He put an arm around me and we walked to the TV. A porno played of a man pumping a woman. Someone removed the movie, stuck another in, the screen blurred with static, and I turned to Caesar. He took another swig from his Corona. I turned back, looking; everyone's face seemed like it was prepped for some funny shit, all smiles and laughs. I folded my arms, watching a blue screen, waiting for the film to be rewound.

"You gonna see some wild shit on here, bro," Eric said as he took a drag from a blunt.

The word STOP appeared on the TV, the film was done. Someone hit play. For the first few moments, the screen played static. Then a shaky camera showed a picture, a bunch of guys kicking the shit out of some motherfucker I couldn't see. I could hear him, though; he was screaming, telling them to stop, begging. Caesar was there. I could see him.

"You know why he's getting beat?"

I looked at him.

"Violation. He didn't come to a meeting."

I nodded, turning back to the TV. The crowd had cleared now; they weren't kicking him anymore. They stood around him, yelling, calling him all sorts of shit. Then it was Caesar who walked forward, the camera jerked, though; I couldn't see anything but grass. Finally, the dick holding it got it right, turning it back on the action, back to Caesar, who stood at the curb, standing over the guy who had been beat. Goddamn, there was a lot of blood pouring out of his mouth. The motherfucker's mouth had been stomped into the cement, no doubt about it. Everyone was laughing but Caesar, who just stared at himself on the tape, watching himself flash the camera his middle finger.

"Dawg, that is the funniest shit."

Someone grabbed the controller. Caesar walked forward.

"Wat you doing?"

He shrugged. "It's done."

Caesar punched him hard in the face, the laughter stopped, and he fell back on the couch, his nose bleeding.

"We haven't seen the best part."

They watched the screen, not a word coming from their mouths, not a laugh, not a motherfucking smile. Fast forwarding through static, Caesar stopped the video. The screen was black now, the picture shaky. You could hear a woman crying. The camera moved on her. She was lying on Caesar's basement table, her bare ass and legs hanging off the end. "It recording?" he asked. "*Si*," the camera guy said back. She started begging. Caesar unzipped his pants and pulled out his dick. She screamed. He slouched over her, "Just pretend I'm your father, *Rican*." I turned away from the picture, my eyes turning toward him; he was smiling. I looked away, back to the TV, to see him on top of her, ass-fucking her. Drool spilled from her mouth. She cried out, and Caesar laughed. The video continued on for about five minutes. No change. Until finally, it ended in static.

"Good movie, no? Motherfucking *Ricans* should learn to keep their ass off our turf."

He looked at me. The others got up.

"We gotta go, Loco."

He smirked, watching me, waiting for an answer.

"Yeah," I shrugged, "real good."

Their feet pounded on the stairs; they were leaving. I turned away from Caesar.

"Pussies." He took another swig from his Corona. "They don't got the balls to understand what I do."

I swallowed. "I gotta go."

He grabbed my shoulder, forcing me to look at him.

"What about you, Miguel, you understand me?"

Looking him in the eyes, I couldn't lie this time: "No."

"You will."

"I gotta go."

He took another drink from his bottle; it was nearly empty. "Tell me what the teacher said?"

"I gotta go, man."

His eyes turned on me, waiting on me, unblinking.

"He told me if I needed help, to come to him."

He emptied the rest of the Corona into his mouth. "Stupid motherfucking gringo." He closed his eyes, his head turned towards the ceiling. "STUPID MOTHERFUCKING GRINGO!" He threw the bottle against the wall. It shattered.

I looked toward the stairs.

"Nobody can break up my family."

"I gotta go."

I was on my way out. He said nothing to stop me, not a word, until I reached the top of his stairs.

"See you tomorrow."

I looked down at him; his back was turned to me.

"What's tomorrow?"

I waited for several seconds. No answer. I left.

That day I couldn't sleep. After seeing those tapes and hearing him say that shit about the teacher, I couldn't get my body to sit still for one motherfucking minute. There was no telling what he was capable of doin': killin', rapin', torturin'—I didn't know. Alls I knew was, I couldn't give up now. No matter how I felt, I was in too deep. And there was no way I was gonna give up, no way.

I got up. It was late, and I could hear my brother downstairs, talking to his girlfriend. Caesar was probably waiting for me at his crib. I had no doubts about going to see him. The way I looked at it, it wasn't really a choice. I couldn't give him any hints, ya know. I had to make sure he thought I was straight with him.

So I left, pretty easy, too, I didn't have to give any answers; my ma and pa were both on vacation in Mexico. And my older bro, he let me skip school today, so I knew I wouldn't have any problems with him. It was all good. I closed the door, locked it, and left.

Caesar was sitting on his porch when I got to his crib, holding a bottle of Corona. He got up when he saw me coming. He was holding a video. My stomach went queasy.

"Got somethin' you should see."

"What is it?"

He opened the front door. "Come on in."

I followed him in, swiftly passing through his kitchen, down a flight of stairs and into his basement.

He handed me the video. "Put it in."

I did. He hit PLAY.

I folded my arms and sat down on the couch. I was nervous. I bit my lip, waiting. The static passed and the picture cleared. A shaky camera moved around a car, past a steering wheel, stopping at the driver-side window. There was a van; the camera was aimed on it. It was hard to see, the window was tinted. Seconds passed before a woman got out. She was tall, white, held a briefcase.

"She fine, no?"

I looked at Caesar. He downed some Corona and wiped his mouth.

"I'm gonna fuck her." He looked down at the bottle he had just drunk from. "Up the ass."

I turned back to the video. The camera had moved to the porch. She was hugging a man. I recognized him; it was my teacher. Two young kids were standing by their legs. I blinked. And when I opened my eyes, the picture was gone, nothing but static.

"Then," he stopped, took another swig from his Corona, wiped his mouth, "I'm gonna mail that bitch a video. So he can watch."

I turned back; he was looking at me. He walked to the refrigerator. "You look like you can use a drink, bro."

I slouched back onto the couch, closing my eyes.

That night, Caesar called. My brother picked up, came into my room, handed me the phone, and said he was asking for me. I took it from him and watched him leave, staring at the phone and remembering the tapes. The woman getting raped, Caesar on top of her. My teacher's wife on tape, him smiling, watching her ass? Maybe there was a good reason for the shit, maybe some Rican gang member had fucked with him? Or maybe he was just trying to scare me, to see if I had what it took to be his bro. I didn't know. Shit, I never even bothered to ask. So what was I doing here, sitting on my bed, worrying? I didn't have the right. I'd be a fool, to stop talking to him and give up my chances in the gang so early. I looked at the receiver as seconds passed. I placed it to my ear.

"Hey, what's up?"

"What took you so long to pick up?"

"I was doing somethin'."

"What?"

I thought for a few seconds. "I was sleepin'."

"Sleepin', eh?" He paused. "You know where I am right now, Miguel?"

"No," I stood up from the bed, walked to my bedroom door, "where?"

"I'm outside your crib," he paused again, "in my black Cadillac."

I wiped some sweat from my forehead and closed my eyes. "You want me to come out?"

"Yeah, we're gonna go somewhere today."

"Where?" I asked, no hesitation.

"Just be outside your house."

He hung up; I put the phone down on my bed, walked in a daze to my closet door, opened it, and grabbed my Bulls jacket. I can't deny that I was nervous about going with him. After seeing those tapes, I didn't know what the hell was gonna go down. But I was prepared, so I left my house that night, not bothering to tell my brother shit when he asked me where I was going. Caesar was outside waitin' when I left, slouched against his car, smoking a cigarette.

He nodded at me, I nodded back; no words were spoken. I got in the front seat.

"So where we going?"

Caesar pulled away from the curb. "Don't worry, *hombre*, we ain't going far."

We drove about four blocks straight before Caesar took a right down a narrow side street. We slowed. Caesar looked at me.

"You're gonna smoke someone tonight, Miguel." His eyes turned towards the backseat; I followed them to where they stopped on a .45.

"This *culo* walks around the neighborhood thinking his face is bulletproof. Motherfucker sells on our turf, on our blocks, disrespecting our authority."

He turned away then and stopped the car at a stop sign. A few seconds of silence passed.

"So what's up, *vato*, you gonna help me do this shit?"

"I made a promise to you, *amigo*; I'm not gonna break it."

He nodded, "Take the gun, then."

I did, grabbing the .45 from the backseat. He turned at the stop sign, driving down an alley. There was a man halfway down, dressed in a black starter jacket, walking with a girl. Caesar sped up, slowing when we neared them, before finally braking the car to a stop. They turned around, stared at us.

"Smoke him."

I wasn't thinking when I opened the car door, got out, and pointed the gun at the kid's head. I was expecting them to run, but instead they just stared. I fired once; but that was all I needed, my first shot hit, he jerked, twisting, before falling onto the ground. Caesar followed my shot up with six or seven more, hitting the girl in the chest and arm. She lay on the ground, still alive. Trying to scream, but only able to gurgle. Bloodstained hands clutching the hole Caesar's gun had put in her chest. The screams grew louder as Caesar walked forward and, without blinking, shot her in the face.

I nearly drank myself into a fucking coma that night. Shit, I barely managed to walk home from Caesar's house to my crib, no lie. Good thing was, I figured out what I was gonna do when I got up in the afternoon. I was gonna tell the teacher everything, and then tell him to leave Chicago. That way, Caesar couldn't get him. I figured it was the only way to go. Either that or I spend my whole life killing people I don't even know, hiding under a blanket of blood.

I crawled outta bed and looked at the clock on my dresser; it was 1:00 in the motherfucking afternoon. This was one day of school I couldn't afford to miss. I jumped outta bed, put my shoes on, and headed for the front door.

It didn't take me long to get to school. I could walk, being only eight blocks away; that made it easy on me. The part that was gonna be a bitch, though, was trying to make him believe that what I had to say was legitimate. I'd figure it out, though. Somehow, I had to.

Once I got to school, I wasted no time bullshitting. I went straight to the drafting room, knowing I could catch his ass in class. I waited. Minutes passed. The bell rang. I moved away from the door. A flood of kids flew out. Once they were all gone, I walked in, looking back only briefly, making sure no one saw me.

"Miguel?"

I closed the door. Turned around. He got up from his desk, alarmed.

"Don't do anything stupid, Miguel."

I raised my arms. "I'm not here to hurt you, man, I'm here to warn you."

"Warn me?"

"Caesar's gonna try and rape your wife. You gotta go somewhere for a while, man. You gotta get outta Chicago."

"Miguel, if this is your idea of a joke . . ."

"It ain't no joke. I'm serious, man."

He folded his arms. "Do you have any proof verifying any of this?"

I thought for a second. "Yeah, he got your wife on video, along with your two kids. Two boys. She a tall woman, she drive a van, a blue van. Carries a briefcase and shit."

"You're not lying, are you?"

I looked at the door. "I gotta go, man, your next class is coming. I don't want no one seeing me here."

"Wait."

"Take my advice, teach, get the fuck outta here, Caesar's one fucked-up guy. He's done this before—believe me when I say he ain't playing."

I left the room just as three kids were coming in. Whether I knew them or not, I couldn't tell, I didn't give myself enough time to look.

Five days went by. And all I could do was sit, watching the phone, waiting. I knew that Caesar knew by now about what I did. I was the only one he told. If the teacher bailed, like I knew he did since his wife didn't make the news, I'd be the one he'd point the finger at. I knew this going in, and I wasn't afraid. Death didn't scare me. It was no match to poverty.

So when my phone rang on the fifth day, I picked up, and wasn't surprised to hear Caesar on the other end.

"Meet me in your alley." He paused. "You don't come, I'll smoke your family."

He hung up. I placed the phone back in the receiver. Went into my closet, got my coat, and went out the back door. My parents were home that day; they got back from Mexico the day before. But they didn't have shit to say to me; they were asleep. Good thing, seeing their faces one more time might have made this hard.

Climbing the fence in my backyard, I looked down my alley and saw him, slouched against a garbage can, smoking, alone. He looked at me. I walked towards him.

"Long time no see, where you been, *amigo*?"

I stopped, ten feet away. "Skip the BS, Caesar, and do what you gotta do."

He took a final drag from his cigarette. "I took you in as family, Miguel." He dropped it. "And this is how you reward me?"

Seconds passed. He turned to face me, reached inside his coat. "You betrayed me, Miguel." His hand came out, holding a .45. "And for that, I'm gonna smoke you."

"I couldn't sit by and let you rape her," I said, watching the barrel as he aimed it at my head. "Wasn't right, he didn't do nothing to you to deserve that."

He smiled. "Is that right?" He laughed. "You stupid fucking *puta*, I could have given you anything."

The last thing I heard was the gunshot. *Bang*. And then I was dead, just like that.

Frozen

EILEEN McVETY

Her first thought was that he'd stood her up. Since seven o'clock, she'd been fidgeting on the stone bench in the snack room, her hopeless face pressed against the thin rectangular window overlooking the ice rink below. The lights of the arena bounced off the slick gray ice, reflecting the dull blur of gliding feet. All those circling bodies—rickety legs on glistening blades, whirlwinds of parkas and fur-lined hoods, hands locked in mitten-to-mitten chains across the bumpy surface, hips careening into dented walls. But there was no sign of him.

It wasn't like Reed to stand someone up, Claudia thought. Was it possible that she'd gotten the time wrong? Could he be waiting outside in the parking lot for her? But no sooner had she latched onto a scrap of hope than she felt it disintegrate. For starters, she specifically remembered Reed saying, "See you tonight at seven." How could she have misinterpreted "tonight at seven"? And why would he be waiting out in the cold for her? Even if he was, he wouldn't wait long before thinking to come inside. No, she determined, clamping her front teeth down on the gnawed-off stump of a fingernail, she'd been stood up.

She waited for a sign telling her what to do next—whether to continue her fruitless vigil, slink away to a corner somewhere and cry herself silly, or simply skate a few laps before phoning her dad for a ride home. And then the stoners walked in. Their stench entered the room first, the sweet but stale pot aroma that burn-outs always seem to carry with them wherever they go. Claudia recognized three boys from the neighborhood. They were a few years older than she was—about sixteen or so, with limp stringy hair and bad complexions. She could feel herself straighten up the second they stormed into the room.

"Yo, Gallagher, gimme a soda!" one of them yelled, pitching coins high into the air.

"You dick," moaned the guy who must have been Gallagher as he busily swatted at the hailstorm of change.

The third stoner, the quiet one, strolled up to the vending machine, a feathered roach clip dangling from his belt loop. Forcing a dollar bill into the slot, he punched the Dr Pepper button with the side of his fist, then belched.

Claudia flinched as the can tumbled down. The stillness of the room had been broken and, with it, her resolve to wait any longer. Her watch now read 7:40. She leaned over to untie her skate, a solemn gesture of defeat, but a burst of orange made her stop and sit up again, orange that flashed through the window like a meteor. It was that scarf she knew so well—the tangerine strip of wool that Reed wore to school every day—that heavenly, wrinkled accessory with the thick, matted fringe. Her heart billowed at the sight of it.

At first, all she could do was watch him. Through the scratched Plexiglas, she studied the leanness of his form, the haphazard way that his hockey skates dangled over the shoulder of his leather jacket. The way he sauntered toward the bleachers, arms swaying by his sides, seemingly unaware of how late he was, made her want to be like him—cool and laid-back. She liked the idea that he wasn't looking for her. Strangely, she wasn't sure whether she'd be as interested in him if he were. No, it was enough that he'd simply showed. It was enough that the two of them were in the same building waiting for one another. The night could almost end now, she thought, because she couldn't imagine it getting any better than this.

She breathed in deeply and exhaled through pursed lips, trying to reach some instant level of Zen to make the rustlings in her stomach disappear. But she was far from tranquil. She was nervous and euphoric and stunned and terrified, and the combination of all those emotions caused her to spring up from the bench. With newfound joy in her feet, she teetered out of the room on blades that no longer seemed equipped to support her. She gripped the railing as she descended the ramp, her ankles turning inward with nearly every step. The fact that she looked like a big klutz didn't bother her. Her skin was electric, the smile in her eyes, as radiant as a million suns. And oddly enough, it seemed that boys were noticing her. She counted at least three heads that sized her up as she passed by. It was if she had slumped into the snack room as Norma Jean and waltzed out as Marilyn. Love had a way of doing that to people, Claudia determined—a way of lighting them from within. She didn't care what all those girls' magazines said, either. All the self-confidence in the world couldn't plant the kind of smile on your face that the right boy could.

Claudia rounded the outside of the rink, her eyes never straying from the stands where Reed sat about halfway up, legs apart, torso hunched forward while he laced up his skates. The lights from overhead frolicked in the chestnut waves of his hair. The nearer she got, the crisper and more refined his features became, like a line drawing morphing into a photograph. It occurred to Claudia just then that she'd never seen him outside of school. She'd never seen him at night. And though he was wearing that same scarf and that same leather jacket with the ripped sleeve that she'd seen so many times before, something about him felt different to her. When she reached his section of the bleachers, she clutched her sneakers to her chest to keep her hands from shaking. She didn't want to do anything drastic like call his name to get him to look up, deciding it would be best to wait until he somehow sensed her presence below.

"Please skate in a counter-clockwise direction *only*," a garbled voice announced from beyond the crackle of a loudspeaker. It was the kind of barely discernible warning that was never enforced, only repeated every fifteen or twenty minutes throughout the course of the night.

The announcement succeeded in lifting Reed's head, and when he noticed Claudia down below, a smile spread across his face, shining like neon. "You're here," he called down to her.

"So are you," she observed. A fat kid with braces waddled past her. She sucked her stomach in to let him squeeze by, refusing to budge from her spot.

"You prepared to skate like a bat out of hell?" Reed said. His cheeks were splotchy with cold-weather redness.

"I didn't know that was our goal," she grinned.

He waved her up. "Come here for a second," he said. "I have to tell you something important."

Her heart racing, she hobbled up the steps, using the metal railing as a crutch in case she tripped or passed out. What on earth could he have to tell her that was so urgent? She stopped when she reached his row, hovering over that heavenly tangle of hair that she longed to grab in big, heaping handfuls. His whole head smelled of dandruff shampoo. The good-smelling kind.

He laid his sneakers on the seat beside him. "I just wanted to prepare you for the crude fact that I skate like a wild man."

She giggled, perhaps too quickly. "Do you?"

"Oh, I'm not proud of it. Not at all. Bad skating runs in our family, though. My father placed fifth in the Skating Wipeout trials of the '36 Olympics."

She was loving this. "The '36 Olympics, huh? That would make him a pretty old man."

"Christ, don't let him hear you say that."

God, he was awesome. He was the only person in the world she could trade banter with like that. She absolutely loved that. She loved him. If she ever had any doubt about it before, she was certain of it now.

"Ready?" Reed asked, standing up. With his skates on, he was a good two or three inches taller, and Claudia liked how the extra height looked on him.

"Ready," she echoed. She dropped her sneakers next to his, then followed him back down the steps. The Rolling Stones' "Nineteenth Nervous Breakdown" was playing over the intercom. Friday nights, the rink played classic rock, Claudia's all-time favorite music. Most kids her age liked their music flashier, more danceable, with hip, urban lyrics, but without much depth or melody. She preferred the songs her parents listened to in high school— songs that no matter how many times you heard them, made you reflect on your life a little differently. "You're an old soul," her dad always told her, and you could tell there was pride in his voice when he said it.

Reed leapt onto the ice with great energy, launching himself into the center of the rink with two or three vigorous lunges. To keep up, Claudia lengthened her strides and fueled each one with leg power she hardly knew she possessed. Maintaining balance was another story. The ice was etched with thousands of broken skate lines which she focused on intently. It was clear that if her eyes strayed too far from her feet, she'd trip and crack her head open.

There were more novice skaters on the rink than usual. You could see them—kids and grownups alike—shuffling along the ice with cautious baby steps, holding still arms out to either side like they were balancing a tightrope. Reed seemed to relish weaving past these amateurs at heightened speeds, stifling a laugh as he humbled them into sinking their heads into their shoulders like turtles. Claudia admired that reckless side of him. She could only imagine how boring it must be to date a guy who acted safe and polite all the time.

They hadn't been skating long when the stoners from the snack room sped by. The three hoodlums were heading in the wrong direction, howling with laughter, and charging in between couples to force their hands apart. "Please skate in a counter-clockwise direction only," the overhead voice repeated. The stoners responded by lifting their heads toward the ceiling-mounted loudspeaker and shooting it the finger.

And then something extraordinary happened. Claudia didn't even realize it at first. Perhaps she was too busy wondering what the stoners did when they weren't hanging out together—whether any of them went to church or had dreams of being anything other than a colossal burnout. Before she knew it, her right palm flushed with a sudden and delicious warmth. When she looked down, Reed's slender fingers were threaded through her own, the tips of them fanned out across the back of her hand. She examined this curious melding together of body parts like it was a jigsaw puzzle, completely distrusting what she saw. Could her eyes be playing tricks on her? She figured the premise was worth testing, so she fed Reed's hand a gentle squeeze. To her amazement, a similar squeeze was volleyed back. And then David Bowie's "Changes" began spilling from the loud speakers. It was as if the soundtrack of her life was being played for all to hear.

It was easier now to keep up with Reed's pace and God, how she loved looking over at him. He was something off the cover of a romance novel, with his jacket zipped open and his scarf sailing behind him. The tips of his ear-lobes were bright red, and Claudia longed to press their cold fleshiness between her thumb and forefinger to warm them up. He was her boyfriend, she thought, daring to utter the word to herself for the first time. On Monday, the two of them would meet by his locker as always, only things would be different. They'd kiss, more than likely, and hold hands on the way to homeroom, and everyone would watch and wait until they were well out of earshot before asking each other in astonishment, "When did this happen?"

What was cool was that Reed didn't give her one of those clenched, worried grins that so many guys give before holding your hand, the kind that begs permission. He had been completely confident in just reaching out to grab hold of her and even more confident in not acknowledging that he'd done it. The great thing, too, was how natural it felt to be hand-in-hand with him. His palm wasn't sweaty or rough, his grip neither crushing nor wimpy. His hand was the perfect blend of softness and strength, and she thanked God more than once that she'd been careless enough to leave her gloves at home.

"This is a great song," Reed called out over his shoulder, his voice a pale buzz amid the clamor of the arena. It was the first time he'd spoken to her since they started skating, and Claudia was anxious to keep the conversation going.

What she came out with, though, was: "Turn and face the strain." It was her favorite lyric of the song and in her mind, the most fitting and thought-provoking thing to say. After she said it, though, she felt like an idiot. Why was it that some of her deepest and most philosophical thoughts sounded completely retarded the second they came out?

"Bowie's God," Reed said, matching his stride to the beat of the refrain. Claudia nodded in agreement, though if she had taken the time to think about it, she probably could have come up with at least three other musicians who were more Godlike.

As Claudia glided next to Reed, a crippling panic seized her—an attack of nerves inspired by the stoners. What if one of them barged in between Reed and her right now? Or what if, by chance, someone were to wipe out on the ice right in front of them, and she and Reed had to break apart to avoid tripping over them? The only way to prevent that from happening, Claudia realized, was to avoid people altogether, which she adopted as her new mission. If someone was skating too close to the back of her, she'd speed up. If anyone up ahead looked in any way suspicious or clumsy, she'd drop back a little, forcing Reed to slow down. Her only goal was to keep the moment going. She didn't care how late it got or how many songs were played or how sore her leg muscles became. She was determined to keep skating until the rink turned its lights off for the night, and the marble-mouthed voice over the intercom ordered them both home.

But after only a handful of laps, barely enough to work up a leg cramp, Claudia felt herself being dragged toward a wall.

"Let's take a break," Reed said, pulling her to the side.

Everything inside Claudia was screaming, "No! No!" but somehow, her feet complied.

Her head was full of questions: how long a break was Reed talking about? Was it the kind of break that meant, "I want to sit down and get to know you better," or simply, "I need to give my feet a rest"? Would he still hold her hand once they were off the ice? Or would their newfound intimacy disappear the moment they kicked the snow from their blades and stepped onto the rubber padding? She thought, too late, that she should have tightened her hold on his hand—that if he felt the increased pressure of her grip, he wouldn't be able to let go. But by the time the thought occurred to her, his hand had already detached itself from hers, and a blast of cold rushed in to fill the void.

They climbed back up the bleachers where their sneakers sat, huddled side-by-side on the rotted wood, like obedient children awaiting their parents' return. This is how their closet would look if they ever got married, Claudia thought with a smile—their clothes strewn and knotted together, collecting chunks of dust, because the two of them would be far too happy and in love to concern themselves with stupid stuff like vacuuming.

Reed plopped down on the bleacher and, loosening the double knot of his skate, yanked the cumbersome load off his foot. "Ugh," he groaned, massaging his toes through the thin cotton of his sweatsock. "I think I'm done for the night."

Claudia's insides wilted. What did he mean he was done for the night?

They'd only just started. But before she had time to wallow in her disappointment, Reed did something daring and remarkable—something that, for Claudia, far surpassed any tame hand-holding experience. He lifted the foot he had just freed and slid it over toward her, rubbing it along the outside of her left skate. She felt that electrifying caress—through the rigid shell of her skate, through two pairs of wool socks, and the Band-Aid that lay across her blistered instep. The tingle ricocheted from toe to sole, from heel to ankle, then abandoned the foot entirely and darted straight up her spine.

Claudia responded by tilting her skate out toward Reed, half expecting the seams to burst from the passion building up inside her foot. She then leaned into him, not so much as to be touching him but enough to create friction between their jackets. She didn't know whether to take her skates off or just let the moment be, to prolong this unbalanced game of footsy for as long as fate, and Reed, permitted it to.

Then he pressed his foot down with greater force, and the caress hardened into a jab. "Lose the skates," he commanded, and something in his voice lost its playfulness.

She untied her skates and, pulling out her feet, removed a pair of socks which she balled up. Reed had stuck his hightops back on but left the laces undone so that the plastic tips slapped against the bleachers with every move of his foot. He leaned back, resting his hands behind his head on the bleacher in back of him and tucking the toes of his sneakers beneath the bleacher in front so that his body resembled a rigidly comfortable column.

And here alongside the sprawled-out glory of his body, amidst the leap and bellow of her hormones, Claudia's mind went screechingly, horrifically blank. She could no more think of a thing to say than she could put her skates back on and perform a triple axel. Her brain had nosedived.

"This place is going to the dogs," he sighed, shaking his head. He was peering down his nose through heavy-lidded, unflinching eyes.

"How do you mean?" Claudia asked.

"It's run-down. The ice is a mess. These bleachers are falling apart."

While Claudia saw his point, for her the rink had always held a certain magic. It was here where she and Katie used to come with their parents on Sunday afternoons, the two of them toting their shiny white skates with the red and blue pompons. She remembered their dad leading them onto the ice, holding out a black leather glove for each girl to grab, as together the three of them inched along the polished surface. Katie always preferred being dragged to actually moving her feet, and their dad was forever tapping her on the back of the thighs to jump-start her legs. Their mom, meanwhile, was content to lean against the wall and watch. "My ankles hurt too much for that," she'd laugh, though she never failed to wave at them after every lap around. She'd be standing with that honey-sweet smile on her face—the kind that came so easily back when she could listen to a person without looking right past them, back when she wore clean clothes every day and understood that the people on TV couldn't actually see you watching them. To pass the time on the rink, their mom would dig the jagged tip of her blade into the ice over and over, creating a little pothole to mark her place along the sidelines.

"So why do you come here?" Claudia asked Reed. She didn't mean the question to sound as confrontational as it came out.

Reed sat upright and leaned in close, his face igniting the pocket of cold air between them. She drew in her breath for a second, half expecting to be kissed, half fearing it. "To escape my miserable home life," he said soberly. When she didn't respond right away, his mouth split open and a devilish laugh leapt out. "I'm just kidding."

She shook her head. "You're a strange one," she smiled, and he nodded, accepting the truthfulness of the remark.

She glanced forward for a moment, returning her gaze to those all-but-forgotten bodies on the ice, watching them spin and stagger like playing pieces on a game board. From the corner of her eye, she could feel Reed staring at her. Either that or he was looking intently at something just beyond her. She ignored the impulse to turn around, continuing to survey the ice like she was frantically searching for someone she knew. But soon, her avoidance of his stare became even more obvious than the stare itself, so she had no choice but to turn and face him.

He was already looking at her. Hard. "Let's get out of here," he said.

"What? Where to?" That was so like her, she thought afterwards. Never one to just go with the flow, always needing a plan, a destination of some sort. What on earth did he see in someone so uptight, anyway?

"Outside," he said.

Now, outside it couldn't have been more than forty degrees, and the November wind was raw and lip-splitting. For the life of her, Claudia couldn't think of what there was to do out there. It wasn't like Reed was old enough to drive, so there was no car to go to. Why would he want to leave right now? They had only skated for about ten minutes and had barely talked on the bleachers much longer than that. By holding hands and playing footsy, they had ventured into the territory of boyfriend and girlfriend, but now it felt like they were slipping backwards.

"What's outside?" she asked, feigning nonchalance, like she was up for anything.

"The golf course. It's way too loud in here."

The suggestion threw her. The golf course Reed was referring to occupied the same grounds as the ice rink. Both belonged to the Windsor Lake Country Club, but unlike the arena, the golf course was private, cut off from the parking lot by an eight-foot-high fence that served the dual purpose of keeping flying balls inside and teenage riffraff out. Signs posted along the fence spoke of hundred-dollar trespassing fines. She knew of people like her sister Katie who wouldn't think about violating a sign like that. But she wasn't Katie. The only thing warnings like that did for Claudia was conjure up images of juvenile detention centers and hefty trespassing fines that she'd have to pay out of her measly babysitting earnings. She wasn't sure why Reed wanted to take her to a cold, deserted golf course anyway, but she didn't object to the idea of going. At least not in words.

They passed down the long, damp-smelling corridor that led outside, skates in tow.

"Did you get a ride here?" she asked Reed in an effort to make conversation.

"I took the bus."

"Really? At this time of night?"

Reed chuckled, rubbing his palms together for warmth. "I've been riding the bus since I was eight. Why? How did you get here tonight . . . your mommy?"

And then it dawned on her: he didn't know. The biggest, most important thing in her life, he knew nothing about. In fact, what did he really know about her? He'd never asked about her family. And he certainly had no clue about her mom: schizophrenic, missing nearly five years. What on earth would he think if he found out? She couldn't say before, but she knew she had to tell him. If he really was her boyfriend, he'd be cool with the news. More than cool, he'd be sympathetic. She imagined the tenderness of his response—the widening of his eyes, the softening of his features, a supportive hand pressed firmly against her cheek. "Oh, my God, that has to be so hard on you," he'd say, or words to that effect. "I'm so, so, so sorry." And he'd cry, and then she'd cry, and in the sorrow of their embrace, their shared pain would bond them to each other for life.

In the parking lot, the muted glow of streetlamps drizzled onto frost-covered car hoods, lending even the most rundown pickups a certain picturesque charm. Reed led Claudia through the tight maze of cars, his path as erratic and unpredictable as the night which lay ahead of them. The wind was picking up speed, and its dampness cut through Claudia's skin.

Fortunately for would-be trespassers, the Windsor Lake Country Club sported a sizeable hole in the bottom of the chain-link fence that surrounded the golf course. For years, the hole endured as many professional repairs as amateur wreckages, until the country club simply gave up the fight and allowed the torn-apart metal links and bent frame to remain. Despite the large NO TRESPASSING sign that hung directly above the unsightly opening, kids continued to climb through with daring bravado. Kids except Claudia, of course.

As if sensing Claudia's unease, Reed crouched through the mouth of the fence first, holding out a hand to help pull her through. She grabbed it with reluctant fingers. The heat had flown out of his palm, but his touch was still confident and reassuring. With her body firmly and illegally entrenched on the other side, he tugged at her wrist. Their shoes chomped through the gravel driveway that led past the brick clubhouse and onto the invisible fairway.

"You dawdler," Reed joked, tightening his grip. Claudia looked around, but no one had seen them. So what if they were trespassing, she thought now, zipping up her jacket. Who better to trespass with?

It was hard to see where they were going, if, indeed, they had a direction at all. Thanks to Reed's swift sidestepping, they were able to avoid smacking into one of the many benches and trash cans that stood up out of the ground as they plodded through the darkness. Claudia no longer thought to ask where they were headed. She was OK with not knowing.

They had been traipsing for some time over lumpy terrain and shallow sand traps before Reed finally stopped along a grassy incline. Claudia could hear the flap of a flag up on the green. "Let's sit here," he suggested, though "here" didn't seem any more appropriate than any other spot they'd traveled over. They tossed their skates aside. When Claudia turned around, she could make out the dark figure of Reed stretched out on the ground on his back. She lay beside him, feeling the brush of his outer thigh against hers. Her shoulder blades and hips butted up against the bone-hard ground which didn't yield at all—only burrowed itself into her body and burned like frostbite on the back of her pant legs. Moonlight sprinkled down from the gray and starless night.

She heard Reed exhale, his breath whistling through his nose. "I like you," he said.

Claudia wanted to scream. Reed Tanner liked her. He'd said it. She'd heard it, the words as clear and unmistakable as a police siren. She looked over at him. His silhouette was lying still, right leg bent. He was talking to her but staring up at the sky.

"I like you, too," she told him, then added, "Sometimes I feel like we're the only two people in school…"

"…who get it?"

"Yes!" she exclaimed, relieved to know he felt the same way.

His index finger was now tracing the outline of her hand, traveling up and down the ramp of each trembling digit, attending to all five fingers, stubby thumb and all. Her heart thumped like hiccups.

"I want you," he said, only now his voice was lead-heavy and without humor. She could see the whites of his eyes moving in. She tilted her chin up and lowered her eyelids, feeling his wet mouth pressing against hers. He kissed her lower lip first, drawing it into his mouth before releasing it, then kissed both lips together. The touch of his kiss started out light, then gained pressure. Claudia's eyes fluttered open to see the shadow of his torso mounting her. His hands were pinning her arms down so that even if she had wanted to move, she couldn't.

"I want you so bad," he whispered with breath like steam. What she heard next sounded at first like a chain rattling, but then turned unmistakably into the clang of a belt buckle. His left hand was still leaning against her but his right was working his pants open. He was kissing her face all over, using his tongue sparingly, like an exclamation point. She wanted him, too, but wasn't sure that this was the way. This was more than she'd ever, ever done with a boy before—more than she ever even thought of doing with Reed. She felt a smooth, rhythmic churning in the area beneath her waist—a slow-moving pivot that filled her jeans with heat. Before she knew it, her crotch was grinding into Reed's, mashing bone against bone. What was happening here, she wondered? And then the answer shot into her head—sex. Sex was what was happening here. Or was about to, anyway. And the second the word popped into her brain, it was as if someone had unplugged her pelvis. Everything simply shut down.

She wasn't sure if Reed ever pulled his penis out. All she felt was grinding and groping, a fumble of coat and pant zippers—hers and his, him tackling both. His leather jacket crinkled with every movement of his body. His wool scarf, still hanging loose around his neck, scoured her cheek. This was too much, she decided. Too much, too fast. A half hour ago they were skating innocently on the ice, and now she was about to lose her virginity on a golf course. No, no, no, this was all wrong. But instead of saying, "No!" or "Stop!" she yelled in a panic-choked voice, "Ouch!"

It was a little girl trick, really, a child's ploy—crying "ouch" in the midst of rough-and-tumble play. Not because anything hurt, but because the word never failed to bring about an abrupt cease-fire in unwanted activity.

"What's wrong? What did I do?" Reed asked, leaping off her.

Her face flushed. "Sorry. Nothing. I—I rolled over on a pinecone." It was the quickest lie she could think of.

And with that, Reed tumbled back on top of her. She felt a light slackening of her muscles, the early buds of pleasure sprouting just below the surface of her skin as Reed's tongue slid inside her ear. But when his hand suddenly appeared inside her jeans, hot against the frigid skin above her panties, Claudia bolted upright and Reed flew backwards.

"Christ! What's going on?"

Claudia took a second to catch her breath. "I just feel we should get to know each other better," she said, still panting. Really, that's all she ever wanted from the evening.

"We do know each other. We're both the school outcasts."

"But I don't really know you. I mean really." Hidden beneath her statement was the implication that he didn't really know her, either.

She thought she caught him rolling his eyes. "Go ahead. Ask me anything," he sighed. But this wasn't the way it was supposed to be. She shouldn't have to fire off questions to him like she were conducting an interview. That wasn't how two people got to know one another.

He tried to kiss her, this time, reverting back to his earlier gentle tugs on her mouth. He probably would have kept going, Claudia thought—distracting her with butterfly kisses on the face while his hands went to town on the rest of her. But her tears got in the way. The first one that slid down her cheek found Reed prying his face away like he'd tasted blood.

She decided not to apologize this time, whispering instead in a shaky but determined voice, "I need to tell you something." She sat up, clasped her knees with frozen fingers, and looked into the glimmering whites of his eyes. A sudden wind shot past. Parched leaves sizzled across the grass, whipping over their bodies.

Claudia gathered her courage. "My mom is schizophrenic." Four words, but they were like a crane lifting a concrete slab off her body. She couldn't stop now. "Five years ago, she left home...left us...and never came back. It's weird because before she got sick, she was the most beautiful woman in the neighborhood. I remember delivery guys turning all red-faced whenever they'd ask her to sign for stuff. But then, she started changing. She stopped taking showers and only slept something like two hours a day. And even though she took pills to make her mind better, it never stayed better. So she left home five years ago, and that was the last we heard from her. I have no idea whether my mom's alive or dead, whether she's on some street corner somewhere, eating out of gutters. Reed, it's so hard having a mom but not *really* having one. It's incredible how hard it is."

Claudia could hear the pasty parting of Reed's lips, the deliberate hesitation in their movement. "Why are you telling me this?" he asked.

Tears flickered cold on her face. She remained still, hoping that he would take the initiative and move closer to her, or at the very least, lay his hand on top of hers to let her know that he'd heard what she said and understood. But his silhouette remained motionless, jacket hanging open and pants undone.

After what felt like an entire day of silence, Reed tucked in and zipped up his clothes. The sound was like the final lowering of a stage curtain. "Listen," he said, "don't think I'm a jerk, but I gotta catch my bus in, like, ten minutes. I really have to go. I'm sorry."

Claudia wiped the tears from her face and, standing up, smoothed her hair and straightened her clothes. They picked up their ice skates wordlessly and plodded back to the parking lot, leaving a gap between them that felt like a canyon. She expected to feel more at that moment—more hurt or anger or humiliation, but all she could feel with an intensity was paralyzing numbness. She couldn't look at Reed and instead gazed through watery eyes at the approaching parking lot whose lights bled into one muddled blur until she blinked.

When they stepped back through the hole in the fence, it was obvious that all the closeness between them had vanished. Reed shifted his weight from one leg to another, glimpsing into Claudia's face only to break up his otherwise prolonged fixation with the ground. She wondered if what she had told him about her mother scared him, but then decided that it didn't matter. By saying to her, "Why are you telling me this?" he had revealed more about who he was than if they had spent all night talking on the bleachers inside. Her eyes drilled into his shifty, cowardly face. Was he ever really all that cute, she wondered. She sensed at that moment that she wasn't so much looking at Reed Tanner as she was witnessing his fall from glory.

They both muttered something about seeing each other on Monday. She could only assume that he headed toward the bus stop because she didn't bother turning around to check. She needed to call her dad. The lights from inside the arena glowed a bluish-white through the windows, and the pavement vibrated from the pulse of some song that sounded faintly like an Elton John tune. Claudia thought of those days when she and Katie used to come here with their parents. Back when the only boy you wanted holding your hand around the rink was your daddy. Back when a smile and a wave from your mom as you completed another lap was worth far more than a thousand kisses on a dark golf course. It was the same arena now as then, but the lightness had gone out of it.

Claudia neared the large wooden double doors that led inside, passing a group of teenagers who were leaning against a bike rack, inhaling cigarettes and coughing out frosty puffs of laughter. Part of her was tempted to ask for a drag, even though she'd never smoked before. It was then that one of the double doors swung open toward her, guided by a tiny red mitten that was curled around the edge. Connected to the mitten was a young girl, no older than four, with blond pigtails and cheeks as rosy as the pink skates she held in her other hand by the laces. The girl's parents followed closely behind—the tall and slender mom carrying a plastic tote filled with sweaters, the dad screwing the lens cap onto the camera that hung from around his neck. As the happy trio brushed past her, Claudia stood frozen, swallowing over a lump in her throat that felt like a fist.

For the first time that night, Reed Tanner was the furthest thing from her mind.

Mai Pen Lai

GAIL WALLACE BOZZANO

This journey happened to someone else. Someone I barely recognize. It
seems strange now that there was a time I didn't know Thailand. I
wasn't born knowing the musky taste of durian fruit or the smell of frangipani
flowers or the screech of a tok kae lizard. A few years ago, I had never led a
dive tour or smelled my own flesh burning or coveted another woman's child.
Thailand has seeped into me, staining my life the way a tea bag bleeds into hot
water. I struggle to remember who I was, that person walking around on the
earth without any of these experiences in her memory. When did my meta-
morphosis begin and when will it end?

I suppose it could have started the day I walked into Walt's office at the
Turner Creek Times and said, "I quit." It could have been the moment I sat in
front of my computer screen reading Mike's e-mailed words: "You should see
this place. Everyone should," and feeling fear and excitement and longing, in
equal measure, speeding up the cadence of my heart. Looking back on it, it
was probably both those things, plus a complicated and dangerous mixture of
outside factors and personal character flaws. And it doesn't really matter now.
I'm not going back over this with some sort of emotional yardstick, trying to
pinpoint the exact moments I screwed up, and where and how much I've

grown. This isn't about that. Tea isn't any better or worse than hot water. It's just different.

One hot August afternoon, I stepped onto a plane in Chicago and, twenty-some hours later, stepped off halfway around the world, into a country I knew almost nothing about. To say that I was in over my head does not even begin to describe the depth of my ignorance. I knew that much at least, and so I clung to the familiar for as long as I could. It's easy to postpone culture shock when you're in an airport. Airports are artificial, like being in purgatory. It wasn't until I left the airport that my odyssey began.

By the time I got through passport control and collected my luggage, I was tired beyond reason. My fatigue felt like an extra piece of luggage that hung from my neck on a rope, dragging me toward the floor. I'd been in Bangkok's international terminal for about an hour by that time, but there was something comforting about being there. I could mingle with the other Americans that had been on my flight—a group of young male backpackers with goatees, a frazzled-looking mother with two half-Asian toddlers in tow—and pretend to them and to myself that I had everything under control. As we moved from one slow-moving line to the next, we could discuss Bangkok's traffic problems and the dangers of malaria in the most abstract of terms. I could convince myself these people couldn't see the woman I really was: an impostor, with only the barest outlines of a plan. I wasn't prepared to step through the doors that led to the main part of the airport and the world beyond. But I couldn't stay in purgatory.

I took a deep breath and stepped into noise and humid air and rank smells and chaos. Crowds of people pressed against the metal rails on either side of the doorway, threatening to knock them over. Brown arms waved wildly, voices screamed in excitement. For a second, I felt like a movie star facing her adoring fans. Then the second was gone, and I remembered that none of this emotion was meant for me. I was suddenly and unequivocally a minority: a pale-skinned, gray-eyed American woman in a sea of black hair and skin that was darker than I'd expected. Not everyone in the crowd was Thai; there were a lot of Indians and others whose race I couldn't guess, Middle Easterners maybe, but for the first time in my life, I was in a place where the "others" were in charge. In spite of this fact, or maybe because of it, I felt invisible. These people were carrying on as if they were welcoming sons and lovers home from a war. There was an urgency to their happiness, as if they didn't find their beloved that very minute, they never would.

I struggled with my luggage cart, which was several sizes too small for my large suitcases, oversized backpack and carry-on bag, and scanned the scrawled lettering on the white cardboard signs that bobbed in the crowd. Vista Tour Group. Snamprogetti Engineering. Welcome Hyundai Group. I was looking for my own name and I didn't see it. I knew Mike wouldn't be waiting for me. After all, it was nearing one in the morning, and Pattaya, the town where he lived, the town that was my final destination, was three hours away. I hadn't asked him to meet me at the airport, and he hadn't offered. Mike was a friend, but not that close a friend. He had told me he'd try to send a car from Pattaya. Look for a sign with your name on it, he'd said. But it wasn't there. I scanned the crowd again, then a third time, just to be sure. But there was nothing, no words bearing the slightest resemblance to my name, Erin Weaver. It was as if I did not exist.

No big deal, I tried to tell the panic that was squeezing at my stomach, making my breath come quick and shallow. Just get a frigging taxi. What's the big deal? My throat was dry. The railing ended abruptly, and now I was in the midst of the crowd, surrounded by people who hugged and kissed and talked and talked. Sweaty arms brushed against mine as people reached to embrace each other. No one bothered to apologize. A chain of young girls walked by, arm in arm in arm, all laughing uproariously. They wore long baggy pajama-like pants in garish colors, T-shirts that didn't match the pants, and plastic flip-flop sandals. They looked like they were on their way to a slumber party. On a piece of floor near the front window an entire family lay sleeping on bamboo mats, as if it was the most natural place in the world to sleep. My cart began veering to the left, and I braced myself and yanked the handle to straighten it. I was still following the backpackers. They strolled through the mayhem calmly, their shoulders back, their pace unhurried, as if they knew exactly where they were going and had all the time in the world to get there. For a few seconds, I thought of catching up to them and begging them to take me with. I would willingly jump into whatever adventure they had planned. I would do whatever they wanted, be whoever they wanted me to be, as long as they didn't leave me. Then my anxiety turned to disgust. Is this what I had turned into, someone who couldn't function without a man? True, I wouldn't be here if it weren't for Mike, but I had a college degree and—up until recently, anyway—was a working professional. Surely I could get myself to Pattaya. If I couldn't handle the unexpected, I should have stayed home.

"Taxi, taxi!" Men in dark blue uniforms yelled the word over and over with the accent on the second syllable. I started to steer my cart toward one of them when I saw the driver. He was standing a little way back from the crush of the crowd, holding a small brown sign that said, "Mrs. Weaver." I raised my arm and waved, feeling weak with relief, laughing a little at the "Mrs." If there was one thing I most definitely was not, it was a missus.

The driver was wearing long dark pants and a white shirt. He was at least half a head shorter than I. "I take your bag," he said, giving me a small, tentative smile that deepened the lines on either side of his thin face. Before I could think of a response, he was stepping up to the cart, reaching for the handle and placing the little cardboard sign on top of the top suitcase. I was happy to give way. The driver wheeled the cart to the right, his feet bracing against its heavy bulk, and headed toward a set of side doors. The crowd parted in front of him, and I followed in his wake. We stepped through the doors into a cavernous parking garage. The air was hot and wet and filled with the stench of gasoline and more subtle but equally unpleasant odors, something like sweat mixed with tropical food. The decay of tropical plants, maybe, although I know we weren't anywhere near the jungle.

The driver led me down a row of cars to a brown Toyota four-door that was dusty and dented. He opened the trunk and started to heave my baggage in. When I tried to help him, he waved me off. "No problem, I can do." I grabbed the door handle on the right rear side of the car and pulled. The door wouldn't budge. "It no work," the driver said when he saw what I was doing. He motioned me over to the other side of the car. I had to yank hard on that door, but I managed to open it and slid into the back seat. I let my head drop back for a second. I was familiar with this level of fatigue—tired, but too wound up to sleep. The car smelled of dust and vinyl and heavy-scented flowers. I lifted my head and looked around. Dangling from the rear-view mirror was a wreath made of red ribbon and flowers, purple blossoms and smaller white buds that looked like popcorn. I wondered briefly about its function. Was it some sort of Buddhist icon or merely an air freshener, the Thai equivalent of those green cardboard pine trees? The steering wheel was on the right side, which threw me for a second. I heard something stirring, a small whisper of cloth and limbs rearranging themselves, in the front passenger seat where the steering wheel should be. I peered over to see a small boy, curled up in sleep. Fluorescent light from the garage spilled onto his white T-shirt, but the rest of him was hard to see. I got a glimpse of high cheekbones, dark lashes, tangled hair, and bony knees pulled up to his chest. He lay perfectly nestled in the bucket seat. It seemed that he belonged to this car, this place and time, and I was the intruder, even though I was the one paying for the ride. The line between public and private seemed to be blurring in a way that I wasn't sure I liked.

The driver got in and slammed his door hard. He stuck a key in the ignition and the car sputtered to life, shaking with the effort. I watched his fingers as they moved over switches on the dashboard. They were long, dark, almost spiderlike. The palms of his hands were pale. The roar of the air-conditioner filled the car, and I felt a cool blast of air ruffle the hair near my right ear. I shivered, although I was wearing a sweatshirt. Those long fingers pulled out a cassette from somewhere and slid it into the tape player's slot. "*Yesterday once more*," crooned Karen Carpenter as the car pulled out of the garage, onto a frontage road, and finally, onto an expressway.

The car was on what I considered to be the wrong side of the road. This bothered me. I expected at any moment the bone-jarring impact of a head-on collision. We were going too fast, hurtling south on a road jammed with traffic. Oncoming headlights rushed toward us on the right side of the car. Each time a vehicle drew near, I cringed. Everyone was speeding, changing lanes without signaling, swerving erratically. My driver was no exception. He would pull up behind a car or truck, tailgate so closely that I could see the dead bugs smashed to the license plate of the vehicle in front of us, then yank the steering wheel to pass on the right or the left—it didn't seem to matter. The car lurched so violently I was sure the sleeping boy would topple off the seat and onto the floor, but he never did.

Pickup trucks with piles of people jammed into the back sped past into the night. We got so close to them that I could see the glint of gold necklaces and rings, see individual strands of hair whipping in the wind. Most of the men and women looked younger than me, and I guessed they were in their early twenties. They wore jeans or those bright pajama pants and long-sleeved, lightweight jackets that rippled and ballooned in the rush of wind. Some of them were laughing and singing. Others slept sitting up, leaning their heads on the shoulders of their companions or draping themselves over large bags and bundles squeezed into the space. One man had a guitar, and I heard him strum one festive chord before the wind caught the rest and we roared past the truck into darkness and more oncoming headlights.

As we headed out of Bangkok's suburban sprawl, the scenery changed. The silhouettes of hotels and high-rises were replaced by smaller buildings, two and three stories high, that I guessed were stores. They looked like egg crates stacked one on top of the other, open to the street. Bright strings of colorful Christmas lights hung down the storefronts in shimmering strands. Then I began to notice the illuminated billboards, one after another, all with the same picture of a smiling, round-faced Thai woman wearing a tiara. She had a motherly look about her. I watched that smiling lady for a long time until my eyelids began to droop and, in spite of myself, I dropped into a dark, dreamless sleep.

Brakes shrieked, and my body jolted forward. Instinctively, I braced myself against the back of the front seat before I was even fully awake. I felt like a tangle of funny bones and skin that would bruise at the slightest touch.

What the hell was the driver's problem? He might just as well have whacked me with a hammer. I wanted to hit back, although I knew it probably wasn't his fault. "What's going on?" I asked, leaning forward and gripping the back of the driver's seat. He grunted and pointed at something outside. In front of the car, two dogs leaped through the twin beams of the headlights. One was white with black spots, the other brown. I caught a glimpse of floppy ears and skin stretched taut over ribs. The little boy was sitting straight up, looking straight ahead. One tuft of his hair stuck straight up from the top of his head, like a bit of grass missed by the mower. The driver said something to the boy in a low voice, and the boy shook his head, still staring straight out the front windshield.

"Are we almost there?" I asked, aware that I was close to whining. "A little bit," the driver said cryptically. I leaned back. No use trying to go back to sleep. I looked out my window and could see nothing, no billboards, no storefronts. Just the outlines of palm trees against a sky sprinkled with stars.

We started up again, only to slow down about half a mile further. Off to the left, glowing like the last oasis in the middle of the desert, loomed a big, modern gas station and mini-mart. A green and yellow sign filled the windshield: BP. The driver turned in and steered toward one of the pumps where several young men squatted around what looked like a checkerboard. They were dressed in green and gold, and when they saw the car they left their game and began to amble toward it. We were their only customers.

The driver turned his head to look at me. "We stop fifteen minute. OK?"

"OK." It occurred to me that he must be tired. It was the middle of the night, even later than that. My plane had been late. He had been waiting at least an hour at the airport. Had his boy been sleeping in the car the entire time? Why wasn't he home in bed?

"Where is the toilet?" The driver pointed in the general direction of the mini-mart. I pushed open the door and was about to step out of the car when the driver said, "You wait." So I waited while he rummaged around under the front seat. As the little boy opened his door and slipped outside, the driver opened the glove compartment and began pawing through wrinkled maps, a withered-looking piece of fruit that I could not identity, and an owner's manual, warped in the humidity. I sat and waited. Finally he turned to me with empty hands, a look somewhere between embarrassment and apology on his face. "Uh, I no have paper. You buy inside." He pointed again toward the mini-mart. I supposed he meant toilet paper. My mind was working slowly.

I stepped into the brightly lit store, which at first glance looked like any gas station anywhere in the States, until I began to inspect the shelves more closely. The contents included stale-looking sandwiches of god knows what, with the crusts cut off, on a half-empty shelf next to two dead flies. Rows and rows and rows of snack foods with foreign names, strange squiggly writing on the bright bags. Some of the names were in English: Prawn chips. Squid treats. A small refrigerator held water bottles and red and orange and green cans of Fanta and Coke. I picked out a bottle of water. My stomach growled, rebelling at being yanked through space and time. I was at once hungry and nauseated. What I really wanted was some plain bread or a bagel, but I settled for a Kit Kat bar. I noticed it was wrapped in red, not orange, paper. I found individually wrapped rolls of toilet paper and paid for the stuff, clumsy with the colorful foreign bills. The cashier didn't look much older than the driver's little boy. He had a piece of white string tied around one wrist and dirt under his nails. He pointed toward the door when I asked him where the toilet was.

I found a small, white, tiled building behind the mini-mart and pushed open the door that said "Lady." Moths fluttered around a white flourescent tube on the ceiling. Three stalls, none with doors. No sink, just a large tile basin filled with water, a yellow plastic bucket floating in it. The floor was soaking wet. I chose stall number three, farthest from the unlocked door. Then I stood there for a minute, staring down at the toilet in dismay. It was only six inches off the ground and didn't have a seat. The white enamel rim widened into two foot-sized shapes on either side of the bowl, their purpose all too apparent. Now, I had done some reading about Thailand and Southeast Asia in general, and so I was familiar with the concept of squat toilets. But it's one thing to be familiar with a concept and quite another thing to be face-to-face with reality when you're jetlagged out of your mind. At that point, you want nothing more than to take care of your most basic bodily needs in some sort of comfort, and this bathroom didn't qualify. Dead mosquitoes lay in puddles of water on the floor. Live mosquitoes trolled up and down the white tile walls. Judging from the lack of smell, the toilet was fairly clean, but I couldn't do it. Not yet. The enamel footholds looked slippery, and I didn't see anything to hang onto. I wasn't in the mood to figure out the logistics of the damn thing, and I certainly wasn't in the mood to fall into it. I could wait a while longer.

I backed out of the stall, pushed open the bathroom door, and began to slink back to the car, and that's when I heard the scream. A small child's voice, high-pitched, hysterical. One long shriek that hung in the air for an agonizing moment, like something defying gravity. I could feel the hair on the back of my neck rising off my skin. The scream was coming from the car. Without thinking, I broke into a run. As I rounded the corner of the mini-mart and the gas pumps and the brown Toyota came into view, I could see the little boy. He was pressed back against the front passenger door of the car. One hand held something that looked like a piece of bread high above his head. His eyes were wide open and focused on a large, tan dog which stood in front of him, wagging its tail in an uncertain oval. The dog was grinning amiably, revealing pink gums and a long pink tongue. It licked its lips and lifted its nose toward the piece of bread. The boy whimpered. As I watched, the driver came hurrying out of the mini-mart and sprinted over to the boy. At the same time, two of the gas-station attendants reached the scene. One grabbed the dog by a crude leather collar and began dragging it away from the boy. The dog went willingly, looking bewildered, its tail still waving faintly. There was a conversation between the driver and the attendants, a lot of hand-waving, and finally, laughter. The boy stood still, his eyes following the dog as it disappeared behind the mini-mart.

I slowed my pace to a walk, not sure what to do, not wanting to intrude. The driver was crouching in front of the boy, both his hands on the boy's shoulders. He was murmuring something in a soft, soothing tone. As I drew nearer, I could see the shiny paths of tears on the boy's dark cheeks. Then I noticed something else. The hand that held the piece of bread had dropped down to his left side. But on his right side, there was no hand. His arm ended just below the elbow in a stump of puckered flesh. I dropped my eyes, trying to look anywhere but at that pale brown stump. It was as if the boy was standing there naked. I swallowed hard, willing my stomach to settle. Something that felt like shame was pushing the blood to my face. I should do something, I thought, but I couldn't think what.

By the time I reached the car, the boy was getting back into the front seat. The driver turned to me, his hands open, showing me his pale pink palms. He smiled thinly, shaking his head. "Sorry, sorry," he said. "My boy no like dogs. One time dog bit him, very bad." I hated the look of pleading I saw on his face. It was none of my business, none of it. I should have kept my mouth shut, but curiosity got the better of me. "His arm?" I asked, touching my left forearm, just below the elbow. The driver nodded vigorously, as if he were pleased that I understood. "Yeah, yeah, his arm," he said, making a chopping motion against his own arm. "Very bad."

"I'm sorry," I said, but the driver was already smiling and opening the back door for me. Then he said something to me in Thai. "*Mai pen lai.*" I had just learned that expression on the airplane, while leafing through my brand-new phrase book. It's said to reflect the Thai's philosophy of life: It doesn't matter. Never mind.

"*Mai pen lai,*" the driver murmured again to the boy, as he started the car and pulled back onto the road. The boy was sitting straight up. The last bit of sleep was shaken right out of me, my full bladder pressing on me like some sort of accusation.

* * *

The wooden shelves outside the temple are overflowing with shoes of all types. Battered dime-store thongs prevail, but here and there are expensive gym shoes, a little girl's pink plastic sandals, women's pumps. Erin slips off her rubber sports sandals, wondering if she'll ever be able to find them again. There isn't room on the shelves, so she sets them carefully at the top of the wide marble steps, as worn in the middle as the flip-flops. The marble is warm underfoot. People are everywhere, and as she stands she is jostled by several squatty Korean women who are clearly part of a larger group. They all wear matching blue T-shirts and blue visors. The leader waves a blue pennant on a tall stick.

Erin searches for Peter's light brown hair and white shirt, but she can't see him. She is surrounded by blue T-shirts and has the sensation of being in the middle of a school of large, stupid fish. Everyone is pushing toward the entrance, so she gives up and goes with the flow. Surely she'll find Peter inside.

Inside, she untangles herself from the Korean tourists and stands near the back, taking it in, temporarily blinded in the dim light. No sign of Peter. The sanctuary is huge; the walls soar to the ceiling several stories above her. The air is as musty and solemn as a library. Everyone is facing the bright figures at the far end of the room, but Erin avoids staring at the Buddhas and all their accessories. She knows it will be too much to take in, and she wants time to savor it. There is only one first time. Suddenly she doesn't mind that she can't find Peter. It seems fitting that she is in the Temple of the Emerald Buddha on her own, free to feel whatever the place gives her to feel this first time.

There are no chairs, just a vast expanse of red carpet. Guards at the back of the sanctuary are motioning for people to sit down, get out of the way. Erin pads across the carpet to the far end of the room, stepping around clusters of people already hunkered down. Then she sits, remembering to keep her feet away and to the side, so that they won't point disrespectfully at those gleaming figures at the front of the room. Noises are hushed, conversations reduced to soft murmurs. She looks around at the walls. Every square inch is covered with faded murals depicting the Buddha's life, and the drama of the epic legend Ramayana. Buddha under the bodhi tree, monsters carrying off Princess Sita. Erin feels a quick pang of regret that she won't be able to stay long enough to understand and appreciate all the paintings, won't be able to unravel the mysteries: Where are those men going with their elephants and gold-tipped spears? Who is the beautiful woman in the pagoda? Erin is sorry that what's at the front of the room snatches all the attention from these lesser, slightly dingy features.

"Don't be," someone says. Erin jumps. She looks around. No one is sitting close enough to her to have whispered into her ear, but that's where the voice came from, next to her ear. For some reason, she turns her head up and to the left, and her eye falls on a figure in a mural. A white animal with a broad chest, a round head, and a mouth as wide open as a viper's. Hanuman, the monkey king, at the front of a legion of soldiers marching on a multi-armed black demon with the same open viper mouth. The monkey king turns his head in Erin's direction.

She blinks, somehow not surprised, although all she had to drink at lunch was a Coke. Hanuman waves a long arm toward the front of the room. "You can look now," he says, his mouth parting into a wider smile. His voice is understanding and kind. Erin lets her eyes travel past the tourists at the back of the room to the worshippers closer to the front. Thai people press their palms together, hands to their foreheads and bow, over and over. They shake their plastic cups of joss sticks, rattling them until some of the sticks fall out onto the floor, and then they pick them up, study them, and repeat the process. An old, bald monk sits placidly behind a small table, next to a wooden stand piled high with incense sticks, lotus blossoms, strings of jasmine flowers, coins. Erin raises her eyes and finally drinks it all in. Golden Buddha after golden Buddha after golden Buddha, sitting, standing, reclining, carefully arranged in groups like a treasured doll collection. Towering above the rest, sheltered from the impure air by a glass case, and from an imaginary sun by a nine-tiered gilt parasol, is the Emerald Buddha. The Buddha everyone has come to marvel at and pray to. The others are apparently mere window dressing.

Strangely, this Buddha doesn't captivate Erin, maybe because it's so far away, so hard to see. Then there's its color. The Emerald Buddha isn't really emerald at all but a deep green jade, the color of a cartoon space alien. It sits primly, no bigger than a cat, a gold robe slung over one shoulder. It reminds Erin of a doll that her mother only allowed her to play with under supervision. It was an antique china doll with brown, fuzzy hair and five different dresses. Because Erin was forced to be so careful with the doll, she began to imagine that it had a stilted, prissy personality. She grew to dislike playing with it and eventually stopped asking to.

"You're missing the point," Hanuman says.

Erin looks around at all the people worshipping the graven image. "Aren't they?" she asks the monkey king. It's not that she disapproves of their practices. Whatever floats their boat. It's just that she has never found a sense of a higher being in any house of worship she has ever set foot in, be it a Methodist church in suburban Chicago or a Buddhist temple in Bangkok. She's finding it particularly hard to take Thai Buddhism seriously when the most revered image in the country looks like a close cousin to E.T.

"Listen," Hanuman snorts in disgust. Then he turns back to his task. Erin listens. The sounds she had heard earlier in the day come floating into the musty air: the slow, melodious chanting of the monks, which is the sound late-afternoon sunlight would make if it had a sound. The tinkling of a thousand spade-tongued bells, hanging from the eaves of every temple. The *ping* of one-baht coins hitting the black iron bowls in the Temple of the Reclining Buddha, resonant as first raindrops.

Erin closes her eyes, basking in the sounds. Time slows, expands, stretches, comes to a rolling stop. There is nothing else in the world, no temple, no Peter, no Thailand, no Erin. Nothing matters but these beautiful melodies. The last coin falls into the last bowl with a lingering *ping*, which fades away. The temple is once again silent. When Erin opens her eyes, the walls are alive, a sea of motion, as if they are a nest of writhing snakes. Figures chase and flee, embrace, and stab at each other. Hanuman's army is in fierce battle with the now-raging demon. The monkey king is too busy grappling with the beast to explain anything. His muscles ripple under his white-painted hide.

Then the big golden Buddhas start to hum to her. They hum softly, without words. They half-close deeply hooded eyes. They vibrate as if struck by a mallet. They are all-knowing and infinitely kind, and their voices sink deep into Erin. If she could just stay here awhile, she thinks, she could understand what they are singing. Tucked away far back in a corner at the far end of the room is a grandfather clock, and the Buddhas are humming in time with its ticking. A feeling of peace creeps over Erin, the feeling she used to get when, as a child, she would hide out in the living room of her grandmother's house in Chicago. The quiet room, where the curtains were always pulled to keep the sunlight from fading the heavily upholstered sofa and matching chairs, and the air always smelled of old books and sugar cookies, the room where you could sit for hours undisturbed, sipping iced tea and reading stories from the children's encyclopedia until you fell asleep on the floor, and when you woke up you'd have a funny pattern on your cheek, the imprint of the carpeting . . .

The Buddhas' humming intensifies, and Erin feels a soft current of air rush past, as if an unseen hand is pushing the hair back from her face. The air is still and warm, the ceiling fans too high up to do any real good, but the breeze returns, gently insistent. Erin looks up, up to the soaring ceiling with its ineffectual fans and gold mosaic pattern, another intricate tapestry she doesn't have time to trace the threads of, and something soft and cool lands on one cheekbone, just under her eyelashes. She touches it in wonder, although a second later there is nothing there to touch but a drop of water. A snowflake.

Snow. A moment later another flake hits her nose. Then her forehead. Snowflakes drift lazily down to the red carpet, as gentle as pink petals falling from a cherry tree in springtime.

"Hurry up," Hanuman growls at her, ducking his head just in time to avoid one of the demons' flailing arms.

Erin hesitates, unsure of what is expected. Again she meets the eyes of the humming Buddhas. Gradually they grow silent, all but one, who keeps humming, slowly, tantalizingly. This Buddha is near the back of the display. He sits in the lotus position, the long graceful fingers of one hand touching the earth. Curving over this Buddha's head is a large hooded cobra, sheltering him from the snow, which is falling faster now, whitewashing the carpet and the worshippers and tourists, obscuring the sanctuary, swirling against the Emerald Buddha's glass case. The Buddha with the cobra nods, raises his down-turned palm slightly, and beckons to Erin. She rises to her feet and steps around and between the people on the floor, who don't seem to notice the snow, even as it collects in globs in their black hair. The snow is icy under Erin's bare feet, and she shivers. Emboldened because the security guards have done nothing to stop her, she walks to the front of the sanctuary, past the offerings, past the Emerald Buddha's podium, past the other Buddhas toward the one with the cobra. It's bigger than it looked from further back. Erin sees the cobra isn't just a plain cobra but a seven-headed beast with rubies for eyes. Crazed grins reveal forked tongues. When the snow hits the snakes' heads and scaled bodies, it evaporates so quickly that it hisses, and curls of steam rise into the air.

Erin stops, suddenly shy. The Buddha beckons again, and Erin knows what she is supposed to do. She stands at the base of the podium, looking into that calm face. Then she starts climbing, scrambling up the gilded podium, which isn't a podium at all but the scaled coils of the snake. She crawls without hesitation into the lap of that beautiful golden man. His robes are warm and smooth, and they shift until she is perfectly curled into them. Long, bronze fingers with bronze fingernails gently, gently stroke her hair. She rests her cheek on a warm, golden thigh. Through half-closed eyes she watches the snow obscure the rest of the sanctuary, blur it as if it is a television picture obscured by static. When the world is almost gone, she closes her eyes. In the Buddha's lap, under the snake umbrella, Erin is safe and warm. This is all she will ever need.

Another Perfect Day

JOSEPHINA GASCA

The sun was shining particularly bright through the bedroom windows that morning when Esperanza Martinique woke up to yet another perfect day. Her short, black hair recently cut into a sharp career coif fell into place just right around the cameo of her face. The red lipstick she wore said powerful, sexy. Her French manicure was impeccable. Her black designer pantsuit maximized and minimized her figure in the most flattering of proportions. Her nyloned feet realized the meaning of heaven when she placed them into her coordinating designer shoes worn to comfortable perfection but with the still-new look to the polish. She knew she was the sharpest knife in the drawer and on top of her game as she sat down to enjoy her cup of mocha. Yes, everyone who was anyone wanted to be her. So when she lifted the lid off the sugar dish, she was undaunted by the emptiness she encountered there. The kitchen, after all, was the room she favored least. While the rest of the rooms in her monochromatically stylish yet cozy new house were arranged according to her particular *feng shui*, the kitchen had yet to be unpacked and made right in her universe.

Esperanza smiled to herself and said aloud, "This is the ideal morning for meeting my new neighbors. Surely, they would be pleased to meet me and to part with some sugar for my morning mocha." She often spoke out loud when she was alone, because even then she sensed that all of her words and thoughts contributed to the greater good.

A few moments later, she stepped from her back door, turned right, and crossed both faultlessly cut, pruned emerald lawns to stand knocking at her neighbor's back door. All the while she thought to herself how the sun always seemed to gladden and shine more brightly in her presence. Even the birds twittered and sang more sweetly when she found herself outdoors.

"Come in, neighbor," a melodious voice chimed in response to her friendly knock. "Come in."

Esperanza entered a kitchen so immaculately white as to be virginal. Her nostrils flared at the assaulting odor of lemony clean. The door slammed hard behind her, and a tomblike silence descended in the cool bright kitchen.

"Welcome to my neighborhood," the woman behind the island said cheerfully. "I'm Holly Hayes." Her voice echoed against the walls. Lemon yellow curtains fluttered over the sink behind her. Holly's hair was the exact color of the curtains, teased into a huge beehive bouffant held in check by more hairspray than Esperanza thought humanly possible for one head of hair to contain. A milky white headband perfectly matched her complexion, just as her eyeshadow, lipstick, rouge, and nail polish perfectly matched her hair color, the curtains, and the polka dots on her very white dress. Her smile was eerie.

"Good morning. I'm—I'm—I'm—" Esperanza stammered, momentarily forgetting her name, much less her errand. She fiddled with the end of her sleeve and noticed with some irritation that a thread had unraveled. She tucked it discreetly into her sleeve and covered the imperfection with her other hand.

Holly fixed her yellow (yes, yellow) gaze on her as she cut a symmetrical eighth from the lemon meringue pie sitting on the countertop in front of her. She set it daintily on a plate. A clear bowl of lemony cleaning solution rested next to the pie. A white scrub brush floated in its center. The kettle whistled shrilly on the stove to her right. Holly arched a yellow eyebrow as her visitor finally finished her sentence.

"I'm Esperanza. Esperanza Martinique."

"Would you like some tea, Esperanza dear?" Holly asked, reaching for the kettle and two teacups from the cabinet beside the stove. All the while, she never averted her gaze from Esperanza's. There was something decidedly cat-like about her expression.

"No," she shook her head. "No, thank you." Her voice sounded small in Holly's kitchen.

"Perhaps you would prefer lemonade, Esperanza dear." Holly glided to the left and opened the glistening refrigerator door to produce a pitcher of cloudy yellow liquid that she poured quickly and expertly into a tall glass without spilling so much as a drop. She held the glass out to Esperanza across the countertop.

"No, thank you, Holly dear," she mocked, squaring her shoulders nervously.

"Are you sure?" Holly asked, tapping a lemon fingernail against the glass.

"Yes." Esperanza forced a smile. "I only came to borrow some sugar for my coffee."

"Coffee?"

She nodded.

"Nonsense." Holly tsk-tsked. "Coffee is a toxic substance. There'll be none of that coffee-drinking nonsense in my neighborhood."

Esperanza's eyes widened with a sudden uncontrollable rage. How dare this woman ruin her perfect start to yet another perfect day with her stupefying vanity? But before she could express the watered-down yet stingingly smart rebuff forming on the tip of her tongue, Esperanza swallowed some lemonade. Her face puckered in response as an explosion of sour lemon water filled her mouth. She clapped the hand hiding the dangling thread over her scarlet lips and clutched the countertop with the other. Her eyes watered.

"Oooh," Holly purred. "My lemonade needs more sugar. Wouldn't you agree, Esperanza dear?"

Just as Esperanza recovered from the sour assault on her taste buds, she sampled a forkful of lemon meringue pie. An overwhelming burst of lemon sweetness filled Esperanza's mouth. Her teeth ached.

"And that," she chuckled, "requires much less."

Esperanza began to step back carefully when Holly's hand clamped down painfully over her wrist and the traitorous black thread. Her skin was as cold and hard as the marble countertop. In that moment, Esperanza's body became paralyzed from the waist down.

"Oh, no, Esperanza dear," she said. "You weren't planning on leaving yet, were you?" She batted false black eyelashes at her. "We haven't even had a chance to have a proper chat." Just then, the shutters banged shut over the window and the door, leaving the curtains to stand at attention over the sink behind Holly. Panicked, Esperanza's dark eyes searched the room only to discover that there were no other exits from Holly's kitchen.

Esperanza's response was nothing more than a gurgle. The offensive tastes were still rolling around on her tongue.

Holly scrunched her nose cutely. "I didn't think so." She opened a drawer on her side of the island, pulled out a cigarette, and set it in the corner of her mouth. Then, she withdrew a banana yellow lighter and lit her cigarette with exaggerated care. She tilted her head back, inhaled deeply, and blew smoke from her nostrils.

Esperanza sputtered and coughed out smoke. Her eyes and nostrils burned as well. Holly jammed her cigarette into her slice of lemon meringue pie, smiling with satisfaction.

"Well, you don't smoke," Holly noted. "That's a good girl. I won't have any smoking in my neighborhood, either. It's a filthy habit." Holly's topaz eyes sparkled. "You don't drink, do you, Esperanza dear?" she asked innocently.

Esperanza shook her head between hacking coughs.

Holly approved. "Very good. However, I suppose it would be pointless to discuss chastity with a woman of your, shall we say . . . ," she paused for emphasis, "your particular ethnic background."

Esperanza suddenly felt as though someone was riffling through the pages of the locked diaries in her mind while she stood there watching, skimming over the most intimate passages of her life with a probing lemon fingernail. She gasped as a tremor passed over her wrist. Holly shuddered from her side of the island. Her eyes slid to half-mast, bright with tears, and her hand closed into a tight fist, tangling at the neckline of her dress, as she rocked with convulsions, screaming. Through it all, she never averted her yellow gaze from Esperanza's. Finally, she quieted, licked her lips, and shuddered into stillness.

Esperanza's head snapped from side to side from the hard invisible slaps delivered across both sides of her face. She resisted the urge to touch her face. Instead, she kept her arm at her side, curling her hand into a fist. Holly's composure was intact and unfazed when Esperanza looked at her through the chaos of her black hair. Holly shook her head disapprovingly, tsk-tsking.

"My, my, Esperanza dear. You have been very, very naughty. But there are ways to remedy even that. You see, there are very strict moral codes to be maintained in my neighborhood as well, Esperanza dear."

Red-faced and stinging, Esperanza struggled to recover her composure, squaring her shoulders against whatever onslaught was yet to come.

Holly examined her carefully and asked, "Did someone die, Esperanza dear?"

She slowly shook her head.

"Then why are you wearing black?"

She gritted her teeth. "I like black."

"Nonsense. I like yellow. Yellow is so much friendlier than black. Wouldn't you agree, Esperanza dear?"

Esperanza stared, her mouth dropping, as the paralysis rose up to her shoulders.

"I don't like to repeat myself," Holly beamed impatiently. Her grip on Esperanza's wrist tightened. "Perhaps you didn't hear me the first time. Now, wouldn't you agree that yellow is so much friendlier than black, Esperanza dear?"

Esperanza winced and nodded.

"I thought so. That's settled then, Esperanza dear." She paused and leaned over the counter to study her even more closely. She toyed with the brush in the clear bowl of yellow cleaning solution, twirling it around with the tip of just one lemon fingernail. "Es-per-an-za," she said aloud, elongating each syllable. "What kind of a name is Esperanza?"

"It was my grandmother's name," she replied cautiously.

"Really? That's so sweet that you were named after your grandmother, Esperanza dear but, well, you see . . ." Holly winked and scrunched her nose cutely. "Esperanza is a trifle too ethnic for my neighborhood. You do want to be happy here, don't you, Esperanza dear?"

"My name," Esperanza argued weakly, "means *hope*."

"Nonsense. We're just going to have to put an end to that right now. *Esperanza* is so very clunky. It just won't do." She tapped a lemon fingernail against her chin, pondering. "I know! We'll change it to Nicki Martin. That's not such a giant leap from Martinique." She sounded out the name. "Nicki Martin. It's a smart and simple name. Wouldn't you agree, Nicki dear?"

She nodded helplessly. She'd lost feeling in her fingers, and her hand was turning a nasty shade of purple under Holly's relentless grip.

"You're a quiet one, Nicki dear, an excellent listener. I can tell. I like that quality in you." She lifted the brush and let the excess cleaning solution drip back into the clear bowl. "We're going to be the best of friends. I can just tell." She lifted Esperanza's wrist, loosening her grip. "However, there is this larger problem of your complexion. I'm afraid your complexion is a trifle more than a trifle too ethnic for my neighborhood. But don't lose hope, Nicki dear. I think we can remedy that, too."

She set to scrubbing away at Esperanza's arm, never averting her feline gaze from her. The sleeve of her black pantsuit along with the unraveling thread rapidly disintegrated under Holly's vigorous scrubbing. The black ran off like dirty dishwater, staining Holly's pristine countertop.

"Oh, don't worry about the mess, Nicki dear," Holly assured her. "It's the least I can do to help my best friend transition into my neighborhood."

Esperanza's eyes widened and her tongue swelled so it felt like a tennis ball had been jammed into her mouth behind her teeth. She silently recited the rosary, ticking off beads with imaginary hands in her mind, calling up her grandmother's ghost kneeling darkly in prayer before the candlelit altar in the chapel of Esperanza's youth. The bristles felt like needles scraping against her skin. Holly smiled toothily, revealing razor-sharp canines. Esperanza's entire body seized up with paralysis at that moment, or she would have begun screaming and never stopped. Her eyes closed just as the countertop ran red. The vision of her grandmother faded into the red, her prayers lost. Her blood pulsed and swirled beneath her eyelids, lava hot with trapped tears, as the brush traveled over the entire length of her body, dissolving clothing, ripping and shredding flesh, scraping and pulverizing her very bones into dust.

Sometime later, Esperanza Martinique coiled unnoticed into a shadow, retreating into a corner of the ceiling in Holly's kitchen, and stared down, observing her own remains. All that was left of her was a conical pile of dust. Holly had cleaned her kitchen very well. She now donned a white lab coat as she swept up the last of Esperanza's remains and emptied them into a big yellow ceramic bowl which she set in her stainless steel sink under the bright curtains hanging like sentinels before the shuttered window.

Holly had come to the final stages of Esperanza Martinique's transformation into Nicki Martin, her new best friend, and Nicki's subsequent transition into her very exclusive neighborhood. She was practically purring with pleasure. Holly carefully scooped out a few dark patches from the powder with a yellow plastic spoon and dumped them into a small white bowl next to the sink. With each scoop, the remaining ethnic members of Esperanza's family were lost. First went her workaholic uncle, Tio Roberto, resolute in his bachelorhood and penny-pinching ways; then, her spinsterish cousin, Hilda, who finally took refuge in her virginity and the convent; and finally, her roguish aunt, Tia Louisa, with the electric black hair and man-eating smile who made up for them both.

Holly positioned the faucet over the bowl. She stepped back, watching the hot water trickle steadily into the bowl. The powder chemically combined with the water, sizzling and bubbling. The bowl rocked dangerously as the substance of Esperanza Martinique reconstituted and rose up rapidly like dough. Holly pinched out a few more dark spots she'd missed here and there and dropped them into the other bowl. With that, Esperanza lost her language and her favorite Mexican recipes and completely forgot how to dance. As the roiling mass struggled with a rush and wail toward the corner of the ceiling, Esperanza's shadow stared and answered with a wail in kind, while Holly dumped the last of the lemony yellow cleaning solution into the bowl at the base of the twisting mass. And the last of Esperanza's culture and unique history was cleansed, disinfected, and bleached from her. The dough fell with a clattering, splat, plop, sigh. Then, it rose up and molded itself into a pale replica of the once-beloved Esperanza Martinique. The shadow in the corner of the ceiling shuddered, visibly shrinking. The yellow liquid rushed up from the feet of the doughy woman to the top of her head and concentrated its lemony brightness in her toenails and fingernails with an instantaneous shimmer. Her yellow hair grew in quickly, replacing her once lovely black hair.

Holly stepped back to admire her handiwork and frowned when her gaze alighted upon a single stubborn black hair hiding in the yellow triangle at her crotch. She plucked it out with one ferocious yank and dropped it into the bowl of leftovers. In the corner, the shadow of Esperanza Martinique hiccoughed as the final secret memory of her Puerto Rican lover—the dark drifter who'd initiated her into the realm of shameless love there in the long cool bed of his pickup under the stars in the long-ago summer of her girlhood—vanished with her into a visionless knot. Holly picked up the bowl of leftovers and walked to the corner. She tapped the wall with one lemon fingernail and the dark knot dropped into the bowl to rest among the pinched fragments of dough, mottled powder, and the single black hair. She pulled open a drawer, snapped a lid onto the bowl, and then closed the drawer with the sealed contents safely tucked away in its recesses.

Holly Hayes clasped Nicki Martin's hands in her own. Her new best friend's eyes blinked open. She smiled up at the topaz eyes reflecting her own, content.

The sun was shining particularly bright through the bedroom windows that morning when Nicki Martin woke up to yet another perfect day. Her short, yellow hair recently cut into a sharp career coif fell into place just right around the cameo of her face. The lemon meringue shade of lipstick she wore said powerful, sexy. Her lemon yellow manicure was impeccable. Her yellow designer pantsuit maximized and minimized her figure in the most flattering of proportions. Her nyloned feet realized the meaning of heaven when she placed them into her coordinating designer shoes worn to comfortable perfection but with the still-new look to the polish. She knew she was the sharpest knife in the drawer and on top of her game as she sat down to enjoy her cup of lemon tea. Yes, everyone who was anyone wanted to be her. So when she lifted the lid of the sugar dish, she was undaunted by the emptiness she encountered there. The kitchen, after all, was the room she favored least. While the rest of the rooms in her monochromatically stylish yet cozy new house were arranged according to her particular *feng shui*, the kitchen had yet to be unpacked and made right in her universe.

Nicki smiled to herself and said aloud, "This is the ideal morning for meeting my new neighbors. Surely, they would be pleased to meet me and to part with some sugar for my morning tea." She often spoke out loud when she was alone, because even then she sensed that all of her words and thoughts contributed to the greater good.

A few moments later, she stepped from her back door, turned left since she was already more than well-acquainted with the neighbor to her right. Holly Hayes was her best friend, after all. Nicki crossed both faultlessly cut emerald lawns to stand with her fist poised to knock at her neighbor's back door. All the while, she thought to herself how the sun always seemed to gladden and shine more brightly in her presence. Even the birds twittered and sang more sweetly when she found herself outdoors. A black shadow, the shape of a dark ill-formed memory, passed on the other side of the lacy curtains of her neighbor's back door. Nicki stepped away from the door with a start, balancing the emptiness of her sugar bowl against the fact that she was feeling somehow lighter and that her clothes felt somewhat looser this fine morning. She took this as a fortuitous sign and crossed both faultlessly cut emerald lawns and sat back down to tea in her own kitchen.

"This is the perfect day," Nicki Martin mused, "to eliminate sugar from my diet once and for all."

The phone rang, jarring Esperanza Martinique from slumber. Her sheets were damp with sweat and her heart thudded in her chest. She rolled over and picked up the receiver from her nightstand and put it against her ear, disgruntled and foggy with sleep.

"Esperanza Martinique, please," said a brusque businesswoman's voice.

"There's no one here by that name," she muttered and then sat up in bed, shaking off the nightmarish memory of Nicki Martin. "I mean, yes, of course," she stammered, "this is she. Esperanza Martinique, I mean. May I help you?"

McDono's

CARLA McCARTY

"I want McDono's!" Tyesha yells from the backseat, her high-pitched voice almost a shriek.

"Me too!" Travelle pipes in, balling his little hands into two tiny fists and smashing them into his thighs.

I glare at them through the rearview mirror, already tired and irritable from having been at the mall all day with a nine-year-old girl who thinks she needs to go to school looking like a supermodel and chooses only the most expensive items in the store that show cleavage she doesn't have and an outie belly button damned near bigger than my breast that she doesn't seem to understand should stay hidden. And a six-year-old boy who thinks a trip to the mall entitles him to at least a hundred dollars' worth of candy, cinnamon rolls, soft pretzels, and frozen coffee drinks, and who wants to impress all the little first-grade girls with gym shoes that cost more than any mortage.

"Yeah, Mom, we want some McDonoooooh's!" Tyesha sings.

"And I told yawl 'noooooo' a long time ago, so quit asking every time we pass one. We got plenty of food at home, and we been to McDonald's fifty times this week. I'm not giving one more single solitary nickel to that old money-grubbing, red-headed, yellow-jumpsuit-wearing hamburger pusher. I said no, and I meant no."

"But, Mommy, I want McDono's too," Tia chimes from her carseat. Tyesha and Travelle gaze down lovingly at their little sister, who is strapped down between them, then look at each other and smile their biggest, cheesiest smiles, 'cause they know I can never resist Tia's requests when she asks me for anything while tied down in that damned carseat, which reminds me of some ancient torture chair.

I'm only a block past the McDonald's we just drove by, and I'm trying to figure out whether I should go back or try and stomach the kids' whining for another few blocks till we reach the next one or, better yet, wait until we get out of the 'hood and closer to home where our property taxes guarantee friendly fast-food service, which I *know* I won't get over here. But then I look in the rearview and Tia bats her big doe eyes at me and I swear the strap of the carseat looks like it's tightening around her ever so slightly, so I do a quick U-turn, causing the guy in the car behind me to screech on his brakes and explode into a mindless rage, honking like a madman. The kids cheer. Tyesha starts clapping loudly, and they all erupt into a ritualistic chant, "McDon-o's! McDon-o's!"

I swerve right up next to the curb on the other side of the street, and one of what seems like hundreds of men standing around uselessly on the corner bends down, a forty-ounce dangling from his hand, and looks into my window. The kids stop chanting and look at him curiously.

"Damn, baby, is it that serious?" he says, then looks me up and down and adds, "and if it is, can I go wich you? We can drop ya kids off at my mama's house."

The kids look at me as if they wonder whether I'll accept the proposition.

Somebody behind the guy shouts in my direction, "Eh, is yo' husband married?"

"Get a job!" I yell back as I jam my foot on the gas, wishing that there was a nice big puddle of water at the curb to splash on all of them. They got their nerve—think I want them. Probably ain't never had a job in their lives. They were probably born on that corner and ain't left it since.

The kids resume their chant: "McDon-o's! McDon-o's!"

I pull into the drive-thru, after having to honk several times at some little ragamuffin-looking children who seemed to have made the parking lot their own personal playground, and I cringe as my car crunches over sixty-five-thousand pieces of broken glass. A reverential silence comes over the car as the kids prepare themselves to yell out their orders (which luckily they already know, 'cause half the little brown strips that usually make up the menu are lying on the ground, broken into little pieces from all the cars rolling over them). We wait for the familiar crackle of the cheap microphone.

Finally, the people inside decide to pretend they're interested in their jobs, and the intercom pops on. From the little speaker we hear the loud, and extraordinarily clear, sound of someone smacking on a wad of gum. After listening to that for about five minutes the gum-smacker decides to grace us with words: "The drive-thru ain't workin'," she says. "You gotta come in."

"Excuse me?" I say, trying to make sure I heard her correctly through all her smacking and popping.

"I said, the drive-thru ain't workin'!" she yelled, amazingly louder than before. "You gotta come in!"

I sit there a minute thinking about debating the supposed dysfunction of the drive-thru with the girl in the brown box, trying to decide whether I should waste time attempting to explain to her that if I can hear *her* and she can hear *me*, then the drive-thru is obviously working fine, but I decide against it. This is what I get for choosing a McDonald's in the 'hood.

I pull into a parking space, thanking God for the promotion a few years ago that got me out of neighborhoods like this. On the other side of me is an old, brown, beat-up 1960-something Buick with shiny silver rims that probably cost more than my annual salary. The guy inside is all laid out in the driver's seat, which is pushed back into an almost horizontal position so the only thing I can really see is the top of his cornrowed head, the cornrows confirming that he didn't get those rims from money he made moving up the corporate ladder. Probably bought them with all the money he saves living for free in his mama's basement.

I get out of the car, followed by Tyesha, and by Travelle who has resumed the McDon-o's chant and is jumping up and down. I unleash Tia from the torture chair, prop her on my hip, and am about to start walking towards McDonald's, when the guy in the Buick sits up, wearing his weight in gold, damn near blinding me. I start to ask him what million-dollar stock he invested in to get all that gold and them expensive rims, but I figure he won't get the joke 'cause I'm sure the only stock he ever heard of is the kind his grandmomma uses to cook her chicken in. He looks me up and down and then looks at my Camry.

"Hold on for a minute," he says into his shiny gold cell phone, then he turns to me and says, "You want me to watch yo' car?" He smiles at me, showing his two gold-capped front teeth. One has the word Big cut out of it, showing the barely white tooth beneath it, and other spells the word Money.

I start to say, *I get you to watch my car then who am I going to get to watch you*—but I decide against it. "No, thank you," I say, grabbing Tyesha and Travelle's shoulders and marching them into the McDonald's.

We walk into the side entrance and almost collide with a little old man who is standing in the line which stretches almost to the back of the store, and I feel sorry for the old guy 'cause he's probably eighty-seventh in line, and he's all bent over and looks like he's going to fall to the floor at any second.

"Watch yo' ass 'fo I pop a cap in it!" he shouts at me through bare gums. Travelle bursts out laughing and Tyesha puts her hand on her hip.

"Don't be talkin' to my momma that way, you old gym shoe." Tyesha gets an attitude real quick and always calls people names that on the surface seem to make no sense, but if you ask her about it she'll be able to explain why she chose that name, like she'll say, "I called him an old gym shoe 'cause the kids at school tease anybody who's not wearing the most up-to-date gym shoes, so being an old gym shoe is really the worst thing in the world to be, 'cause you all beat up and don't nobody like you and you get teased all the time." That's just how Tyesha is, always got an explanation for everything. Tia is in my arms looking down at her sister proudly.

I snatch Tyesha's hand, pulling it off her hip, and drag her to the line before Grandpa decides to make good on his threat. Travelle is still laughing hysterically, holding his belly and pointing at the old man who keeps turning around and looking at us. He puts his hand in his pocket. I bend down and tell Travelle that if he doesn't stop laughing I'm going to take his gym shoes back to the store, and he stops immediately, like somebody flicked a switch, and the old man takes his hand out of his pocket, turns around and resumes his crouch.

There must be at least seventy people behind the counter, so I can't understand why the lines are so long, but then I realize that only two of the six registers are open and half of the teen-aged workers are either just standing around, staring into space or huddled into little chit-chat groups by the French-fry bins. I consider trying to get a manager to open up another line but I see the girl in the blue-and-white striped managerial shirt standing in the center of one of the french-fry social groups, and I wonder why black folks in these little fast-food joints think that "manager" is synonymous with "vacation"—like that raise from four dollars an hour to five dollars an hour has moved them to the top of the food chain, and now they can just kick back and let the big bucks roll in.

The little girl standing next to me, who must be about five years old, smiles at me, and I wait for her head to tip over from the weight of her damn-near floor-length curly-weave braids, but she must be used to them, 'cause she holds her head up just fine. She picks up a crop of French fries drowned in so much ketchup that they lie limply across her small fist, and she's about to put them into her mouth, but the boy next to her, who looks to be maybe two years older, snatches the fries from her, leaving the tips still squashed in her hand,

and stuffs the stolen fries greedily into his mouth, making guttural munching noises.

The woman across the table from them hops up, snatches the boy's arm, yanks him out of the seat, and pulls off her belt all in one motion. She gives the boy several whacks on the butt, each whack punctuated with a word: "Didn't—I—tell—you—not—to—eat—your—sister's—French—fries?" The boy starts crying, probably more from embarrassment than anything else, 'cause the belt is made of cheap patent-leather-look plastic and is spaghetti-strap thin, so it can't be hurting him much. The little girl is laying her head on the table, and I can't figure out if it's because she's crying or because the heavy braids were finally too much for her to bear.

Travelle tries to hold back a snicker, and Tyesha is still staring angrily at the old man who is now at the counter, placing his order.

I peek out the door and make sure Mr. Goldfinger isn't hot-wiring my car. He isn't.

What seems like hours later, we make it to the front of the line. The girl behind the counter, who's wearing so much Vaseline on her lips that I can see my reflection in them clear as day, mumbles something unintelligible and I say, "Excuse me?" and she yells at the top of her lungs, "Hello, welcome to McDon-o's, can I take your order!?" in a tone so hostile that if she'd added the word 'bitch' in there somewhere it would have fit perfectly. Her eight-foot-high blue-streaked French roll, partially covered by a too-small hairnet, stands defiantly immobile as she rolls her neck. She rolls her eyes, too, exposing blue eye shadow that matches the streaks in her hair perfectly.

I say, as calmly as I can—hoping the girl will learn by example, but seriously doubting it—that I would like a Filet-o-Fish meal, and I order a Chicken McNugget Happy Meal for Tia. The girl punches in the order with the tip of her long curving nails, which are covered in some pasty-looking translucent nail polish, and trapped in the inch-thick gook are bits and pieces of torn-up one- and five-dollar bills with thousands of fake diamonds scattered on top, and I think, *She's probably got more money in her nails than she gets in her paycheck.*

The crooked, greenish tattoo just above her wrist, that she probably did herself, reads, with all the grammatical accuracy of a three-year-old, *Peachy love Pee-Wee,* and after I read it I wonder why black folks always have to give themselves all these weird names and nicknames. It's like we still ain't got over the fact that during slavery we couldn't name ourselves, so now we're making up for lost time, and you got folks going around saying, "My name is Lacretia Barnetta Kenyatta Shardonay Jones, but everybody calls me "Coochie." I swear, it's just a mess.

I tell Tyesha to give the nice woman her order, and Tyesha says, "I would like a Cheeseburger Happy Meal with an orange pop and no mustard on the cheeseburger, please." I smile proudly, glad that I got her out of the 'hood before she picked up bad habits from the 'hood-rat kids who probably would have said, "Yeah, I wont me a mu-a-fuckin' cheese-buga happy mu-a-fuckin' meal." I instruct Travelle to tell the woman what he wants. He starts off nicely too, also saying, "I would like . . . ," but he's interrupted by the cashier, who screams, "Wait a minute, wait a minute! I gotta find the mustard key!" All four of us stare at her dumbly while she stares, just as dumbly, at the cash register's keyboard.

"Hey, Aquamonetta!" she yells across the room.

I look around for a mermaid-looking creature to surface from some hidden underground pool, but Peachy seems to be talking to the blue-and-white striped manager who pokes her head out from the center of the french-fry huddle and yells, "Hunh?"

"Where's the mustard key?"

The manager makes a wet, clicking noise with her tongue, says "Girrrrrrrl, I'm trying to tell them 'bout what happened last night," and she stomps away from the group and over to Peachy. "Heah it is, right here." She points to a big, yellow key and runs back to her group to finish her story.

"Oh," Peachy says to herself, and she still takes another hour to finish punching in Tyesha's order.

Some lady comes in the side door, ignores the line, and walks right up next to me at the counter. "I called in an order," she announces, and Peachy looks up at her.

"What's the name?"

"Tito."

Peachy yells toward the back, "Tito is here to pick up they order!" and some man comes from the back carrying a greasy-looking bag. He tells the woman to step over to the last register.

The three young men behind us start snickering and one of them says, "Eh, I put a Big Mac on layaway, and I'm here to pick it up!" They laugh loudly, but Peachy and the rest of the workers ignore them.

Peachy finally finishes with Tyesha's order. We can tell she's done 'cause she looks up at Travelle and stares at him until he rattles off his order. "I would like a cheeseburger Happy Meal with . . ." I hold my hand up to his face, stopping him from saying, "with no pickles." We don't have another five hours to waste while Peachy searches for the pickle key. Travelle is just going to have to pick them off today.

"What-choo want to drink?"

"I would like an Oreo McFlurry."

Peachy sucks her teeth and looks at him with her lips poked out sarcastically. "What-choo want to drink?" she repeats.

I interject. "He *said* he wants an Oreo McFlurry."

She rolls her eyes and turns to me. "I asked him what he want to *drink*. A McFlurry is ice-cream," she sneers.

"Well-just-give-him-a-Coke-and-a-McFlurry-on-the-side," I say through clenched teeth, not even bothering trying to tell her that every other McDonald's we've been to has let us get a McFlurry in place of a pop. I'm trying hard to hold back my temper—the old ghetto in me is dying to get out—but I keep it civil for the kids' sake and Peachy's too, 'cause she don't want me to get black up in here.

She punches in the order then rattles off unenthusiastically, "Would you like to add crispy bacon skrips to your orders for the low price of thirty cents each?"

I ask Tyesha and Travelle if they want bacon strips on their cheeseburgers, and they say no.

"You want bacon on yours?" Peachy asks.

"I ordered a Filet-o-Fish," I say.

She just stares at me.

"No, Peachy, I do not want bacon skrips on my fish." I hope she'll understand me now that I'm speaking her language.

Peachy saunters off to get our order. While I wait I look up at the smiling picture of Ronald McDonald, who looks severely out of place in this McDonald's. It seems like he should have his arms crossed over his chest and a baseball cap tilted to the side with a dialogue bubble that reads "Mc-Don-O's!" And I keep looking around expecting to see Hamburglar, The Fry Guys and Grimace, the big, purple precursor to Barney, sitting in a hoopty out in the parking lot blasting Tupac and Biggie Smalls from the car stereo and checking out the honeys.

Years later, Peachy returns with our order. She collects the money and just as we're about to trudge away from the counter she smiles and says, "A'ight, girl, have a good night!"

Ain't too many places you can go where somebody can call you "girl" and it just sounds so…right. I look at her, for the first time really, and I smile back. "You too, girl, you too."

The kids and I stroll out into the parking lot. I walk around to the passenger side and strap Tia into her seat, where she immediately falls asleep, 'cause it's way past her bedtime. Tyesha and Travelle hop in and start digging for the prize in their Happy-Meal bags. The guy in the beat-up Buick next to me pokes his head out of the window and says, "I watched your car for you anyway," and I say thanks. He reaches into his inside coat pocket. "I own a little shop down the street." He hands me his card. "You ever need some rims, you come see me. I'll give you a good deal."

"Thank you, I sure will." I climb into the car and drive off, nibbling on my fries.

"We were in there forever," Tyesha says to no one in particular.

"Yeah," I say, "next time I'll call in our order."

The Daffodils

Mama drove me and Akira to the kindergarten every morning.

We had a blue Nissan Sunny with four doors and a stick shift. Inside, the car always smelled like vinyl because the seats were made of it, and the smell was thicker in summer because the sun scorched the seats through the glass. The smell made me feel like throwing up, so I always rolled my window down a little for fresh air. I couldn't roll it all the way down because Mama said it was dangerous, so I breathed only through my mouth when I was in the car. Sometimes I had to shut my mouth to swallow my own spit, but when I did, a tiny bit of the air was sucked into my nose and I had to smell the vinyl. Usually, I took the risk, but sometimes I pinched my nose as I swallowed to make sure that absolutely no air would get through. It worked well, but also made my eardrums puff out. I didn't like the feeling at all, but it was better than smelling the stink. I couldn't believe that Akira's mouth was shut all the time when he was not talking, and he seemed to have no problem. Mama didn't seem affected in any way by the smell, either. In fact, I was the only one in my family who had the problem, and none of my many friends from kindergarten who got a ride in our blue Sunny suffered from it, as far as I knew. I just couldn't believe it.

Akira and I sat in the rear seat. Every morning, Mama would step on the brakes suddenly and I would be thrown forward and bump my head on the back of the front seat. She was not as good as Papa at starting the car or shifting gears, either. When she shifted gears, I was pulled forward a little, then thrown back against the cushion. It was fun in a way, but it could give me slight motion sickness. I believed that Akira also had some difficulty, sitting right next to me, even though we never talked about it, because after one point, we simply quit sitting when Mama drove us to our kindergarten. Instead, we stood on the floor in the rear, holding onto the backs of the front seats. We could put our hands on the front seats' shoulders, but since they were taller than we were, we had to adjust by spreading our arms to grab their edges. The first position made our shoulders feel numb and the other tired our hands, so we moved our hands quite often between the two. It must have been tougher for Akira because he was shorter than me. Despite the problems, standing like that in the car was a great idea, because we didn't get thrown back and forth anymore. Also, if we tilted our heads, we had a good view through the windshield. It was much better than looking out from the side windows, because the view moved toward us instead of scrolling. We changed sides in the back of the car day after day. When I took the right side, which was the driver's side, I had to be careful not to disturb Mama with my fingers.

Mama had a strange habit of talking into the air when she was driving. I didn't know exactly what she was doing or for what reason she was doing it, but it wasn't that she was humming a song or just muttering to herself. She was clearly talking to someone, and frequently, she was not only talking but arguing. She would nod and shake her head, and as she got more aggressive, her voice became almost as loud as when she talked to a real person.

"Yukio isn't such a child," Mama said one morning, during an argument with someone whom she was seeing through the windshield.

"What?" I said from the rear seat because she had called my name, and her self-talk snapped off in the middle of a sentence. I could see her eyes in the rearview mirror, and I could see that she had lost herself for a second, as if she didn't know where she was.

"Huh?" she said and glanced at me in the mirror.

"What about me?"

"It's nothing," she said.

Five seconds later, she was talking to the air again:

"Oh, that's not true, *sensei*...I told you the same thing last month, *sensei,* would you remember that? Excuse me, *sensei,* but that's not what Yukio has told me . . . . Why do you believe the boy's story but not Yukio's? Yes, you sure are . . . . There is still a bruise on his shin under his sock after two weeks

. . . *Sensei*, pardon me, but did you even know that Yukio had a big purple bruise? But that isn't fair, *sensei*…Then why didn't you tell his mother about it at that time? Are you saying that Yukio is lying to his own mother? *Sensei*, Yukio never lies to me. Our son is not such a child."

I never paid much attention to Mama's self-talk, but I couldn't ignore her when she said I wasn't the kind of child who would ever lie to his mother, because I knew she was wrong about it. This made me feel like I was causing a problem, though I really didn't know what it was.

On another morning not long after that, there was an unusual smell in the car. It was the sweetest scent I had ever known and it was coming from a bunch of daffodils that lay diagonally on the front passenger's seat. I had a good view of the daffodils because I was standing behind Mama that morning. I couldn't imagine how a bunch of flowers could be more beautiful than that.

Mama had bought the daffodils the day before and kept them carefully in our kitchen sink overnight. She had included some full buds in the bunch, so they would bloom later. The buds of the daffodils were long and pointy. One of them, the largest one, was split open a little, showing the wet inside like a live clam. The open ones looked very fresh and lively. The outer petals were a cool, light yellow, and the inner tube-like petals were a strong canary yellow. The yellows of the petals were so bright that everything else in the world seemed like faded black and white. The white waxed paper was carefully wrapped around the bunch like a *kimono,* and the flowers were arranged to come out from the V-shaped opening in the paper. They appeared like crazy trumpets, but then they reminded me of modest young ladies. Each flower and bud had its own look, as if each had a mind just like a person.

Mama stopped the car on a grade, behind a white car, and past it I could see the rail crossing.

"So, Yukio-chan, do you remember what Mama told you before we left home?" she said.

The crossing bars were down, and the red lights were flashing. It looked like there was a strange glowing creature that flipped up and down between the pair of lenses. I could hear the *clang-clang* of the alarm that came in through the open space of the window next to me. The sound matched the flashing lights at first, but the timing went off, little by little.

"Yukio-chan?" she said again.

Before we left home that morning, Mama had called to me from the kitchen. I was watching *Let's Play with Mama! Ping Pong Pang!* on TV in the living room with Akira. When I went to the kitchen, Mama was rewrapping the bunch of daffodils in the waxed paper above the sink.

"Can you give the flowers to Shimakawa-*sensei* when you see her in kindergarten today?" she said, carefully adjusting the paper around the bunch. "Aren't they pretty?"

It was just an ordinary day, and no one in my class had brought such a great surprise for our teacher. So I asked Mama if Shimakawa-*sensei* knew that I was bringing the flowers to her. Mama smiled slightly and said that it was all right if the teacher didn't know about it. I asked Mama why I was doing this, but she didn't answer. I was afraid that Shimakawa-*sensei* might ask me the reason for the sudden present. My classmates would want to know why, also.

"Why doesn't Mama give it to *Sensei*?" I said. But Mama insisted that *I* should give it to her.

"What are you going to say to Shimakawa-*sensei* when you give the flowers to her?" Mama said. I didn't know what to say.

"*Sensei!* Here's some flowers!" Mama said loudly. "Can you say it?"

It sounded like something some bad child TV actor would say, whom I couldn't stand to watch.

"Come on. Why don't you rehearse it here now when Mama's watching? Mama plays *Sensei,* OK?" said Mama, and she offered me the bunch so I could give it back to her while repeating the line. I couldn't raise my hands to take the flowers.

"What's the matter? Here, take it. It's better if you practice now so you won't forget what to say when you see Shimakawa-*sensei* in kindergarten, right?" I felt like crying. Then we were late. Mama brushed her teeth quickly at the kitchen sink, wet a towel with hot water from the instant heater, then wiped my face and Akira's face with it. Through the wet steamy cloth, I could feel her fingers digging into the corners of my eyes and my nostrils. Mama's hands were always strong when she did that, but that morning, she was a little rougher than usual.

I thought that Mama had forgotten about the line, because she didn't mention it in the car until we stopped before the crossing. I'd been too optimistic. The train had not yet reached the crossing, and she was watching me in the rearview mirror.

"Why don't you say it now as practice?" she said. The yellow train finally appeared. The steel wheels made heavy train noises as they passed over the rails' joints. All the train cars were densely packed with adults in suits.

"Yukio, don't think you can get away from this by just keeping your mouth shut." The alarm stopped and the bars rose up.

"Come on. Say it now."

"But why?" I said, wriggling my body.

"You don't need a reason to give flowers to someone," she said, turning her head to watch me directly, and then opened her mouth to say something else.

A full honk blasted behind us. Mama's eyes flinched. She turned back to the driving position and released the parking brake, and we rolled backwards. For a second, I felt like we were falling, and then we stopped with a jerk. More honks flew out. Mama was helter-skelter in her seat, and finally we moved forward. The white car was already far away, at the crest of the hill. Crossing over the bumpy rails, Mama bowed to the rearview mirror.

"*Sumimasen,*" she said weakly. I looked back. A light-duty truck followed closely behind us. The driver was an unshaven, suntanned man with a filthy hand towel tied around his head. He was yelling something at us.

"*Sumimasen,*" Mama was still apologizing to the mirror. I couldn't help sobbing like a girl. When I looked to my side, Akira's eyes were filling up with tears, and a big drop ran down his nose. He wiped the tears with his sleeve and held onto the back of the driver's seat again. Mama said nothing after that. Her eyes looked moist, too, but I couldn't see well through my own tears. I peeked at the daffodils again. They were still powerfully beautiful, giving off the sweetest scent, as if they were not afraid of anything.

Mama parked the car outside the main gate of the college, and we walked to the kindergarten's entrance, where Mama handed the daffodils to me.

"Here, can you give it to your teacher as Mama has told you?" she asked. Her voice was nice and gentle, so I nodded to her, though I wasn't sure if I could say the line.

Akira and I changed our shoes in the entrance hall and stepped onto the corridor. Mama was waving goodbye to us from the front walk. Akira crossed the corridor and went into his Class Peach. I walked right to Class Red which was next to Class Peach.

I barely held the neck of the bunch of daffodils in my hand. The flowers were taller than my torso and head, so they blocked my view, but they weighed almost nothing considering their size. The corridor was always dark when I came inside, but that didn't help the daffodils to lose their brightness. Rather, they seemed to be shining more powerfully than ever before. It was like holding the sun in my hand, and I couldn't help squinting.

Some of my classmates were running around in the corridor. They stopped running as they saw me and the daffodils. A couple of girls ran into our classroom, and Shimakawa-*sensei* came out, pulled by the girl's hands. I raised the flowers to her. She smiled like she was very happy, and bent herself down to receive the bunch. She held it using both hands like she was holding a baby.

"Thank you very much, Yukio-kun," she said. "They are so pretty." She didn't ask anything.

Shimakawa-*sensei* borrowed a vase from the principal's room for the daffodils. It was the largest vase in the kindergarten. The vase was made of thick glass and was shaped like it had been twisted by the top and the bottom while the glass was still hot. The stems of the daffodils were too long even for the vase, so the teacher cut off the thick green stem bottoms one by one with her large scissors on a table in our classroom. They snapped with the hard metallic sound of the colliding iron blades. Inside, the stems looked juicy and fibrous. She arranged the flowers in the vase on top of the shelves by the door. That day, our classroom was brighter than usual, and smelled better than usual.

At the end-of-the-day recess, Shimakawa-*sensei* formally announced in the class that the flowers were from me. She was sitting on a chair facing us, and we were sitting directly on the floor.

"My mother bought them," I said to the teacher, feeling like I was shrinking, because all my classmates were listening, and I wasn't used to calling Mama "my mother" at all. But I had to say it because I didn't want to take credit from her.

"They are so pretty, aren't they?" the teacher said to my classmates, pointing at the vase with her hand.

"They are so pretty," the girls said, looking at the daffodils. Even the boys were looking at them and nodding to our teacher. One of the boys asked the teacher why some of the flowers were not blooming, and I got a twitch in my heart.

"That's because," the teacher said smiling, "Yukio-kun's mom picked some buds so they will bloom later, and so we can see the flowers for a much longer time." I was glad that she knew it, and my classmates seemed to understand her account.

"Now let's say 'Thank you' to Yukio-kun together," the teacher said, and looked at me. Everyone turned their heads to see me. They were all smiling.

"*Domo arigato*," the teacher said slowly. Some of the class said it along with her. The others said it following her. Then she read a picture book for us. I do not remember what it was, because I was thinking:

"Mama will ask me whether I could give the flowers to *Sensei* or not. I can say that I did, because I did give them to *Sensei*. I can even tell Mama how happy *Sensei* was and how she announced to the class about the flowers in the recess and how everyone thanked me for that. Mama will be happy to know that. But she should also ask me whether I could say the line when I gave the flowers to *Sensei* . . ."

I didn't say it. It wasn't that I forgot about it. In fact, the line was spinning around my head as I held out the bunch for the teacher that morning. A strange voice was yelling in my head, "Say it!" and another voice was saying calmly behind it, "You don't have to say it if you don't want to." I listened to the second voice, because I didn't want to say it. I didn't want to say it because it was too obvious. It was like saying, "*Sensei*, there's the sky!" in the middle of a field with my finger pointing up.

"I can lie," I thought. "Mama won't know . . . . Just say 'yes' when she asks me if I said it . . . but then Mama might want to know *Sensei's* response to the line. In that case, I would have no choice but to tell Mama a second lie, because there was no response to the line, because I never said it . . ."

I didn't know if I could lie to Mama twice in a row and act completely natural. Even if I could, that would make me really bad. I was positive that Mama would be upset if she got to know I didn't say the line. And I was sure that she would get mad if she found out that I was trying to cover up my failure with lies.

When the recess was over, my classmates were going out of the room to meet their moms outside the entrance hall. I remained standing alone in the room, crying hard like the end of the world had come.

"What's the matter?" Shimakawa-*sensei* said, leaning down to look at me face to face. She was propping her body with her hands on her knees. I didn't know what to say, so I kept crying until it stopped naturally.

When we walked out of the entrance hall, I was still feeling extremely nervous. I saw Mama among other moms and my friends. Akira was running around her, laughing with his friend. Mama saw me and waved. She was smiling.

Suddenly, I felt like nothing mattered anymore and everything was all right again. I ran to Mama, smiling too, and she took my hand without a word.